AF656399

Encyclopaedic Dictionary of

BIOLOGICAL SCIENCES

ENCYCLOPAEDIC DICTIONARY OF BIOLOGICAL SCIENCES

Vol. 5

K. NARANG
R. RANI
M. PRAKASH

ANMOL PUBLICATIONS PVT LTD
New Delhi-110002

ANMOL PUBLICATIONS PVT LTD
4374/4B, Ansari Road
Daryaganj, New Delhi-110 002

Encyclopaedic Dictionary of Biological Sciences

© Reserved

First Edition, 1991
ISBN 81-7041-462-8 (Set)
ISBN 81-7041-467-9 (Vol.5)
Reprint 1994
Reprint ... 1998

PRINTED IN INDIA
Published by J.L. Kumar for Anmol Publications Pvt. Ltd. New Delhi
and Printed at Mehra Offset Press.

Preface

The *Encyclopaedic Dictionary of Biological Sciences* (set of six volumes) has been carefully compiled and edited to meet the long felt needs of increasingly large number of, those who have to deal with the different aspects of biological sciences in colleges, universities, and research institutes. These volumes provide a speedy means of reference to easily interpreted definitions of the terms selected from botany, zoology, environmental science, ecology, genetics, biochemistry, forestry, agriculture geomorphology, cell biology, plant pathology, anatomy, evolution and ecology.

This set of dictionary is more or less encyclopaedic in its contents and style of representation which is evident from the comprehensiveness of its coverage and contextual relevance of explanations with illustrations and chemical formulae wherever necessary.

The entries in this dictionary have been written in a clear and explanatory style to provide both straight forward definitions and invaluable background information. The presentation throughout has been aimed at sustaining the interest of readers while enriching their vocabulary and comprehension of technical terms and expressions.

Throughout the process of compilation and editing these volumes our sincere effort was to make the dictionary as a ready reference for undergraduate and post graduate biological, agricultural, environmental, medical, marine and biochemistry students and also for those appearing for competitive examinations, research scholars, teachers and authors.

The editors express their thanks to their friends and colleagues whose continuous inspiration have initiated them to bring out these volumes.

The Editors

P

P_1. In genetics, the first parental generation; the parents in a particular cross, considered to be homozygous unless otherwise stated.

P680. A special form of chlorophyll *a* with a light absorption peak of 684 nm. It is one of the constituents of the photosystem II light-gathering centre of photosynthesis. The absorption of light energy by the P680 molecules causes, among other things, the formation of a.

P700. A special form of chlorophyll *a* with an absorption peak for light of 700 nm wavelength, found within the photosystem I light-gathering centre of photosynthesis. Other ordinary chlorophyll *a* molecules are also present and these absorb light energy and pass it to p700, creating a charged form, $P700^+$. Electron transfer occurs from photosystem II, electrons being passed on ultimately to produce NADPH, the reduced form of NADP.

Pacarana. A South American rodent (Dinomys branickii) similar to a paca.

Pacemaker

1. (Or sinoatrial node). A small mass of specialised muscle cell in the mammalian heart, found in the wall of the right atrium near the opening for the vena cava. The cells initiate and maintain the heart beat by their rhythmic and spontaneous contractions they stimulate contractions in the rest of the heart muscle. The cells themselves are controlled by the

autonomic nervous system, which determines the heart rate. Similar pacemakers occur in the hearts of other vertebrates.

2. An electronic or nuclear battery-charged device that can be implanted surgically into the chest to produce and maintain the heart beat. These devices are used when the heart's own pacemaker is defective or diseased.

Pachyderm. A large, thick-skinned, hoofed mammal, as an elephant, rhinoceros, or hippopotamus.

Pachytene. The period in the first prophase of meiosis when paired homologous chromosomes are fully contracted and twisted around each other.

Pachytene Stage. A stage in the early prophase of mitosis during which pairing of the chromosomes is completed and chromosome become shorter and thicker. It follows the zygotene stage and precedes the diplotene stage.

Pacinian Corpuscle. A capsulated sensory end organ for deep pressure.

Paedogenesis. Reproduction by larval or other immature forms. Larval paedogenesis occurs in insects of the genus Tanytarsus (order Diptera, family Chironomidae). in which larvae produce eggs that can hatch into larvae which develop into males or females. Pupal paedogenesis occurs in insects of the genus Henria (order Diptera, family Cecidomyidae), in which pupae can produce broods of larvae. This mode of reproduction results from hormonal imbalances in the immature stages.

Paedomorphosis. Evolutionary change that results in the retention of juvenile characters into adult life. It may be the result of neoteny or progenesis. It permits an 'escape' from specialization, and has been invoked to account for the origin of many taxa, from subspecies to phyla.

Paenungulata (infraclass Eutheria, cohort Ferungulata). Superorder comprising herbivorous animals which diverged from the primitive Palaeocene ungulate stock to become 'subungulates' or 'near ungulates'. The superorder includes the orders Hyracoidea (hyraxes), Proboscidea (elephants, their ancestors, and other elephant-like forms), Pantodonta, Dinocerata, Pyrotheria, Embrithopoda, and Sirenia (sea-cows or mermaids). In all of them the ulna and fibula are complete, and the upper bones of the limbs are long. The digits bear nails but not hoofs. Molars are specialized for grinding, and the incisors and canines are often reduced and modified to form tusks.

Pagina. *bot.* The blade of a leaf.

Pain An acutely uncomfortable reeling or sensation of discomfort or distress, usually the result of stimuli which are injurious to the body, which may result from dysfunction, excessive stretching or contraction of distensible structures, inadequate or excessive blood supply, bacterial infection, presence of foreign proteins, mechanical injury, or trauma. It is usually associated with impaired function.

Painted. With colored streaks or blotches of varying intensity.

Pairing. (Synapsis). The close association between homologous chromosomes that develops during the first prophase of meiosis. The two chromosomes move together and the exact pairing of corresponding points along their lengths occurs as they lie side by side. The resulting structure is called a bivalent.

Palaceous. Spade-shaped, said of leaves.

Palaeobotany. The branch of palaeontology concerned with the study of plants through geological time, as revealed by their fossil remains (also palynology). It overlaps with other aspects of plant study, including anatomy, ecology, evolution, and taxonomy.

Palaeocene. The earliest geological epoch of the Tertiary period. It began about 65 million years ago, following the Cretaceous period, and extended for about 11.5 million years to the beginning of the Eocene (the Palaeocene is sometimes included in the Eocene). It was named by the palaeobotanist W. P. Schimper in 1874. A major floral and faunal discontinuity occurred between the end of the Cretaceous and the beginning of the Palaeocene: following the extinction of many reptiles the mammals became abundant on land. By the end of the epoch primates and redents had evolved.

Palaeoclimatology. The study of climates of earlier geological periods. This is based largely on the study of sediments that were laid down during these periods and of fossils. The changes in the positions of the continents as a result of continental drift and plate tectonics complicate the study.

Palaeoecology. The study of extant and fossil organisms with a view to establishing the nature of the life of past ages and the environmental conditions that prevailed. Details of the environment in which given fossil organisms lived can be assumed from a knowledge of the prevailing climatic conditions in which the rocks that contain them were formed. However difficulties arise in distinguishing between the environment in which the organism lived and the environment in which it was buried.

Palaeolithic. The Old Stone Age, lasting in Europe from about 2.5 million to 9000 years ago, during which man used primitive stone tools made by chipping stones and flints.

Palaeontology. The study of fossils. The branch dealing with the study of plant fossils is termed palaeobotany which includes palaeoethnobotany, the study of fruit and seed remains found in archaeological sites. Palaeontology requires a knowledge of the way in which fossilization takes place and of the type of rock in which the fossil is found, a knowledge of the environmental conditions that prevailed when the rock was laid down, and an appreciation of the geological time scale so that the fossil can be dated.

Palaeozoic. The first of the three eras of the Phanerozoic. It began 570 million years ago and lasted 345 million years. The Cambrian Ordovician and Silurian Periods together form the Lower Palaeozoic sub-era; the Devonian Carboniferous and Permian the Upper Palaeozoic sub-era. During the Palaeozoic two major orogenies occurred the Caledonian during the Lower Palaeozoic and the Variscan in late Palaeozoic times. The faunas of the Palaeozoic are noted for the presence of many invertebrate organisms including trilobites, graptolites, brachiopods, cephalopods and corals. By the end of the era, amphibians and reptiles were major components of various communities and giant tree-ferns, horsetails, and cycads gave rise to extensive forests.

Palea (pale valvule). The upper of the pair of bracts beneath each floret (flower) in the inflorescence of a grass the other being the lemma. The palea is usually thin, narrow, and parallel sided. It usually has two ribs which may project as prominent keels. Compare glume.

Palaeozoology. The branch of palaeontology concerned with the study of animals throughout geological time, as revealed by their fossil remains.

Palama. The web in a web-footed bird.

Palate. The roof of the mouth; it separates the nasal and mouth cavities. In Mammalia and Crocodilia bones project inward from the jaws to form a false palate below the original palate, so extending the nasal cavity and moving its opening to a position in the throat. In mammals the bony part of the (false) hard palate is extended at the rear of the mouth by membrane and connective tissue which form the soft palate.

¹Palatine. Of or pertaining to the palate.

²Palatine. The palatine bone.

Palea. The upper scale or bract which, with the lemma, encloses a single flower of a grass spikelet.

Paleobotany. The study of fossil plants.

Paleocene Epoch. The first epoch of the fertiary period marked by the rise of archaic placental mammals and birds.

Paleolithic Period. A period in early human culture characterized by the use of stone instruments which, with the Neolithic period, comprises the Stone Age.

Paleontolgy The study of animals and plants of former geological periods as represented by their fossil remains.

Paleozoic Era. An era of geological history following the Proterozoic and preceding the Mesozoic, commonly called the Age of Ancient Life. It was marked by the rise of of land animals and plants.

Palingenetic. Pertaining to characteristics developed during the life of an individual that are inherited from ancestors.

Palisade Mesophyll. Photosynthetic chlorenchyma tissue composed of more or less elongate cells arranged in radial columns. Palisade mesophyll occurs with spongy mesophyll as a ground tissue in the leaves of many mesophytes. Here the palisade mesophyll is usually on the adaxial (upper) side of the leaf, whereas in many xerophytes it forms the bulk of the mesophyll and is present on both sides of the leaf. When the stem has taken over much or all of the photosynthetic work of the plant, the cortex may consist largely of palisade parenchyma.

Palisade Parenchyma. The photosynthetic tissue of a leaf, forming one or more layers of chlorophyll-containing cells (palisade cells) which, with the spongy parenchyma, comprises the mesophyll of a leaf.

Pallial Groove. In chitons, a groove between the foot and the mantle.

Pallial Line. A linear scar on the inner surface of a bivalve shell marking attachment of the mantle.

Pallial Sinus. An indentation in a pallial line, marking point of attachment of the siphon retractor muscle.

Pallium

1. *zool.* The mantle of a mollusk, brachiopod, tunicate, or bird.
2. *embryol.* The thin wall of the lateral vesicles of the telencephalon.
3. *anat.* The cerebral cortex.

[1]Palm. A monocotyledonous plant of the order Palmales, most possessing a large, unbranched trunk bearing at its tip a cluster of large leaves, as the coconut palm.

[2]Palm

1. The inner surface of the hand from wrist to proximal ends of fingers.
2. The corresponding part in the forefoot of a tetrapod.

Palmae (Arecaceae). A monocotyledonous family of mainly tropical trees, the palms. It contains about 2780 species in about 210 genera. The growth form of a palm is characteristic, the plant usually consisting of an unbranched trunk with a crown of large leaves at the apex. When branching does occur, *e.g.* in Hyphaene (doum plams), it is dichotomous. The leaves may be pinnate, as in the feather palms, or the leaflets may all arise from the tip of the midrib, as in fan plans, palm inflorescences are large and may contain thousands of flowers in a panicle or spike. In some palmss, *e.g.* Metroxylon sagu (sago palm), the inflorescence is terminal, and the plant dies after flowering. The fruits are usuallo one-seeded drupes or berries, which may attain a considerable size. Many palms are of economic importance, examples being the coconut plam (Cocos nucifera), the date palm (Phoenix dactylifera, and the oil palm (Elaeis guineensis).

Palmar

1. Of or pertaining to the palm of the hand or manus.
2. Of or pertaining to the ventral surface of the wing of a bird.

Palmate (digitate)

1. Describing a compound leaf having four or more leaflets arising from a single points. The leaves of the horse chestnut (Aesculus hippocastanum) and of lupins (Lupinus) are examples.
2. Describing a form of venation in which several equally prominent veins branch out from the base of the leaf blade.

Palmella Formation. A stage in the development of certain flagellates in which they lose their flagella, undergo division, and form a multicelluar, gentinous mass.

Palmelloid. Describing a type of colonial growth form in which an indefinite number of cells are held together after division in a mucilaginons matrix. Palmelloid forms are characteristic of certain blue-green algae, *e.g.* Merismopedia, and various eukaryotic algae.

Palmitic Acid. A sixteen carbon saturated fatty acid. It is the commonest saturated fatty acid in plants, forming a high proportion of plant fats. It is also on the synthetic route, to other fatty acids such as stearic and oleic acids.

Palp. An elongated sensory organs, usually near the mouth, in many invertebrates. Examples are the tactile head appendages of polychaete worms, the ciliated flap of tissue that produces feeding currents in bivalve molluscs, the distal part of the mandibles of crustaceans, and the olfactory parts of the first and second maxillae of some insects.

Palpal Organ. An intromittent organ on the pedipalp of an arachnid.

Palpate

1. Possessing a palp or palpi.
2. To touch or feel for purposes of diagnosis.

Palpebral. Of or pertaining to the eyelids.

Palpifer. A palp-bearing sclerite on the stipes of an insect maxilla.

Palpiger. A palp-bearing sclerite on the mentum of an insect labium.

Palpitation. A rapid pulsation, throbbing, or beating, as that of the heart.

Palpon. A tactile zooid in certain siphonophores; a dactylozooid.

Palpus pl. **Palpi.** A palp.

Palsy. Paralysis.

Paludal. Of or pertaining to marshes.

Palus. A thickened ridge between the columella and sclerosepta in the skeleton of a coral.

Palustrine. Growing in or inhabiting marshes.

Palynology (pollen analysis). The study of pollen grains and spores, and especially their use in reconstructing the vegetational history of an area. The outer coat, or exine, of a pollen grain or spore is very characteristic for a given family, genus, or sometimes even species. It is also very resistant to decay, particularly under anaerobic conditions.

PAN (peroxyacetyl nitrates). Air pollutants formed during the production of photochemical smog. They are serious eye irritants and cause crop damage. They are thought to result from the interactions of reactive hydrocarbons and nitrogen oxides (which are by-products of the combustion of hydrocarbons, *e.g.* by internal-combustion engines) in the presence of strong sunlight when these substances accumulate in the atmosphere due to a temperature inversion. Other products of photochemical smog include ozone and aldehydes.

[1]Pan. A shallow area or depression containing standing water which usually dries up during the dry season.

[2]Pan. The leaf of the betal pepper (Piper betle) or a masticatory made of these leaves smeared with lime to which slices of betel nuts and flavoring substances are added.

Panbiogeography. Term coined by L. Croizat to describe a new synthesis of the sciences of plant and animal distribution. The main features are that consistencies recur in distribution patterns and that analysis of these produces 'tracks' (joining areas of common floras and faunas) and 'nodes' (where different tracks meet). These ideas from the basis of the new school of vicariance biogeography.

Pancreas. A gland in vertebrates lying between the duodenum and the spleen. Under the influence of the hormone secretin it secretes digestive enzymes (mainly trypsinogen (trypsin), amylase, and lipase) into the duodenum via the pancreatic duct. It also contains groups of cells—the islets of Langerhans—that function as an endocrine gland, producing the hormones insulin and glucagon, which regulate blood sugar levels.

Pancreozymin. A hormone secreted by the duodenal mucosa which stimulates the secretion of enzymes by the pancreas.

Pandemic. Of continental or worldwide distribution, said of a disease.

Pandurate. Fiddle-shaped, as certain leaves.

Pangenesis. A new disregarded theory formulated by Charles Darwin that suggested a mechanism by which acquired characteristics may be inherited. He postulated that there were particles (pangenes) carried in the body fluids from all the organs of the body to the reproductive cells. These particles then influenced the gametes that in turn influenced the characteristics of the succeeding generation.

Panicle. A racemose inflorescence in which the flowers are formed on stalks (peduncles arising alternately or spirally from the main axis. Each stalk is a raceme. The peduncles may be long and spreading, as in oats (Avena), a short, resulting in a spikelike inflorescence, as in timothy grass (Phleum pratense). The panicle is thought to be the most primitive form of racemose inflorescence from which the other types have probably evolved. The term is also sometimes used to describe any type of branching inflorescence.

Panmictic. Characterized by random mating and crossbreeding, said of populations.

Panmixis. Unrestricted random crossing. It is probably fairly rare but the term may be applied to crossing that appears to be random with respect to a particular character or gene. Compare assortive mating.

Panniculus. *anat.* A layer or membrane.

Pansy. A garden flower (Viola tricolor) of the violet family, Violaceae.

Panther

1. In the Americas, the cougar (puma, mountain lion).
2. In India, any of the large leopards, especially Felis pardus.

Pantocolpate. Describing a pollen grain having many colpi.

Pantothenic Acid. A compound, formula $CH_2OHC(CH_3)_2CHOHCONHCH_2CH_2COOH$, that is the precursor of coenzyme A. It is synthesized by plants and bacteria but not by vertebrates, which consequently require it is a vitamin-in the diet.

Pantropic. Affecting more than one type of tissue, said of viruses.

Panzootic. Affecting many species of animals, said of a disease.

Papain. A protein-digesting enzyme (protease) occurring in the fruit of the West Indian papaya tree (Carica papaya). It is used a digestant and in the manufacture of meat tenderizers.

Papaw. An American shrub or tree (Asimina triloba) or the large cylindric, pulpy fruit it produces. Also pawpaw.

Papaya, The oblong, yellow, edible fruit of a tropical tree (Carica papaya), the source of papain, proteolytic enzyme. Also called mamao.

Paper Chromatography. A widely used chromatographic technique for separating the components of mixtures using absorbent paper as the stationary phase. A sheet or strip of paper, with a concentrated spot of the mixture on a pencil-drawn base line, is vertically suspended in a suitable solvent (the mobile phase), that seeps slowly upwards through the paper by capillary action. The compounds in the mixture travel upwards with the solvent and separate out at different levels. When the solvent reaches a level near the top of the paper, this point (the solvent front) is marked. The paper is removed and dried. Colourless compounds may then be developed either by spraying the paper (the chromatogram) with a suitable chemical, such as ninhydrin, or by viewing the paper in ultraviolet light. The compounds can then be identified either by comparing them with chromatograms of known standard solutions run at the same time, or by calculating the Rf values.

Paper Wasp. A social vespid which constructs a nest out of papery materials, as the bald-faced hornet and the yellow jacket.

Papery. Resembling paper in appearance or texture; chartaceous.

Papilla. A projection from a cell, usually of the epidermis, often regarded as a kind of trichome. Papillae are often swollen and covered with wax and in xerophytes may serve to protect from sunlight and excessive water loss.

Papilionaceous. Having a pealike flower, as the pea and other legumes.

Papilla. A nipple; a small nipplelike eminence or projection.

Papillate. Possessing papillae.

Papilloma. A neoplastic growth on a surface epithelium, as a wart.

Papillose. Covered with or bearing numerous papillae.

Papovavirus. One of a group of DNA-containing viruses that produce tumours in their host. Papilloma types produce nonmalignant tumours (such as warts) in all vertebrates; polyoma types produce malignant tumours in only certain classes of vertebrates (not including man).

Parenteral. Not by way of the intestine or digestive tract, with reference to substances being taken into the body.

Paresis. General paralysis.

Pappose. Resembling a pappus; possessing a pappus; downy.

Pappus. A modified calyx made up of aring of fine hairs, scales, or teeth that persist after fertilization and aid the wind dispersal of the fruit, often by forming a parachute-like structure. It is seen in members of the Compositae, *e.g.* dandelions (Taraxacum) and thistles (Carduus). The pappuses of an inflorescence may form a 'clock'.

Papula pl. **Papulae.** One of the numerous ciliated projections on the body surface of echinoderms which functions in respiration and excretion. Also called dermal branchia.

Papule. A small, solid elevation of the skin; a pimple.

Parabasal Body. A minute body of unknown function laying close to the basal granule in certain protozoans, as trypanosomes.

Parabiosis. The experimental joining together of individuals so as to form parabiotic twins.

Parachordal. Alongside the cephalic portion of the notochord, as parachordal cartilages of the embryonic skull.

Parachuting

1. Ballooning.
2. Wind dispersal of seeds which bear a parachutelike tuft of hairs, as the dand on seed.

Paracone. The exterior anterior cusp of an upper molar tooth.

Paraffin Method. A widely-used procedure employed in the preparation of tissues for microscopical examination. Steps include killing and fixing, dehydration, clearing, embedding in paraffin, sectioning, and mounting of sections. Tissues may be stained before or after sectioning.

Paraganglia Small masses of chromaffin tissue located between the kidneys in lower vertebrates, as fishes.

Paragaster. The spongocoel, the central cavity of a sponge.

Paraglossa. The outermost of a pair of lobes on the labium of certain insects.

Paraglycogen. A polymerized product of glycogen which forms a reserve food supply occurring as refractile granules in various protozoans.

Paragnath

1. One of a pair of chitinized processes bearing jaws in the lining of the eversible pharynx of certain polychaetes, as Nereis.
2. A lobe on the lower lip or metastoma of certain crustaceans.

Parahormone. A substance resembling a hormone in many respects but differing in that it is not a secretory product, as carbon dioxide.

Parallel Evolution (parallelism). The development of similar adaptations in related organisms as a result of being subject to similar selection pressures. Thus the different species of a genus with a wide distribution may show the same adaptations to similar environments in widely separated regions. The development of divided submerged leaves in various species of crowfoot, *e.g.* water crowfoot (Ranunculus aquatilis) and river crowfoot (R. fluitans), is an example. However the phenomenon is not of widespread occurrence and some authorities deny its existence.

Parallelism

1. A similar course of evolution followed by two unrelated groups of organisms.
2. The occurrence of superficially similar organs in unrelated groups, as the eye in a squid and man.

Parallelodromous. Describing a form of leaf venation in which two or more primary veins originate at the base of the lmina and run to the apex in an essentially parallel manner. The leaves of many monocotyledons have this type of venation. In traditional terminology such venation is simply termed parallel.

Paralysis. Loss of sensation or loss of muscular function usually due to an injury to a nerve or a lesion within the central nervous system.

Paramecium (suborder Peniculina). Genus of ciliate protozoa in which the cells are elongated or ovoid, and range in size from 0.05—0.33 mm, depending on species and conditions. Body cilia are arranged uniformly, and two contractile vacuoles are usually present. There are many species. They are common in various types of aquatic environments, and feed mainly on bacteria.

Paramere

1. One of the halves of a bilaterally symmetrical animal or of a metamere.
2. In radially symmetrical animals, a perradius and half of an interradius on each side.
3. One of a pair of copulatory structures lying lateral to the penis, in certain insects.

Parameter. A quantity that characterizes and describes a population.

Paramifosis. Mitosis in which chromosomal behavior is a typical, as in protozoans.

Paramylon. A polysaccharide occurring in the form of ovoid granules (paramylon bodies) in various protozoans; paramylum.

Paramylum. A polysaccharide that is the assimilation product of both green and colourless algae of the Eugle-nophyta.

Paramyxoviruses (Paramyxoviridae). Groups (family) of viruses in which the virions are enveloped and contain a single molecule of RNA. Paramyxoviruses are responsible for a range of diseases in humans and other animals, including mumps, measles, and Newcastle disease.

Paranthropus. Genus recognized by some authorities to describe the robust australopithecines, often classified as Australopithecus robustus or A. boisei. They were early protohominids, the sister group of Homo Members of the genus, often called 'nutcracker man", were characterized by enormous molars and premolars, and reduced front teeth. They were common at such sites as Olduvai and Koobi Fora, in the Late Pliocene and Early Pleistocene.

Parapet. The collar of a sea anemone.

Paraphyletic. Describing a group of organisms that does not contain all the descendants of a common ancestor. In plant classification, the dicotyledons are a paraphyletic group because their ancestors also gave rise to the more advanced monocotyledons.

Paraphysis. A sterile unbranched usually multicellular hair borne amongst the reproductive structures of many bryophytes, algae, and fungi. Paraphyses are protective and in some cases are throught to aid in dehiscence.

Parapodium

1. In Polychaeta, usually biramous, muscular, lateral projections of the body, paired and extending from the body segments, more or less compressed laterally, and bearing setae; in free-swimming forms they are used for locomotion, and in sessile forms to fan water.

2. In opisthobranch Mollusca, lateral projections from the side of the foot which form fins used in swimming.

Parapophysis. A process on the body of a vertebra with which the capitulum of a rib articulates.

Parasexual Recombination. A form of recombination seen in the progeny of certain heterokaryotic fungi; which does not involve meiotic segregation. The sequence of events involved is termed the parasexual cycle and is as follows : two genotypically distinct nuclei in a heterokaryon fuse to give a diploid heterozygous nucleus; the diploid nucleus multiplies alongside the haploid parent nuclei in the heterokaryon; a homokaryotic diploid mycelium is established from a diploid conidium; recombination occurs during crossing-over in mitosis; a haploid nucleus is formed by progressive shedding of chromosomes from the diploid nucleus.

Such recombination has been observed in various ascomycetes, basidiomycetes, and imperfect fungi. It accounts for the occurrence of new strains of pathogenic imperfect fungi. It has also made feasible the study of the genetics and 'breeding' of imperfect fungi.

Parasitemia. The presence of parasites in the blood, especially the malarial parasite.

Paraproct. A podical plate.

Parapsid. Designating a type of skull in which a single opening, the upper supratemporal fossa, exists, as in certain extinct reptiles.

Parapsis pl. **Parapsides.** A lateral sclerite on the thorax of an insect. Sometimes called scapula.

Parasite

1. An organism which lives in or on another organism from which it derives its nourishment.
2. The smaller of a pair of conjoined twins.

Parasite-mix. A parasitocoenosis.

Parasitica. One of the two customary divisions of the suborder Apocrita (order Hymenoptera). The Aculeata are the stinging forms (ants, bees, and wasps) and the Parasitica are those whose larvae parasitize other insects. There are four principal superfamilies : Ichneumonoidea, Chalcidoidea, Cynipoidea, and Proctotrupoidea.

Parasitism. Interaction of species populations in which one, typically small, organism (the parasite) lives in or on another (the host), from which it obtains food, shelter, or other requirements. Parasitism usually implies that some harm is done to the host, but this interpretation must be qualified. Effects on the host range from almost none to severe illness and eventual death, but even where such obvious immediate harm accrues to the individual host it does not follow that the relationship is harmful to the host species in the long term or in an evolutionary context—for example, it might favour beneficial adaptation in the host species population. Obligate parasites can live only parasitically. Facultative parasites may live as parasites or as independent saprophytes. Ectoparasites live externally on the host. Endoparasites live inside the body of the host. A partial parasite is a plant that carries out photosynthesis, but that relies on its host for other nutrients and needs, *e.g.* support. Compare commensalism; mutualism; and neutralism.

Parastichy. An imaginary spiral around a stem apex joining adjacent leaf primordia. Two parastichies can be visualized running in opposite directions (diagram). If a plant is described as having, for example, (3+5) or 3/5 phyllotaxis, this means that the shallower of the two parastichies joins every third primordium formed at the apex (1, 4, 7, 10, etc.) and the steeper parastichy joins every fifth primordium (1, 6, 11, 16, etc.)

Parasitocoenosis. The combined populations of organisms, plant and animal, which live together in a host organ or in the entire host, as all the organisms (bacteria, yeasts, molds, protozoans, worms) which live in the intestine of a vertebrate, or all the organisms (ecto-and endoparasites) which live in or on a single host.

Parasitoid

1. A parasite which lives within its host only during its larval development, eventually killing the host.
2. A mite of the superfamily Parasitoidea, as the red mite or roost mite of poultry.

Parasitology. The study of parasites and parasitism.

Parasitosis. A pathological state or condition caused by parasites.

Parasymbiosis. Mutualism.

Parasympathetic. Pertaining to that division of the autonomic nervous system which comprises the craniosacral outflow. Includes cranial nerves III, VII, IX, and X and sacral nerves 2, 3, and 4 containing preganglionic fibers which synapse in terminal ganglia with postganglionic neurons.

Parasympathetic Nervous System. Part of the autonomic nervous system. Its nerve endings release acetylcholine as a neuro-transmitter and its actions tendto antagonize those of the sympathetic nervous system. For example, the parasympathetic nervous system increases salivary gland secretion, decreases heart rate, promotes digestion (by increasing peristalsis), and dilates blood vessels, while the sympathetic nervous system has opposite effects.

Paratenic Host. In parasitology, a transport host.

Parathormone. A hormone, PTH, secreted by the parathyroid glands, which regulates calcium and phosphorus metabolism.

Parathyroid Glands. Two pairs of endocrine glands situated behind, or embedded within, the thyroid gland in higher vertebrates. They produce parathyroid hormone (parathormone), which controls the amount of calcium in the blood. A low level of calcium stimulates hormone secretion, which increases transfer of calcium from the bones to the blood (compare calcitonin).

Paratonic. Not automatic; due to external causes, with reference to plant movements.

Paratonic Movement. A movement exhibited by a plant or plant part in response to an external stimulus. Taxes, tropisms, and nastic movements and mechanical hygroscopic and turgor movements are all examples of paratonic movements Compare autonomic movement.

Paratype. A specimen other than the isotype or holotype cited in the original publication of the name of a taxon. A paratype can also be one of a collection of syntypes, following the selection of a lectotype. Although of little significance nomenclaturally, paratypes are of considerable importance to the taxonomist, who may not be able to see other type material of a particular taxon.

Paraxial. Lying near or alongside the main axis of the body.

Paraxonic. Having the axis of symmetry between the third and fourth digits, as in even-toed ungulates. Compare mesaxonic.

Parazoan. Any member of the Parazoa, a division of the Metazoa which includes the Porifera (sponges), characterized by lack of organized tissues and absence of a digestive cavity.

Paranchyma

1. In plants, tissue composed of thin-walled, live cells permeated by air spaces.
2. In Platyhelminthes, the tissue, composed of cells and intercellular spaces, filling the interior of the body.
3. In other animals, the essential cells of an organ,

as opposed to blood cells, cells of connective tissue, etc.

Parenchymatous. Resembling, of the nature of, or composed of parenchyma.

Parenchymula Larva. The stereogastrula of a sponge.

Parent

1. A father or mother.
2. Something which brings forth offspring, as a parent cell.

Parichnos An area of tissue made up of disintegrated cells seen at the base of the sporophylls in the strobili of Lycopodium and in the leaves of various fossil relatives of Lycopodium, such as Lycopodities and Lepidodendron.

[1]Parietal

1. Pertaining to the wall of an organ or of the body. Compare visceral.
2. *bot.* Attached to the wall of an ovary, with reference to ovules or placenta.

[2]Parietal. A paired membrane bone forming a part of the roof and sides of the cranial cavity.

Parietal Body. The parapineal body, the anterior portion of the epiphyseal apparatus located anterior to the pineal body; present in lower vertebrates, as in Sphenodon where it forms a third eye.

Parietal Cell. A cell of a gastric gland which secretes hydrochloric acid.

Parietal Placentation. A form of placentation in which the placentae develop along the fused margins of a unilocular compound ovary, as in violets (Viola).

Paripinnate. Describing a pinnate leaf in which all the leaflets are paired. Such leaves are seen in vetchs (Vicia), the terminal leaflet having been replaced by a tendril. Compare imparipinnate.

Park

1. In ancient farming systems, the enclosed fields lying between the inner fields next to the farm buildings, and the larger, outer fields used only seasonally for pasture.
2. Enclosed land on which deer are or were kept.
3. Land, usually woodpasture, enclosed by a pale, and intended for the keeping of deer.
4. In modern use, an area of land set aside for public enjoyment and designed to resemble semi-natural land.

Parotid Gland. A salivary gland located anterior to the ear, its duct opening into the mouth cavity; a compound tubulo-acinous gland composed of serous cells.

Parotoid Gland. A poison gland in the skin of an amphibian.

Paroxysm. A sudden, violent, uncontrollable action.

Parr. The young of salmon and other marine fishes, especially those with short vertical marks (parr marks) along sides of body.

Parrot. Any of a number of brilliantly colored birds of the order Psittaciformes with hooked beaks and loud raucous voices, including the parakeets, macaws, cockatoos, lories, lorikeets, lovebirds, and allied species.

Parrot Fever. Psittacosis.

Parrot Fish. A brightly colored tropical fish of the family Scaridae with parrotlike jaws, as Sparisoma, Scarus.

Parted. Cleft or divided, but not entirely to the base, with reference to leaves.

arthenitae. The sporocysts and redia of flukes.

Parthenocarpy. The production of a fruit without the setting of seeds. The process is an irrelevance in the life history of a plant and is unusual in that it appears not to benefit the plant it any way. Parthenocarpy is most often seen in plants with numerous ovules in the fruit, *e.g.* fig and melon. In some species, *e.g.* cucumber, pollination is not required to stimulate parthenocarpy.

Parthenogenesis. Development of an individual from an egg without fertilization. It occurs in some groups of animals (*e.g.* flatworms, leeches, aphids, rotifers), it which males may be absent, and plants (*e.g.* dandelion). The egg (ova) that develop in this way are usually diploid, so all offspring are genetically identical with the parent. Commonly parthenogenesis with only females in the population alternates with ordinary sexual reproduction, which allows the recombination of genetic material and presents a need for males. This alternation is called heterogamy.

Parthenogone. A parthenogenetically produced individual.

Parthenogonic. Reproducing by parthenogenesis.

Parthenogonidium. In colonial protozoans, an asexual reproductive zooid, as in Volvox.

Parthenospore (azygospore). A thickwalled resting spore that develops parthenogenetically from an unfertilized gamete. Parthenospores are formed by certain algae, *e.g.* Protosiphon, and fungi, *e.g.* Entomophthora muscae. They may give rise to more gametes or to a haploid individual. Compare zygospore.

Parthenote. A haploid individual produced by parthenogenes.

Partial Dominance. In genetics, incomplete or semidominance; the production of an intermediate phenotype in individuals heterozygous for the gene concerned. For example, in Mirabilis jalapa (the four-o'clock plant), individuals with red petals bred in a pure line when crossed to a pure line with white petals will yield individuals with pink petals in the first filial generation. The red phenotype (and its determining allele) is said to be incompletely dominant over the white phenotype (and its allele). The impact of a gene at the level of the phenotype depends on its dominance relations, but also on the conditions of the rest of the genome and on the conditions of the environment.

Particulate Inheritance. The determination of inherited characteristics by stable discrete factors that remain unchanged from one generation to another. Differences observed between parents and offspring are thus due to the recombination rather than modification of such factors. The particulate nature of inheritance was established with Mendel's work. Earlier theories formulated without experimental evidence tended to the idea that the characteristics of parents blended together in the offspring (blending inheritance).

Parturition. The act of giving birth to young at the end of the gestation period. Hormons probably cause the process to start but the mechanism is not fully understood.

Parus (tits, chickadees; family Paridae). Genus of small, olive brown, or grey birds which have yellow, white, or buff under-parts. Many have black caps and bibs, some have crests. Many frequent gardens, readily using nestboxes. They feed particularly on nuts, which many store. There are 47 species found in Europe, Africa, Asia, and N. and C. America.

PAS Reaction. The Periodic Acid Schiff reaction, a cytological technique by which the localization of polysaccharides within a cell can be accomplished. It is dependent upon the Feulgen reaction.

PAS Reagent. The Schiff reagent, basic fuchsin which has been bleached with sulfurous acid.

Passage Cell. Any of the thin-walled cells found at intervals in the endodermis, generally opposite the protoxylem poles. It is believed that passage cells provide an easier route for water and dissolved solutes to pass through from the cortex to the protoxylem.

Passeriform. Passerine.

[1]Passerine. Of or pertaining to the order Passeriformes, the largest order of the class Aves containing the perching birds, numbering over 5100 species. Includes the suborder Passeres (Oscines) which comprises the songbirds.

[2]Passerine. Any bird of the order Passeriformes.

Passive

1. Note active.
2. Resulting from or brought about by outside forces.

Passive Transport. The movement of substances across a plasma membrane which does not involve the expenditure of energy by the cell. Compare active transport.

Pasteurization. The treatment of milk to destroy disease-causing bacteria, such as those of tuberculosis, typhoid, and brucellosis. Milk is heated to 65°C for 30 minutes or to 72°C for 15 minutes followed by rapid cooling to below 10°C . The method was devised by the French microbiologist Louis Pasteur (1822-95).

Pastoralism. Human way of life that depends economically largely upon grazing domesticated animals (*e.g.* cattle, sheep, goats) or semi-domesticated animals (*e.g.* reindeer)l which provide food, clothing, hides used to make shelters, etc. Often the number of stock owned by an individua, herdsman is a measure of his wealth and social status. Some seasonal migration is often associated with pastoralism, so that pastoralists are often semi-nomadic.

Pasture. Grass or other plants used for feeding grazing animals, or land bearing such that is used for grazing.

Patagium

1. *ornith.* The patagial membrane, a web of skin which extends from body to wing.
2. In mammals, a fold of skin between fore and hind limbs as in flying squirrels and flying lemurs.
3. The wing membrane of a bat.
4. A lateral process on the thorax of certain insects, as in lepidopterans.

Patella (kneecap). A small rounded movable bone that is situated in a tendon in front of the knee joint in most mammals (incluing humans). The function of the patella is to protect the knee.

Patelliform

1. *zool.* Shaped like a limpet of the genus Patella.
2. *bot.* Disc-shaped with a narrow rim.

Patent

1. *anat.* Exposed, open, said of tubes or ducts.
2. *bot.* Patulous, spreading.

Paternal. Of or pertaining to the father or mole parent; inherited from the male side.

Pathogen. An agent able to cause disease. The term is often restricted to agents that are themselves living organisms.

Pathogenesis. The sequence of changes occurring in the development of a disease.

Pathogenicity. Virulence.

Pathology. The scientific study of disease, including causes, symptoms, signs, and various structural and functional alterations which may occur in its course.

Patristic. Describing similarity between two or more taxa that is due to common ancestry. The concept of patristic relationship is purely phylogenetic and thus not used in the construction of phenetic classifications.

Patronymic. In nomenclature, a name derived from a person or persons.

Pattern Analysis. Any analysis for the detection of a non-random distribution of organisms, *e.g.* nearest-neighbour analysis, or classification techniques. However, the term is applied more particularly to the detection of patterns in the distribution of individuals of a given plant species in a community by comparing the observed number of individuals per quadrat with the expected number derived from the Poisson series (based on a population that is dispersed at random). The correspondence is tested for statistical significance either by comparing observed numbers with those predicted using the χ^2 test, or by comparing the variance : mean ratio for the data with the value for the Poisson series of unity. Where this ratio is significantly greater or less than unity, the population is respectively overdispersed (contagious) or underdispersed (regular). Though first applied to studies of plant ecology, the technique is now widely used in other fields.

Patulous. Expanded, open, dilated.

aunch

1. The rumen.
2. The abdominal cavity and its contents.

Paurometabolous. Pertaining to the group Paurometabola, which comprises insects which undergo gradual metamorphosis, as orthopterans, hemipterans.

Pauropod. An arthropod of the class Pauropoda, comprising mostly minute, terrestrial forms living in damp places, as Pauropus.

Paw. The foot of an animal, especially the clawed foot of a quadruped.

Pea. A round, edible seed produced in dehiscent pods by the vine, Pisum sativum, a legume, or the plant which produces it, of the pea family, Leguminosae.

P each

1. A tree (Prunus persica) of the rose family, Rosaceae.
2. The fruit, a drupe with a fleshy pericarp, of the peach tree.

Peacock. The male of the peafowl, with elongated, erectile, ocellated tail feathers of striking iridescent colours.

Pea Carb. One of a number of small crabs of the family Pinnotheridae, most of which are commensals inhabiting the tubes and burrows, and the mantle, cloacal, and pharyngeal cavities of various invertebrates.

Peafowl. One of a number of gallinaceous birds of the genus Pavo, especially P. cristatus, a domesticated species, a native of India.

Peahen. The female of the peafowl.

Peanut. A bushy, creeping annual (Arachis hypogaea); a legume; or its fruit which ripens underground.

Peanut Worm. A sipunculid.

Pear. The fleshy fruit, a pome, of a tree (Pyrus communis) or the tree which produces it, a member of the rose family, Rosaceae.

Pearl. A dense, lustrous body which develops as an abnormal growth in the inner layer of the shell of certain mollusks due to a foreign object or parasite lodging between the mantle and the shell and nacre being deposited about it in concentric layers.

Pearl Organ. A cornified area of the epidermis which appears in certain teleost fishes during the breeding season.

Pearl Oyster. One of several large, marine bivalves of the family Pteridae, a source of pearls, found principally in the Persiat Gulf, and off the coasts of Australia and Lower California, as Avicula (Pteria) and Margaritifera.

Peat. A mass of dark-brown or black fibrous plant debris produced by the partial disintegration of vegetation in wet places. It may accumulate in depressions. When subjected to burial and hence pressure and heat it may be converted to coal. Peat is used to improve soil and as a fuel, especially in Ireland and Sweden.

Peat-borer. Implement designed to extract peat cores with the minimum of disturbance. The most familiar is the Hiller peat-borer, which consists of a short screw auger head to ease penetration of the peat, backed by a chamber which can be opened and closed at the required sample depth, the sharp cutting edge of the chamber assisting detachment of the sample in more consolidated peats. The principale alternatives are the piston sampler, which is particularly good for loose peats, and the Russian borer, which allows easier removal of the complete peat core than is possible with the Hiller borer, but which is more difficult to use in compacted peats since it has no screw auger head.

Pecan. A hickory tree (Carya illinoensis) or the thin-shelled nut it produces.

Pecking Order. Name given to the hierarchical social organization found in some insect species, *e.g.* ants, bees, and in many vertebrate species. It is so called because the phenomenon was first described for chickens. Social organizations of this type have survival value, *e.g.* clustering in bees generates and maintains sufficient warmth to ensure survival during winter temperatures low enough to kill the same individuals if isolated. Colonies may also have a regulatory function operating against growth in excess of immediate environmental resources.

Pecten

1. pl. *pectines*. A comblike structure, as *a.* a serrated, fan-shaped structure in the eye of a bird; *b.* the pollen rake, a part of the pollen packer of a honeybee; *c.* a sensory structure attached to the second mesosomatic segment of a scorpion.
2. pl. *pectens*. A scallop, a bivalve of the geneus Pecten.

Pectic Substances. Pectins and related polysaccharides, in which galacturonic acid, galactose, or a derivative of these is a major component. Besides the pectins found in cell walls and middle lamellae, large quantities of pectic substances are found in some fruits, *e.g.* apples, pears, and citrus fruits. Pectins are used in the food industry as gelling agents in jams, etc.

Pectin. Any of a group of water-soluble substances present in plant tissues which, in the presence of sugar (65-70%) and proper acid concentation (pH 3.2—3.5) causes the formation of jelly.

Pectinate. Shaped like or having teeth resembling a comb; comblike.

Pectoral. Of, pertaining to, or located in the region of the breast or chest.

Pectoral Fin. One of the paired anterior lateral fins of a fish.

Pectoral Girdle (shoulder girdle). The bony or cartilaginous structure in vertebrates to which the anterior limbs (pectoral fins, forelegs, or arms) are attached. In mammals in consists of two dorsal scapulae (shoulder blades) attached to the backbone and two ventral clavicles (collar bones) attached to the sternum (breastbone).

Pedal. Of or pertaining to the food or feet.

Pedal Cyst. A podocyst.

Pedal Disk. The basal disk of a hydrozoan.

Pedal Ganglion. A ganglion in the foot of various mollusks.

Pedal Gland. A gland in the food of a rotifer or a mollusk.

Pedalium. The flattened, basal portion of a tentacle in certain coelenterates, as the cubomedusae.

Pedate

1. *bot.* Designating a palmately lobed leaf in which the two side lobes are also divided.
2. *zool. a.* Having podia or feet, with reference to holothuroids. *b.* Having a foot or feet.

Peddler. The larva of the tortoise beetle, which possesses a forked caudal process to which cast skins and excrement are attached, the whole forming a shield over the body.

Pedalfer. A soil in which the soluble line has been leached from the surface layers by heavy persistent rain. It is thus acid and the rate of decomposition of soil litter is consequently slow. Iron and aluminium hydroxides are abundant. Pedalfers are one of the two main types of zonal soils (compare pedocal) and include brown earths, podsols, and tundra soils.

Pedicel. The stalk attaching individual flowers to the main axis (peduncle) of the inflorescence. It often develops in the axil of a bract and its internal structure is typically stemlike. The pedicel may act as a temporary storage organ for sugars prior to seed development.

Pedicellaria. A small pincherlike organ on the body surface of various echinoderms.

Pedicellate. Borne on a pedicel.

Pedicle. A pedicel or peduncle.

Pediculosis. Infestation with lice.

Pediform. Shaped like a foot.

Pedigerous. Bearing feet or limbs.

Pedigree Method. A plant breeding technique that is used to create entirely new varieties of plants that combine the best qualities of selected existing varieties. The method is limited to self-pollinating species. Parents are selected and artificially crossed. A few (say six to ten) of the resulting F_1 hybrid seeds are sown widely spaced to encourage prolific seed set. Assuming the parents were homozygous, the F_1 plants should all be identical. The seed from each plant is harvested separately and grown, again widely spaced, in separate 'family' plots. The genotypic variability becomes apparent in the F_2 and the characteristics of each plant are noted. The seed from a small number (perhaps only 1%) of promising plants is harvested to grow on to the F_3. The seeds from each plant are again sown in separate plots and in this way the 'pedigree' of each plant can be recorded. By noting the variability within each of the F_3 plots it may be determined which plants of the previous generation depended excessively on heterozygosity for vigour. At this stage whole families of plants may be discarded. As heterozy by is approximately halved each generation, increasing emphasis is placed in succeeding generations on selection between rather than within families. If breeding a crop plant, then at about the F_6 generation seeds from selected plants are grown closely spaced as would occur in normal field conditions. Yield may then be determined. From this point selection is entirely between families. By the F_8 generation the remaining selected lines may be assumed to be over 99% homozygous and they are bulked up for variety trials. Compare back-crossing.

Pedipalp. One of the second pair of appendages in arachnids, resembling a leg in appearance and structure; in scorpions they are well developed chelate structures.

Pedocal. A soil in which lime accumulates in the surface layers, which consequently become alkaline. Pedocals occur in regions with light rainfall and are usually fertile as they may be rich in potash and phosphates as well as lime. In persistently dry conditions calcium salts may be deposited on the soil surface. Pedocals are one of the two main types of zonal soils (compare pedalfer), and include the chestnut-brown soils, chernozems, and red desert soils.

Pedology. The science of the study of soils, including their origin and characteristics and their utilization.

Peduncle. The main stalk of a plant that bears the flowers, which may be solitary or grouped in an inflorescence. Compare pedicel.

Pedunculate. Possessing a peduncle.

Peking Man. Pithecanthropus (Sinanthropus) pekinensis, a species of prehistoric man related to the Java man.

Pelage. The hairy coat of a mammal; wool, fur, hair.

Pelagic. Describing the organisms that live in the surface waters of a sea or ocean, such as plankton.

Pelagic Life. All the life of open waters, as plankton, nekton, neuston.

Pelican. A large, fish-eating bird (Pelecanus erythrorhynchos) with a long, flat bill bearing a large, distensible gular pouch.

Pellagra. A deficiency disease resulting from inadequate intake or absorption of niacin or niacinamide.

Pellet

1. A small, spherical mass of material, as food or medicine.

2. *ornith.* A mass consisting of the undigestible remains of animals regurgitated by predatory birds, as herons and owls which swallow their prey whole.

Pellicle (periplast). A membrane surrounding the protoplast in some unicellular algae that lack a cellulose cell wall, for example Euglena. In many cases, it is believed to consist of numerous semirigid overlapping rings. The pellicle may be rigid or flexible.

Pellucid. Clear; transparent.

Pelt. The hide or skin of a fur-bearing mammal, especially when undressed.

Peltate. Describing a structure that is circular, with the stalk inserted in the middle, such as the leaf of the garden nasturtium (Tropaeolum majus), the hairs on the undersurface of the leaves of sea buckthorn (Hippophae rhamnoides), or the sporangiophores of certain cycads.

Pelvic. Of or pertaining to the pelvis or pelvic girdle.

Pelvic Fins. Fins.

Pelvic Girdle (pelvis; hip girdle). The bony or cartilaginous structure in vertebrates to which the posterior limbs (pelvic fins or legs) are attached. The pelvic girdle articulates dorsally with the backbone; it is made up of two halves, each produced by the fusion of the ilium, ischium, and pubis.

Pelvis

1. Pelvic girdle.
2. The lower part of the abdomen in the region of the pelvic girdle.
3. A conical chamber in the kidney into which urine drains from the kidney tubules before passing to the ureter.

Pen

1. *bot.* The midrib of a leaf.
2. *zool. a.* The horny, internal shell of a squid. *b.* A female swan. Compare cob.

Pendant. Hanging downward, suspended.

Pendulous. Pendant.

Penetrance. The proportion of individuals of a specified genotype who manifest that genotype in the phenotype under a defined set of environmental conditions. If all individuals carrying a lethal mutation die prematurely, then the mutant gone is said to show complete penetrance. An organism may not express the phenotype normally associated with its genotype because of the presence of modifiers, epistatic genes, or suppressors in the rest of the genome; or because of a modifying effect of the environment. Expressivity describes the degree or extent to which a given genotype is expressed phenotypically in an individual.

Penetrant. A type of nematocyst with a tube which, when discharged, penetrates prey producing a toxic effect.

Penguin. A short-legged, aquatic, flighltess bird of the southern hemisphere with wings adapted for swimming, as Aptenodytes patagonica, the king penguin of the family Spheniscidae.

Penial. Of or pertaining to the penis.

Penial Setae. Copulatory setae in a male nematode.

Penicillate. Ending in a tuft of hairs, like that of a brush.

Penicillin. Type of antibiotic produced for example by fungi of the genus Penicillium. Penicillins are active against certain types of bacteria (mainly Gram-positive species) and are widely used in the treatment of diseases caused by those bacteria. (Pencillin G was one of the first antibiotics to be used for the treatment of disease). There is now a wide range of chemically-modified penicillins, each with slightly different properties. They function by inhibiting the synthesis of bectrial cell walls.

Penicillium (class Hyphomycetes). Form-genus of fungi which form branched conidiophores bearing phialids. Conidia appear as greyish-green or bluish-green powdery masses on white mycelium. Most species are saprotrophic and cosmopolitan in distribution. Many species produce important antibiotics, including penicillins. Some species are used in the manufacture of certain types of cheese.

Pennirparallel. Craspedromous.

Penis. The male reproductive organ of mammals (and also of some birds and reptiles) used to introduce sperm into the female reproductive tract to ensure internal fertilization. It contains a duct (the urethra) through which the sperms pass. The penis becomes erect during precopulatory activity, either the filling with blood or haemolymph or by the action of muscles, and can be inserted into the vagina (or cloaca). In mammals the urine also leaves the body through the penis.

Penna pl. **Pennae.** A contour feather or pluma as distinguished from a down feather (plumula).

Pennaceous. Penniform; like a feather.

Pennate. Pinnate.

Penniculus. A curved band of cilia in the cytopharynx of certain ciliates.

Prestore. To store data prior to processing.

Penniform. Pennate; resembling a feather, said of certain muscles.

Pennsylvanian Period. The Upper Carbonaceous, a period of the Paleozoic era marked by warm and humid climate and the formation of great coal forests and swamps.

Pensile. Hanging or pendant, with reference to the nest of certain birds.

Pentacula Larva. The final larval stage in the development of a sea cucumber.

Pentadactyl. Having five digits in the hand or foot.

Pentadactyl Limb. A limb with five digits, characteristic of tetrapod vertebrates (amphibians, reptiles, birds, and mammals). It evolved from the paired fins of primitive fish as an adaptation to locomotion on land and is not found in modern fish. The limb has three parts (illustration) : the upper arm or thigh containing one long bone, the forearm or shank containing two long bones, and the hand or foot, which contains a number of small bones. This basic design is modified in many species, according to the function of the limb, particularly by the loss of fusion of the terminal bones.

Pentadelphous. In groups of five, with reference to the filaments of stamens.

Pentamerous (5-merous). Describing flowers in which the parts of each whorl are inserted in fives, or multiples of five. This is the most commonly found arrangement in dicotyledons.

Pentandrous. With five stamens.

Pentapetalous. With five petals.

Pentasepalous. With five sepals.

Pentastomid. A tongue worm, a parasitic, wormlike animal of the class Pentastomida (Linguatulida), phylum Arthropoda, as Linguatula serrata, inhabiting the paranasal sinuses of carnivores.

Pentosan. A polysaccharide in which the major monosaccharide subunits are pentoses. The most common monosaccharide components of pentosans are xylose and L-arabinose. Many hemicelluloses are pentosans, although they are usually heteropolymers containing other sugars besides the pentoses.

Pentose. Any five-carbon sugar. Common pentoses are ribose, deoxyribose, xylose, and arabinose. Pentoses are synthesized from hexoses in the pentose phosphate pathway, from carbon dioxide in the Calvin cycle, or by decarboxylation of nucleoside diphosphate sugars. Polymers of pentoses are collectively, termed pentosans.

Pentose Phosphate Pathway (phosphogluconate pathway, hexose monophosphate shunt). A complex multifunctional metabolic pathway involving oxidation of glucose and formation of three-, four-, five-, six-, and seven-carbon sugars.

In the pentose phosphate pathway glucose 6-phosphate is first oxidized and decarboxylated to a five-carbon sugar with the concomitant formation of NADPH. The five-carbon sugar then undergoes various combinations and transformations, similar to those of the Calvin cycle, leading eventually to the reformation of glucose 6-phosphate.

Although the pathway can be used for the oxidation of glucose, it is more important as a source of five-carbon sugars, as a pathway for the oxidation of five-carbon sugars, and as a source of NADPH for such purposes as fatty acid synthesis.

Pentoxylales. An order of extinct gymnosperms from the Jurassic, the affinities of which are uncertain.

Peony. A flower (Paeonia) of the buttercup family, Ranunculaceae.

PEP. Phosphoenolpyruvate.

Pepo. A type of berry with a hard exterior derived either from the epicarp or noncarpellary tissue of the plant. In members of the Cucurbitaceae the hard exterior is formed from the receptacle of the flower.

Pepper

1. A pungent spice obtained from plants of the genus Piper, black pepper being obtained from the dried ripe fruit of P. nigrum.
2. Any of a number of plants of the genus Capsicum or their fruits, the source of cayenne or red pepper and paprika.

Peppermint. The dried leaf and flowering top of Mentha piperita, the source of peppermint oil, used as a flavoring and a carminative.

Pepsin

1. An enzyme present in gastric juice which catalyzes the hydrolysis of proteins and polypeptides.
2. A substance containing this enzyme obtained from the mucosa of the stomach of a hog.

Pepsinogen. The precursor (zymogen) of pepsin produced by the chief cells of gastric glands.

Peptidase. Any hydrolase enzyme that catalyses the hydrolysis of peptides. The distinction between proteases and peptidases is not a clear one—peptidases often have protease activity and vice versa.

Several types of peptidase can be distinguished. Exopeptidases can only attack terminal peptide bonds while endopeptidases attack bonds within the peptide chain and are often specific to certain types of peptide linkage. Aminopeptidases attack the amino terminal of peptides and carboxypeptidases attack the carboxy terminal. Dipeptidases attack only dipeptides.

Peptide. A molecule consisting of a number of amino acids covalently joined by peptide linkages. Small peptides containing only a few amino acids are known an oligopeptides while larger peptides are called polypeptides. Most oligopeptides arise as breakdown products of proteins but a few have specific functions. For example, the tripeptide glutathione activates some enzymes and protects lipids from autooxidation.

Peptide Linkage. The union of an amino group (NH_2) with a carboxyl group (COOH), as occurs in the union of two or more amino acids.

Pepsin. An enzyme, secreted by cells lining the interior of the vertebrate stomach, that catalyses the breakdown of proteins.

Peptide. Any of a group of organic compounds comprising two or more amino acids linked by peptide bonds. These bonds are formed by the reaction between adjacent carboxyl (—COOH) and amino (—NH_2) groups with the elimination of water (illustration). Dipeptides contain two amino acids, tripeptides three, and so on. Polypeptides contain more than ten and usually 100-300. Naturally occurring oligopeptides (of less than ten amino acids) include the tripeptide glutathione and the pituitary hormones vasopressin and oxytocin, which are octapeptides. Peptides also result from protein breakdown, *e.g.* during digestion.

Peptone. A product of the hydrolysis of a protein, intermediate between a proteose and a peptide.

[1]Perch. A horizontal bar, pole, or limb of a tree upon which birds sit or roost.

[2]Perch

1. A small, freshwater percomorph fish of the family Percidae, especially Perca flavescens, the yellow perch.

2. Any of a number of freshwater or marine spiny-finned fishes as the climbing perch (Anabas testudineus), the pike perch or yelleye (Stizostedion vitreum), or white perch (Roccus americanus).

Percomorph. Of or pertaining to the Percomorphi (Percomorphida), an order of ray-finned fishes which includes the perches, basses, sunfishes, mackerels, and tunas.

Peregrine. Foreign exotic; wandering, migratory.

Pereiopod. A thoracic appendage of a crustacean which functions as a walking leg.

Perennation. The survival of biennial or perennial plants from one year to the next by vegetative means. In biennials and herbaceobs perennials the aerial parts of the plant die down and the plants survive by means of underground storage roots (*e.g.* carrot), rhizomes (*e.g.* couch grass, Solomon's seal), tubers (*e.g.* dahlia), bulbs (*e.g.* daffodil, snowdrop), or corms (*e.g.* crocus, gladiolus) These perennating organs are also frequently responsible for vegetative propagation. Woody perennials survive the winter by reducing their metabolic activity (*e.g.* by leaf loss in deciduous trees and shrubs).

Perennial. A plant that lives for many years. There are two types. Herbaceous perennials survive each winter as underground storage or perennating organs, such as bulbs, corms, rhizomes, and stem and root tubers. The foliage leaves and flowers die back in winter. Woody perennials are trees and shrubs whose aerial stems have woody tissues and persis above ground. They may be deciduous or evergreen. Compare annual, biennial, ephemeral.

Perfect. *bot.* Having both stamens and pistil, with reference to flowers.

Perfoliate. Describing a sessile leaf in which the base of the lamina extends either side of the node and joins together on the far side so the stem is completely encircled. This formation is also seen when pairs of sessile leaves unite at their bases, as in the perfoliate honeysuckle (Lonicera caprifolium).

Perforation. An opening, especially one of the flumerous openings in vessel members of xylem.

Perforation Plate. The remains of the end walls between two adjacent vessel elements in a vessel of the xylem, forming an opening between the cells, thus facilitating the free movement of water through the vessel. Perforation plates are present in some ferns, some gymnosperms (Gnetales), and most angiosperms, and are believed to have evolved independently in the three groups. Compare sieve plate.

Perfusion

1. The spreading of a liquid over or through a substance.
2. The introduction of a fluid into an organ or tissue by injection into the blood vessel supplying the structure.

Perianth. The part of a flower situated outside the stamens and carpels. In dicotyledons it consists of two distinct whorls, the outer of sepals (calyx) and the inner of petals (corolla). In monocotyledons the two whorls are similar and often brightly coloured. In wind-pollinated flowers both whorls may be reduced or absent. In many horticultural varieties the number of perianth parts is multiplied, but the resulting 'double' flowers are often sterile.

Periblast. In a highly telolecithal ovum, the rapidly dividing cells about the margin of the blastodisc.

Periblem. A plant hisiogen which gives rise to the cortex.

Peribranchial. Surrounding the gills.

Peribranchial Cavity. The atrium of tunicates and lancelets.

Pericardial Cavity. The cavity in vertebrates that contains the heart and is bounded by a membrane (the pericardium). It is part of the coelom.

Pericardial Sinus. The portion of the hemocoel in invertebrates which surrounds the heart.

Pericardium

1. In vertebrates, the closed membranous sac enclosing the heart consisting of outer parietal and inner visceral layers.
2. In invertebrates, the pericardial sinus.

Pericarp

1. In seed plants, the wall of the ripened ovary or fruit, usually consisting of three layers, exocarp, mesocarp, and endocarp.
2. In red algae, an urn-shaped structure surrounding the carposporophyte.

Pericentric. Pericentral, located near or about a center.

Perichaetium, Any of the leaves or bracts surrounding the sex organs of bryophytes or the structure formed by such a whorl. Those enveloping the archegonia are sometimes termed perigynia while those around the antheridia are termed perigonia.

Perichondrium. A fibrous membrane which forms an investing membrane about cartilage except at articular surfaces.

Perichordal. Surrounding the notochord, as the perichordal sheath.

Periclinal. Parallel to the surface. The periclinal wall of a cell is thus one that is parallel to the surface of the plant body. A periclinal division is one that results in the formation of periclinal walls between daughter cells. Such a division results in an increase in girth of the organ. In cylindrical organs, such as stems and roots, the term tangential may be used in place of periclinal, usually in descriptions of cell walls. Compare anticlinal.

Periclinal Chimaera. A chimaera in which tissues of one genetic type completely surround tissues of another genetic type. The ornamental shrub Laburnocytisus adami is a periclinal chimaera that originated from the grafting of Cytisus purpureus onto a Laburnum anagyroides stock. The epidermis is composed of Cytisus cells and the internal tissues of Laburnum cells. Externally it is not obvious that this graft hybrid is a chimaera but occasionally shoots arise consisting solely of tissues from one or other parent. The seeds, which derive from the internal tissues, are always Laburnum. Investigations into the stability of this chimaera led to the tunicacorpus theory of apical organization.

The variegated leaves of certain plants are examples of periclinal chimaeras that have originated from a plastid mutation preventing chlorophyll synthesis. The mutation may occur in either the second layer of the tunica (L2) or the corpus (L3). Differences in colour appear between the leaf margins and the centre of the leaf because the margins are derived from the L2 while the centre is composed of both L2 and L3. Thus if the mutation occurs in the L2 then the margins are white and the centres green (the underlying green L3 tissues are not masked by the white L2 tissues). This type of variegation is seen in Pelargonium.

Pericycle. A plant tissue comprising the outermost layer of the root vascular tissue, lying immediately beneath the endodermis. Lateral roots originate from the pericycle.

Periderm. A protective tissue of secondary origin, comprising the phellogen, phellem, and phelloderm and replacing the epidermis as the outer cellular layer of the stem and root in plant axes exhibiting secondary growth. In such tissue the functions of stomata are performed by lenticels. Periderm also often develops at the site of a wound or other recently exposed surface, thus helping to prevent the entry of pathogens. Compare bark, rhytidome.

Peridinin. A xanthophyll pigment characteristic of algae in the Dinophyta.

Peridiole. A spore-producing structure in certain basidiomycetes.

Peridium. The two-layered outer wall of certain fungal fruiting bodies. It is most obvious in the ascocarp of gasteromycete fungi, in which it consists of an outer exoperidium and an inner endoperidium. In puffballs (Lycoperdon), the exoperinium sloughs off or breaks up into a number of scales, while in the earthstars (Geastrum) it peels back over the endoperidium to give the characteristic star-shaped fruiting body. A peridium is also seen in the aecium surrounding the aeciospores of rust fungi and in the ascocarp of certain Erysiphales.

Perigenous. Describing an angiosperm stomatal complex in which the subsidiary cells are not derived from the same initial as the guard cells. Compare mesogenous.

Perigonium

1. In bryophytes, an anotheridium and its surrounding leaves.
2. In angiosperms, a perianth.

Perigynium

1. In liverworts, a tubular extension of the stem or thallus which encloses the archegonium.
2. A saclike structure (utricle) which encloses the ovary in sedges.
3. The reduced perianth in various sedges.

Perigynous. Designating flowers in which the sepals, petals, and stamens are attached above the ovary to the margin of a cup-like receptacle.

Perigyny. The arrangement of floral parts, intermediate between hypogyny and epigyny in which the sepals, petals, and stamens are inserted on the receptacle at about the same level as the ovary. Perigynous flowers, *e.g.* cinquefoils (Potentilla), are seen when the receptacle becomes flattened or concave, in contrast to hypogynous flowers in which the receptacle is convex.

Perilymph. The fluid of the inner ear that fills the space between the bony labyrinth and the membranous labyrinth. Compare endolymph.

Perimysium. The fibrous membrane which surrounds a bundle (fasciculus) of muscle fibers.

Perineum

1. The region of the outlet of the pelvis including the pelvic floor and associated structures.
2. In a restricted sense, *a.* in a male, the region between the anus and the scrotum; *b.* in a female, the region between the anus and vulva.

Perineurium. The fibrous sheath which surrounds a bundle (fasciculus) of nerve fibres.

Period. A time interval during which a certain series of events occurs, as *a. geol.* a subdivision of an era; *b. physiol.* the menses.

Periodontal Membrane. The membrane of connective tissue that surrounds the root of a tooth and anchors it to its socket in the jawbone. Fibres of the periodontal membrane pass into the cement covering the root, which provides a firm attachment.

Periosteum. A fibrous connective tissue membrane which covers the surface of bone, its innermost layer containing osteoblasts.

Periotic. About or around the ear.

Peripheral Nervous System. All parts of the nervous system excluding the central nervous system. It consists of all the cranial and spinal nerves and their branches, which link the receptors and effectors with the central nervous system.

Periphery. An external surface or boundary; the outer regions of a body or structure.

Periphysis pl. **Periphyses** Sterile hyphae in an ascocarp, especially those lining the osteolar canal.

Periphye. A bacterium which grows attached to a solid surface.

Periphyton. The organisms adhering to submerged plants.

Periplasmodium. A multinucleate structure which develops from the wall of a sporangium in ferns of the order Salvinales.

Periplast. The surface membrane or pellicle of certain algae.

Peripneustic. With spiracles arranged in a row along the side of the body.

Periproct. The structure surrounding the anus in a sea urchin.

Periproctal. About or surrounding the anus or rectum.

Perisperm. Nutritive tissue derived from the nucellus present in some seeds, as the pine, water lily.

Perispore. An extra layer that may surround the spore in some species, particularly certain ferns.

Perissodactyla. An order of mammals having hoofed feet with an odd number of toes. They are all herbivores and include the tapirs, rhinoceros, and horse. The teeth are large and specialized for grinding. Cellulose digestion occurs in the caecum and large intestine. Fossils of the Eocene epoch, 60 million years ago, show that these animals were at that time already distinct from the cloven-hoofed Artiodactyla.

Peristalsis. Progressive wavelike movements occurring in the intestines or other tubular structures in which a wave of contraction moves along the tube preceded by a wave of relaxation.

Peristome. Single or double ring of teeth which fringes the mouth in many types of moss capsule; the peristome can be seen when the lid of a ripe capsule falls or is removed. The teeth are hygroscopic; jerky movements of the teeth on changes in humidity levels aid in the dispersal of the spores.

Peristomium. The segment or segments behind the head and surrounding the mouth, as in various polychaetes.

Perithecium (pyrenocarp). The type of ascocarp characteristic of the Pyrenomycetes. It is a flask-shaped structure with a pore or ostiole opening to the exterior.

Peritoneum. The thin layer of tissue (serous membrane) that lines the abdominal cavity of vertebrates and covers the abdominal organs.

Peritreme

1. The edge of an opening to a shell.
2. A sclerite surrounding the spiracle of an insect.
3. A sclerite surrounding, or a chitinous tube leading to the stigma of an arachind.

Peritrich. A ciliate protozoan of the order Peritrichida, as Vorticella.

Peritrichia (class Ciliatea). Subclass of ciliate protozoa which have a well-developed system of oral cilia. Body cilia are mostly absent, but are present in some immature stages. Cells are variable is shape, and may be sessile or free-swimming. Some are colonial, some have a shell-like lorica. There is one order, with many genera. They are found in freshwater and marine habitats.

Peritrichous. Describing bacteria that have flagella all over the surface of the cell. Bacteria with flagella at one or both ends of the cell are termed polan.

Peritrophic. Surrounding food.

Peritrophic Membrane

1. A chitinous tube free within the cavity of the midgut of insects which separates food from the lining epithelium.
2. A thin, mucoid sheath surrounding the feces of certain crustaceans.

Permanent Stain. A stain that lasts for a long time without fading and does not damage the specimen. A single stain may be used, such as fast green for macerated tissues, or a tissue section may be double-stained, using, for example safranin and the counterstain light or fast green. Aqueous dyes, such as safranin, should be used before the section is dehydrated, and light green on completion of dehydration. Clearing and mounting follow. Compare temporary staining.

Permanent Teeth. The second and final set of teeth that mammals produce after shedding the deciduous teeth. An adult human normally has 32 permanent teeth, consisting of incisors, canines, molars, and premolars (dental formula). These usually appear between the ages of approximately 6 and 21 years.

Permanent Wilting Point. The point at which the amount of water in the soil has dropped to such a level that the plants begin to wilt and will not recover, even if moved to a cool and dark place, unless more water is added to the soil. It occurs when the water potential of the soil is the same as, or lower (more negative) than the water potential of the plant. The amount of water retained in the soil when the permanent wilting point is reached varies depending on the plant species and the type of soil.

Permeant. An animal which can move readily from one area to another.

Permeability. The sum of the factors associated with the transfer of substances across a plasma membrane.

Permeate

1. To pass into or through a substance.
2. To pass through the pores of a membrane.

Permian. Final period of the Palaeozoic Era, which began 280 million years ago and lasted 55 million years. It is named after the central Russian province of Perm. The period is often noted for the widespread continental conditions that prevailed in the northern hemisphere and for the extensive nature of the southern hemisphere glaciation. Many groups of animals and plants vanished during the Permian, including the rugose corals, trilobites, and blastoid echinoderms.

Permo-triassic. A period encompassing the Permian and Triassic periods. It is considered a single period by certain authorities, as the prevailing conditions make it difficult to draw a boundary between the rocks of the Permian and Triassic. Intense earth movements and a period of mountain building and volcanic activity occurred resulting in the extinction of many groups of organisms and the appearance of new forms.

Peronium. In certain medusa, an epidermal tract containing nematocysts, muscle and nerve fibres, extending from the inner surface of a tentacle onto the exumbrella.

Peronosporales. An order of the Oomycetes containing both saprobic and parasitic fungi, many of which are serious plant pathogens. Its members, which number about 300 species in some 16 genera, are found in damp terrestrial habitats and include : Pythium (many species of which cause dampingoff of seedlings); Phytophthora infestans (late blight of potato); Plasmopara, Peronospora, and Bremia (various downy mildews), and Albugo (white blister rusts).

Peroxidase. An enzyme, common in plants, which catalyzes removal of oxygen from hydrogen peroxide.

Peroxisome. A microbody that contains amino acid oxidases, urate oxidases, and catalase. The latter catalyses the decomposition of hydrogen peroxide, produced by the activity of the other enzymes, to oxygen and water.

Persistent. Describing pesticides that take a long time to break down and become inactive. Such pesticides give longer protection than nonpersistent pesticides but are not suitable for use soon before harvest. Some are harmful to the environment as they accumulate in food chains and poison wildlife. Examples are the weedkiller MCPA and the insecticide DDT.

Persister. An organism, as a bacterium, which has been exposed to an antibiotic, as penicillin, and survived, or a culture derived from such an organism.

Personate. Designating a bilabiate corolla, the throat of which is closed by a projection, the palate.

Persoonia (family Proteaceae, subfamily Persooniodeae). Genus of small, xerophytic trees and shrubs, which have entire, alternate leaves. The flowers are bisexual, solitary, and axillary, or in short racemes. They are yellow or white. The calyx is often cylindrical. The fruit is a drupe with one seed, a juicy exocarp, and a hard, thick endocarp. There are seven species, endemic to Australia, where they are found throughout the arid regions, often as components of heathlands.

Perspiration. Sweet; the secretion of sweat glands.

Perula

1. The scale of a leaf bud.
2. The mentum of an orchid.

Perulate. Bearing scales, with reference to a leaf bud.

Pervious. Open, pertorate; capable of admitting passage.

Pes pl. **Pedes.** The foot or hindlimb of a vertebrate, comprising the tarsus, metatarsus, and digits.

Pessimum. The least favorable conditions under which an organism can survive.

Pessulus. A skeletal structure in birds which crosses the lower end of the trachea.

Pest. Any organism that damages crops or reduces their yield or that irritates or injures livestock. The term is more often used of animals that cause physical damage, for example locusts or rodents. Organisms that causes disease are more commonly termed pathogens or parasites.

Pesticide. Any chemical used to kill pests, such as an insecticide, fungicide, or herbicide.

Pestilence. An infectious disease which is especially virulent and devastating in its effects, as the bubonic plague.

Petal. An individual unit of the corolla. Petals are thought to be modified leaves with a simplified internal structure, having only one vascular bundle compared with the several normally found in leaves and sepals. Insect-pollinated plants tend to have large, often yellow or white, scented petals often with a nectary at the base and honey guides. patterning the surface. The petals of wind-pollinated plants, when present, tend to be small and dull coloured. Compare sepal.

[1]Petaloid. Like or resembling a petal

[2]Petaloid. In echinoid, and ambulacral area shaped like a petal, radiating from the center of the aboral surface.

Petalous. Possessing petals.

Petiolar. Pertaining to, borne on, or arising from a petiole.

Petiolate. Possessing a stalk or petiole.

Petiole. The stalk that attaches the leaf lamina to the stem. The point of attachment is often strengthened by a widening of the base of the petiole. Some leaves (sessile leaves) lack a petiole and are joined to the stem at the base of the lamina. Sessiles are characteristic of most monocotyledons.

The petiole is generally similar in structure to a stem except that the vascular and strengthening tissues are asymmetrically arranged so as to bear the weight of the lamina. The different patterns of veins evident in petioles are useful taxonomically. Various modifications of the petiode are seen. Some are flattened and bladelike (phyllode). Others are inflated, as in Eichhornia crassipes (water hyacinth), where they aid buoyancy. In many species the base of the petiole sheaths the stem, as in Heracleum mantegazzianum (giant hogweed). The base of the petiole may be modified as a pulvinus. The petioles of some climbing species, *e.g.* Clematis, are haptotropic. The base of a fern rachis is sometimes termed a petiole.

Petrel. One of a number of oceanic birds of the family Procellariidae, commonly called stormy petrels or Mother Carey's chicknes.

Petricolous. Living in, on, or among rocks.

Petri Dish. A shallow circular flat-bottomed dish made of glass or plastic and having a fitting lid. It is used in laboratories chiefly for culturing bacteria and other microorganisms. It was invented by the German bacteriologist J.R. Petri (1852-1921).

Petrifaction. The conversion of organic matter into stone by the interstitial addition or gradual replacement, molecule by molecule, of the original substance, as trees of the petrified forest in Arizona.

Petrophilous. Inhabiting rocks or frequenting rocky areas.

Petrous. Hard, like stone, as the petrous portion of the temporal bone.

Petunia. A flowering herb (Petunia) of the nightshade family.

Pewee. A small bird of the flycatcher family, Tyrannidae, as the wood pewee (Contopus virens).

Peyer's Patch. An aggregated mass of lymph nodules in the wall of the small intestine, usually the ileum.

Peyote. Mescal buttons, the dried flowering tops of the cactus (Lophophora williamsii).

Pezizales (cup fungi). An order of the Discomycetes in which the asci are operculate and are contained within a hymenium. It contains about 700 species in some 90 genera The hymenium lines the surface of the cuplike apothecium and may be brightly coloured, as in Sarcoscypha coccinea. the scarlet elf cup. The group also contains the edible morels (Morchella).

P_{fr}. The active form of the plant pigment phytochrome that has a peak of light absorption in the far red of the spectrum, *i.e.* at about 725—730 nm. It is interchangeable with the P_r form.

PGA. Petroylglutamic acid (folic acid), one of the B-complex vitamins, effective in treatment of anemia.

pH. A measure of the hydrogen ion concentration, $[H^+]$, and hence of the acidity or alkalinity of an aqueous solution. It is the logarithm of the reciprocal of $[H^+]$, *i.e.* $\log_{10}$ (1/ $[H^+]$). The concentration of H^+ in a litre of pure water *i e* a neutral solution) is 10^{-7} moles, giving a pH value of 7. One integer on the pH scale indicates a tenfold difference in H^+ concentration. The lower the pH value, the higher the concentration of H^+ and vice versa.

Phacidiales. An order of the Discomycetes whose members, which are divided between about 250 species and 64 genera, have inoperculate asci. It includes the plant pathogen, Rhytisma acerinum, which causes tar spot of sycamore.

Phaeophyta (brown algae). A division of algae in which the green chlorophyll pigments are usually masked by the brown pigment fucoxanthin. Brown algae are usually marine (being abundant in cold water) and many species, such as the wracks (Fucus), inhabit intertial zones. They vary in size from small branched filaments to ribbonlike bodies (known as kelps) many metres long.

Phaeophyte. Any plant of the division Phaeophyta which includes the brown algae, mostly marine plants some reaching enormous size, as the kelps and rockweeds. Some are the source of algin.

Phage. Bacteriophage.

Phagocyte. A cell that is able to engulf and break down foreign particles, cell debris, and disease-producing microorganisms (phagodytosis). Many protozoans and certain mammalian cells (*e.g.* macrophages and monocytes) are phagocytes. Phagocytes are important elements in the natural defence mechanism of most animals.

Phagocytosis. Process by which a cell membrane can invaginate and enclose externally derived, solid material which a vacuole, without disrupting the continuity of the cell surface. Subsequently this vaculuole will fuse with a lysosome and its contents will be wholly or partly digested.

Phagotroph. An organism that ingests or engulfs solid particles of food.

Phalanger. Any marsupial of the family Phalangeridae, arboreal mammals with long tails.

Phalanges. The bones that make up the digits of the hand or foot in vertebrates. They articulate with the metacarpals of the hand or with the metatarsals of the foot. In the basic pentadactyl limb there are two phalanges for the first digit (the thumb or big toe in humans) and three for each of the others.

Phalanx pl. **Phalanges**

1. *zool.* A bone of a finger or toe.
2. *bot.* A bundle of stamens united by their filaments.

Phallales. An order of the Gasteromycetes containing the stinkhorns. There are about 70 species in some 21 genera.

When mature the basidiocarp wall of the stinkhorn is broken open by an expanding stalk, which rapidly grows carring the foul-smelling spores at its tip. A common species is Phallus impudicus.

Phallus

1. The peins.
2. *embryol.* The embryonic structure from which the penis or clitoris develops.

Phanerogam. Any plant of the Phanerogamia, a group in order classifications which included the flowering or seed plants. Compare cryptogam.

Phanerophyte. One of Raunkiaer's life-form categories, being a plant whose perennating buds or shoot apices are borne on aerial shoots. Such plants are the least protected of those in Raunkiaer's scheme and therefore are most typical of environments where drought, cold, and exposure to strong winds are relatively infrequent. Several subcategories are recognized, the most universal being : (a) evergreen phanerophytes without bud scales (tropical trees) or with bud scales; and (b) deciduous phanerophytes. These groups may be subdivided further according to height, as nano-(less than 2m), micro- 2—8 m), meso- (8—30 m), and mega- more than 30 m) phanerophytes. Other subgroups are epiphytie, stem succulent, and herbaceous phanerophytes, the last being confined to humid tropical environments. Compare chamaeophyte; cryptophyte; hemicryptophyts; and therophyte.

Phanerozoic. Geological time since the end of the Precambrian, represented by rock strata containing clearly recognizable fossils. It comprises the Palaeozoic, Mesozoic, and Cenozoic ears and has extended for about 570 million years from the beginning of the Cambrian period. Fossils are extremely rare in Precambrian rocks.

Pharate. The state of an insect that has formed a new cuticle but that is still covered by the old. An insect moults at the end of each instar (stage in its development), the pharate state occurring during the moulting process. There is some argument in the literature as to when each instar ends. Some say it is when the new cuticle is completed, others that it is when the old cuticle has been sloughed.

Pharyngeal. Of or pertaining to the pharynx.

Pharynx. The part of the gut that lies between the buccal cavity and the oesophagus. In primitive vertebrates (*e.g.* Amphioxus) it occupies almost half the length of the alimentary canal. Probably its original function was connected with the sifting of particles of food, but in lower vertebrates it is concerned with respiration and gill slits or lungs open into it.

Phase

1. Little-used term in biostratigraphy, related to time. According to early geologists it was the time-equivalent of a zone.
2. In chemistry and in other fields of geology frequent reference is made to the 'phases' of liquids and to a 'phase boundary' (the line marking the contact between two constituent or liquid phases).

Phase Contrast Microscope. A microscope that enables living, and hence normally transparent, material to be viewed by converting (invisible) differences of phase in the transmitted light to (visible) differences of contrast. Light passing through a specimen changes its phase by different amounts due to differences in thickness or refractive index. The phase contrast microscope converts these differences to differences in amplitude, which can be seen as shades of grey (because the greater the amplitude of a wave the more bright or intense is the light). The effect is produced by using a special condenser together with a glass plate (the retardation plate) in the objective. The condenser produces a certain pattern of light, often a hollow cone. This is matched in the retardation plate by a similar pattern produced by a groove in the plate. Any light that is not diffracted by the specimen will pass through the groove in the retardation plate and remain unchanged in phase. Any light that has been diffracted been diffracted by the specimen will pass through the thicker part of the retardation plate and hence be slowed even further. Contrast results from combination of the direct and refracted light. If they are out of phase by half a wavelength the difference produces destructive interference of the light so producing contrast. When this technique is used in conjunction with a time-lapse cine camera it enables such events as cell division to be filmed and later speeded up, a technique known as cinemicrography.

Phase Diagram. Graphical method for examining stability in biological systems, *e.g.* host—parasite relationship. The system variables (the number of frost and parasite organism) at different times are plotted against one another, and change over time is shown by a line connecting the co-ordinate points for successive time values. The form of the resulting curve indicates the stability of the system. A line spiralling inward indicates damped oscillations favouring ultimate stability; an outward spiral suggests ultimate instability. By testing different values for the number of organisms it is possible to establish limits for stability. The technique has considerable practical relevance in agriculture.

Phasmid. A small, pouch-shaped sensory receptor located postanally in certain nematodes.

Phellem (cork). The compact protective tissue that replaces the epidermis as the outer cellular layer in plants with secondary growth. It is the outer layer of the periderm and consists of numerous more or less isodiametric cells arranged in radial rows, with thick waxy suberized cell walls. Commercial cork is obtained from the cork oak Quercus suber, in which the same phellogen is active each year (bark). It consists of thinwalled unsuberized cork cells (phelloids) and is stripped from the tree approximately every nine years.

Phelloderm (secondary cortex). Parenchyma tissue of secondary origin, derived centripetally from the phellogen. Cells of the phelloderm may, be distinguished from those of the cortex by their arrangement in radial columns reflecting their origin from the phellogen.

Phellogen (cork cambium). The cambium that arises external to the vascular cambium in many plant axes undergoing secondary growth. It gives rise to the phellem and phelloderm.

Phelloid. Phellem.

Phenetic. Describing a system of classification of organism based on similarities and differences in as many observable characteristics as possible. A phenetic system does not aim to reflect evolutionary descent, although it may well do so. Compare phylogenetic.

Phenocopy. A condition in which an acquired or artificially induced characteristic is identical with that produced by a gene, as pigmentation induced by ultraviolet rays.

Phenogenetics. Developmental genetics, the study of gene action in relation to developmental processes.

Phenogram. Dendrogram.

Phenolics (phenols) Compounds containing a benezene ring directly substituted with one or more hydroxyl groups. The simplest member is phenol (carbolic acid), formula C_6H_5OH. Plant phenolics are widespread and extremely diverse and include the flavonoids. Simple phenolic compounds containing one or two rings are not as common as the flavonoids, though hydroquinone, coumarin, and the cinnamic acids are widely distributed. The amino acid tyrosine also contains a phenolic ring. Less common are such phenolics as catechol, phloroglucinol, and pyrogallol. Lignin is a phenolic, probably being formed from coniferyl alcohol, a derivative of cinnamic acid. Tannins are also derived from phenolics.

Phenology. The science which deals with relationships between weather and cyclic biological phenomena, as migrations of animals, flowering of plants.

Phenolphthalein. A hydrogen-ion indicator that is colourless in acids and red in alkalis.

Phenotype. The observable manifestation of a specific genotype: those properties of an organism produced by the genotype in conjunction with the environment that are observable. Organisms with the same overall genotype may have different phenotypes because of the effects of the environment and of gene interaction. Conversely, organisms may have the same phenotype but different genotypes, as a result of incomplete dominance, penetrance, or expressivity.

Phosphorus (P). Element, required by plants in the oxidized form, as orthophosphate. The special chemical properties of this compound are utilized in reactions in which energy is transferred often involving ATP. It is also a good buffer helping maintain a neutral pH. The leaves of phosphate-deficient plants become dark green or blue-green and a reddish pigment may develop Growth is generally reduced.

Phenylthiocarbamide. PTC, a substance which is bitter to some individuals but tasteless to others.

Phenoxyacetic Acids. A group of compounds some of which show auxin-like activity. Various chlorine substituted forms cause a disruption in metabolism particularly at the meristems and have been widely used as selective weed-killers. An important factor in the use of phenoxyacetic acids as weedkillers is their immunity from the plant's endogenous IAA oxidizing system, which can normally inactivate superfluous auxins. Examples of such compounds are 2,4-D, 2,4,5,-T, and MCPA.

Phenylalanine. An aromatic nonpolar amino acid with the formula $C_6H_5CH_2$ $CH(NH_2)COOH$ (illustration at amino acid). The biosynthetic pathway shikimic acid to phenylalanine from erythrose 4-phosphate and phosphoenolpyruvate is similar for all the aromatic amino acids. Phenylalanine and the other aromatic amino acids are precursors of a large number of aromatic compounds, mostly found only in plants. Deamination of phenylalanine yields cinnamic acid, important in the synthesis of lignin. Phenylalanine is also a precursor of such alkaloids as morphine and curare (*i.e.* the isoquinoline alkaloids).

Pheromone. An ectohormone; a substance produced and discharged by an organism which induces a physiological response in another of the same species, as the sexual attractants of insects.

Phialospore. A type of conidium found, for example in many of the Eurotiales and Hypocreales. Phialospores develop at the tips of specialized finger-like cells termed phialides.

Phlegm. Mucus, especially thick, viscid mucus discharged through the mouth.

Phloem (bast). A vascular tissue whose principal function is the translocation of sugars and other nutrients. The phloem is composed mainly of sieve tubes, sclerenchyma cells, and parenchyma cells, including companion cells. It occurs in association with, and usually external to, the xylem.

Phloroglucinol. A red dye (usually acidified with hydrochloric acid) that stains lignin in plant cells red.

Phosphagen. A compound found in animal tissues that provides a reserve of chemical energy in the form of high-energy phosphate bonds. The most common phosphagens are creatine phosphate, occurring in vertebrate muscle and nerves, and arginine phosphate, found in most invertebrates. During tissue activity (*e.g.* muscle contraction) phosphagens give up their phosphate groups, there by generating ATP from ADP. The phosphagens are then reformed when ATP is available.

Phosphatide. Phospholipid.

Phosphoenolpyruvate (PEP). An important phosphorylated intermediate of glucose metabolism. In glycolysis PEP is the immediate precursor of pyruvic acid, while in the synthesis of glucose from acetyl-CoA, PEP is formed from oxaloacetate generated in the glyoxylate cycle. In C_4 plants PEP is an intermediate in the Hatch-Slack pathway. The aromatic amino acids, and hence a large number of other aromatic nitrogenous compounds, are also synthesized from PEP.

Phosphoenolpyruvate Carboxylase (PEP carboxylase). The enzyme that is responsible for carbon dioxide fixation in C_4 plants and in plants exhibiting crassulacean acid metabolism. It catalyses the carboxylation of phosphoenolpyruvate to oxalocetic acid.

Phosphogluconate Pathway. Pentose phosphate pathway.

Phosphoglyceric Acid (HGA). The phosphorylated derivative of the three-carbon glyceric acid. It may be phosphorylated at the second or third carbon giving 2-phosphoglyceric acid or 3-phosphoglyceric acid respectively. 3-phosphoglycerate is the first product of the dark reactions of photosynthesis, two molecules being formed by the carboxylation and cleavage of ribulose bisphosphate. It is also an intermediate in glycolysis being formed from 3-phosphoglyceroyl phosphate, two molecules of ATP being formed in the process. It is then converted, via 2-phosphoglycerate, to phosphoenolpyruvate. 3-phosphoglycerate is the precursor of the amino acid serine.

Phosphoglyceride. (phospholipid, phosphatide, glycerophosphatide). Any of a group of complex lipids similar to acylglycerides except that the third hydroxyl group is phosphorylated, *i.e.* the backbone is glycerol 3-phosphate rather than glycerol. Common phosphoglycerides include phosphatidylcholine, phosphatidyl-ethanolamine, and phosphatidylinositol (all found primarily in seed tissues), and phosphatidylglycerol (found in leaf tissue).

Phosphoglycerides are the major lipids in most plant membranes, although glycolipids are important components of chloroplast membranes.

Phospholipid (phosphatide). One of a group of lipids having both a phosphate group and one or more fatty acids. Glycerophospholipids are based on glycerol; the three hydroxyl groups are esterified with two fatty acids and a phosphate group, which may itself be bound to one of a variety of simple organic groups (*e.g.* in lecithin it is choline). Sphingophospholipids are based on the alcohol sphingosine and contain only one fatty acid linked to an amino group. With their hydrophilic polar phosphate groups and long hydrophobic hydrocarbon 'tails', phospholipids readily form membrane-like structures in water. They are a major component of cell membranes.

Phosphoric Acid. H_3PO_4, an important compound in cellular metabolism.

Phosphorolysis. The process by which glucosidic bonds of glycogen are broken at the 1—4 linkage by reaction with inorganic phosphates resulting in the formation of glucose-1-phosphate or Cori ester, a reaction catalyzed by phosphorylase.

Phlox. A flowering herb of the genus Phlox.

Phoresis. A form of symbiosis in which the host transports the symbiont, as barnacles on whales on or sessile ciliateson arthropods; phoresy.

Phoronid. Any invertebrate of the phylum Phoronidea within contains a small number of lophophorate, coelomate marine animals of uncertain relationships, as Phoronis..

Phorozooid. A specialized zooid in certain pelagic tunicates which acts as a nurse bearing gonozooids.

Phosphate Bonds. High-energy bonds, designated as PMP bonds, especially those in the molecules of adenosine triphosphate (ATP) which are the principal sources of energy for cellular activity.

Phosphocreatine. Creatine phosphate, $C_4H_{10}N_3O_5$, a source of energy for cellular activity.

Phospholipid. A phosphatide; a compound formed of a lipid and an ester of phosphoric acid, as lecithin, cephalin, sphingomyelin.

Phosphoprotein. A protein combined with a phosphorous-containing compound.

Phosphorescence

1. The emission of light without heat, as occurs in certain bacteria, fungi, protozoans, insects, and fishes.
2. The reemission of light waves of a different wavelength and for a considerable time following subjection to certain types of radiation.

Phosphorus. Symbol : P. A nonmetallic element, atomic number 15, atomic weight 30.9, important as a macronutrient for plant growth. It is essential for the formation of nucleic acids, lipoproteins, and energy-carrying molecules and is involved in many aspects of metabolism, especially carbohydrate metabolism. Phosphorus occurs in soil minerals as the apatites and as calcium phosphate rock. It is absorbed by roots as the PO_4^{3-} ion, this ion acting as an important buffer in the cell sap. Deficiency results in poor root growth, bluish, bronzed, or purple leaves, and poor germination, ripening, and seed set. Phosphorus can be applied to soils as inorganic basic slag or superphosphate or in various organic materials, guano and bonemeal containing a particularly high percentage.

It is often applied in combination with nitrogen and potash in compound fertilizers.

Phosphorylase. An enzyme which catalyzes the phosphorolysis of glycogen.

Phosphorylation. The union of a substance with phosphorus or the phosphate radical, PO_4^{3-}.

Phosphotransferase. Kinase.

Photic. Pertaining to light.

Photic Zoone. The upper layer of a sea or a lake, in which there is sufficient light for photosynthesis. The limit of the photic zone varies from less than a metre to more than 200 metres, depending on the turbidity of the water.

Photoautotroph. An autotroph that obtains the energy for synthesizing organic food substances from inorganic components directly from sunlight. Photoautotrophs include most green plants and some photosynthetic bacteria. Compare photoheterotroph.

Photoantotrophic. Using light energy to synthesize organic compounds from inorganic substances, as in all green plants.

Photochemical Smog. Hazy condition of the atmosphere due to the reaction of hydrocarbons with molecules of nitrogen oxide in sunlight which produces complex organic molecules of peroxyacyl nitrates (PNA). In humid conditions these molecules produce smog. Such phenomena are common in large urban areas (*e.g.* the Los Angeles basin and Athens) where there are stable atmospheric condition and a high level of hydrocarbon input from incamplete combustion in car engines. Natural photochemical reactions occur in the high atmosphere with the absorption of radiation by oxygen to produce ozone.

Photoheterotroph. A photosynthetic or ganism that requires a supply of organic compounds as a source of hydrogen

The purple nonsulphur bacteria are obligate photoheterotrophs and also require certain organic growth substances. Some of the purple sulphur bacteria are faculative photoheterotroph in that under certain conditions they use organic acids rather than reduced sulphur compounds as a hydrogen source.

Photo-ionization. The absorption of solar energy in the upper atmosphere (mesosphere and thermosphere) by oxygen (O and O_2) and nitrogen oxide (NO) molecules, accompanied by the release of electrons. The removal of the negatively-charged electrons leaves atmos or molecules as positively-charged ions. Ionic concentration varies throughout the ionosphere.

Photolithotroph. Phototrophic organism in which photosynthesis is associated with the oxidation of an inorganic compound (or element, in the case of some photosynthetic bacteria). For example, green plants obtain energy from sunlight by photosynthesis, during which water is oxidized to yield oxygen.

Photolysis. Decomposition resulting from the action of light, as in the dissociation of water in photosynthesis.

Photolysis of Water. The photosynthetic splitting of water into gaseous oxygen and reducing equivalents. Two molecules of water are split to produce one molecule of oxygen, four electrons, which go through the electron transport chain, and four protons. The electrons and protons eventually reduce NADP to NADPH. This in turn is utilized in the reduction of carbon dioxide to carbohydrate.

Photon. A quantum, or the unit of visible light; the unit of all radiant energy.

Photomicrograph. Micrograph.

Photomicrography. The use of photography to obtain a permanent record (a photomicrograph) of the image of an object as viewed through a microscope.

Photonastic. Pertaining to nastic movements resulting from changes in light intensity, as the opening and closing of flowers at night.

Photonasty. A nastic movement induced by external light stimuli. Some flowers, *e.g.* those of the garden marigold (Calendula officinalis), exhibit these movements and oped on exposure to light.

Photoorganotroph. An organism which utilizes light energy in the manufacture of food from organic materials.

Photoperiodism. The responses of an organism to changes in light intensity or in length of days, as *a.* in animals, seasonal and cyclic events as migrations, reproductive cycles, changes in pelage or plumage; *b.* in plants, the growth and development of flowers and fruits, the shedding of leaves, or onset of winter dormancy.

Photophile. Describing a phase during which light promotes flowering. In one theory advanced to explain photoperiodism it is suggested that short-day plants are in the photophile phase during the day but at night they are in the photophobe (or skotophile) phase when light inhibits and darkness promotes flowering. The alternation between photophile and photophobe phases is seen as a type of circadian rhythm. If the period of daylight extends beyond the photophile phase into the photophobe phase, as would occur with a short-day plant on a long day, then flowering is inhibited.

Photophobe. Photophile.

Photophore. Luminous organ, modified from a mucous gland, found in the skin of fish. Rows of photophores are present in many deep-sea fish, which apparently can produce flashes of blue-green to orange light at will. The photophores secrete a compound which glows when activated, or contain colonies of phosphorescent bacteria.

Photopsin. A component of iodopsin, a visual pigment present in cone cells of the retina.

Phosphatide. A phospholipid.

Photopic Vision. The type of vision that occurs when the cones in the eye are the principal receptors, *i.e.* when the level of illumination is high. Colours can be identified with photopic vision. Compare scotopic vision.

Photophosphorylation (photosynthetic phosphorylation). The production of ATP from ADP and inorganic phosphate utilizing light-induced photosynthetic electron transport as a source of energy. Two types of photophosphorylation occur, noncyclic and cyclic. In noncyclic photophosphorylation electrons are passed from water to $NADP^+$ via photosystems I and II. During the transfer of electrons from the primary electron acceptor of photosystem II (termed C550) to P700 through plastoquinone, plastocyanin, and various cytochromes, one molecule of ATP is formed. In cyclic photophosphorylation only photosystem I is involved. Energy absorbed by P700 releases electrons, which are absorbed by a primary acceptor termed P430. Electrons then pass, via cytochrome b_6, into the chain connecting the primary electron acceptor of photosystem II to photosystem I. A molecule of ATP is formed as the electron passes down to P700. Cyclic phosphorylation does not produce reduced $NADP^+$.

Photoreceptor

1. *zool.* A receptor which is capable of being stimulated by light rays, as an eye or ocellus.

2. *bot.* A structure containing a light-sensitive pigment, as an eyespot or stigma.

Photorespiration. Respiration that occurs in plants in the light. It differs from dark respiration in that it does not occur in the mitochondria and is not coupled to oxidative phosphorylation. The rate of CO_2 release by photorespiration in C_3 plants can be three to five times greater than that released by dark respiration. Since the process does not generate ATP it appears to be extremely wasteful. It has been estimated that photosynthetic efficiency could be improved by 50% if photorespiration were inhibited. In C_4 plants photorespiration is hardly detectable, possible because synthesis of glycolic acid, the substrate for photorespiration, is much lower in C_4 plants (about 10% of that of C_3 plants). This could be because the concentration of CO_2 in the bundle sheath cell is so high that oxidation (instead of carboxylation) of ribulose bisphosphate is prevented.

Some C_3 plants, *e.g.* the grass Panicum miliodes, have a leaf structure comparable in some respects to the Kranz structure of C_4 plants. Such plants also tend to have reduced rates of photorespiration. These observations have stimulated research into the possibility of breeding C_3 plants with slower photorespiration rates.

Photoreversibility. The capacity of opposite responses occurring through the action of a single photoreceptor.

Photosensitive. Sensitive to or capable of being stimulated by light.

Photosynthesis. Term given to the series of metabolic reactions that occur in certain autotrophic organisms, whereby organic compounds are synthesized by the reduction of carbon dioxide using energy absorbed by chlorophyll from sunlight. In green plants, where water acts both as a hydrogen donor and as a source of released oxygen, photosynthesis may be summarized by the empirical equation :

$$CO_2+2H_2O \xrightarrow[\text{light}]{\text{chlorophyll}} [CH_2O]+H_2O+O_2\uparrow$$

(oxygen being released as a gas). Photosynthetic bacteria are unable to utilize water and therefore do not produce oxygen. Instead they may use hydrogen sulphide (purple and green sulphur bacteria) or organic compounds (purple non-sulphur bacteria) as a source of hydrogen.

Photosynthetic Bacteria. A group of phototrophic bacteria that contain a green pigment, bacteriochlorophyll, similar to the chlorophyll of plants, that enables them to photosynthesize. They obtain hydrogen from hydrogen sulphide or other reduced sulphur compounds (or occasionally from molecular hydrogen or organic acids) and fix carbon dioxide by the Calvin series of reactions. There are three groups of photosynthetic bacteria : namely the green sulphur bacteria (Chlorobiaceae or Chlorobacteriaceae); the purple sulphur bacteria (Chromatiaceae or Thiorhodaceae); and the purple nonsulphur bacteria (Rhodospirillaceae or Athiorhodaceae). Together these form a suborder of the Pseudomonadales. In the purple bacteria additional red and brown pigments are also present.

Photosynthetic Phosphorylation. Photophosphorylation.

Photosynthetic Pigments. The plant pigments responsible for the capture of light energy during the light reactions of photosynthesis. The green pigment chlorophyll is the principal light receptor, absorbing blue and red light. However the carotenoids and various other pigments also absorb light energy and pass this on to the chlorophyll molecules.

Photosystems I and II (pigment systems I and II, PSI and PSII). Two photochemical systems containing photosynthetic and accessory pigments and electron carriers that operate in sequence to perform the two light reactions of photosynthesis and so bring about photophosphorylation and reduction of $NADP^+$ (diagram). PSII contains chlorophyll *a* (P680) that absorbs light of 684 nm wavelength most efficiently. When activated by light it produces a strong oxidant that oxidizes water to oxygen, hydrogen ions, andelectrons. The electrons are transferred via a primary electrons acceptor (possibly C550) and plastoquinone and the cytochrome chain to PSI. The energy released when each electron is transferred is used to transform a molecule of ADP to ATP. PSI contains chlorophyll *a* (P700) that absorbs light of 700 nm wavelength most efficiently. When P700 is activated a strong reductant is produced that reduces $NADP^+$ to NADPH.

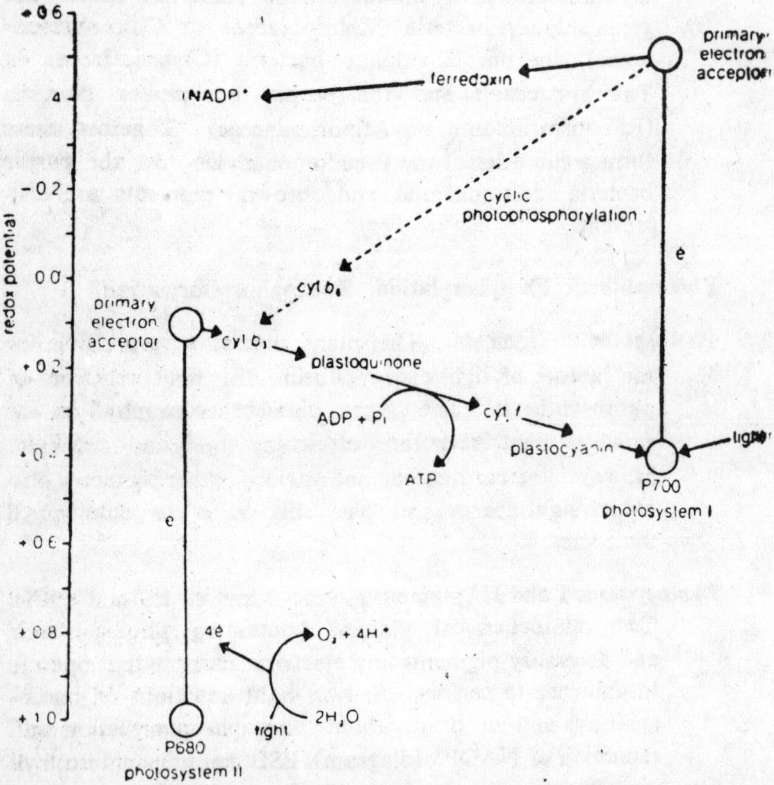

The Z scheme depicting electron transport between photosystems II and I.

Phototaxis. A taxis in response to external light stimulation. Cells of Chlamydomonas swim freely towards a light source to enhance photosynthetic efficiency but will swim away if the source is too intense (positive and negative phototaxis respectively). Some chloroplasts also show phototaxis within cells, aligning themselves with respect to the incident light.

Phototroph. An organism that derives the necessary energy for the synthesis of organic compounds directly from sunlight. The term encompasses both photoautotrophs and photoheterotrophs. Compare chemotroph.

Phototrophic. Designating organisms which can utilize radiant energy, as green plants.

Phototropic. Responding to light as a stimulus.

Phototropism. A tropism in response to light. Thus, shoots show positive phototropism by growing towards a light source. Work with oat (Avena) coleoptiles has shown that the stimulus is received in the tip of the seedling and that the response is effected by increased growth on the relatively shaded side, triggered by auxins, which pass from the tip more readily on the shaded side. Removal of the tip destroys the phototropic response. Most roots are a phototropic.

Phragma pl. **Phragmata.** A dorsal apodeme in insects and other arthropods which serves for attachment of muscle fibers; endotergite.

Phragmoplast. A system of fibrils that persists at the outer edge of the equator of the spindle at early telophase. As the cell plate forms in the equatorial region the fibrils become dispersed. The term is used by some authorities to mean the developing cell plate.

Phragmosis. Using a part of the body to close a burrow.

Phragmosome. In plant mitosis, one of the many small bodies present in the equatorial plane which contribute to the formation of the middle lamella of the cell wall.

Phreatophyte. A plant with extremely long roots reaching to the water table.

Phrenic

1. Of or pertaining to the diaphragm.
2. Of or pertaining to the mind.

pH Scale. A logarithmic scale for expressing the acidity or alkalinity of a solution. To a first approximation, the pH of a solution can be defined as $-\log_{10}c$, where c is the concentration of hydrogen ions in moles per cubic decimetre. A neutral solution at 25°C has a hydrogen-ion concentration of 10^{-7} mol dm^{-3}, so the pH is 7. A pH below 7 indicates an acid solution; one above 7 indicates an alkaline solution. pH stands for 'potential of hydrogen'. The scale was introduced by S. P. Sorensen in 1909.

Phycobilin (biliprotein). Any of the blue or red pigments found in the blue-green and red algae. Like the carotenoids they are accessory pigments in photosynthesis, but unlike the chlorophylls and carotenoids they are water soluble. Structurally they are very similar to the porphyrin part of the chlorophyll molecule, except that they contain no magnesium. The three classes of phycobilins are the phycoerythrins, phycocyanins, and allophycocyanins.

Phycobilisome. A small particle, about 30 nm across, many of which are found on the membranes of the lamellar system of blue-green algae. Phycobilisomes are thought to be aggregations of the pigment phycobilin. They are also found in the plastids of red algae between the photosynthetic lamellae.

Phycobiont. The algal partner in a lichen, which is either a unicellular green or blue-green alga and often a member of the genus Trebouxia. If a blue-green alga (*e.g.* Nostoc; Rivularia, Gloeocapsa) is present the lichen is usually gelatinous. The number of algal genera involved in lichens

(24 have so far been discovered) is relatively few compared to the large numbers of lichenized fungi. Compare mycobiont.

Phycocolloid. One of a number of complex, colloidal substances present in the cell walls of various brown algae, as algin, fucoidin.

Phycocyanin. Any of the blue pigments that form one of the two major classes of the phycobilins. They are found in all blue-green algae and in some red algae and act as accessory pigments in photosynthesis.

Phycoerythrin. Any of the red pigments that form one of the two major classes of the phycobilins. They are found in all red algae, and act as accessory pigments in photosynthesis. They absorb the dim blue-green light that reaches the lower levels of the ocean where the algae grow, and pass in onto chlorophyll so that it may be used in photosynthesis. The deeper in the sea an alga lives, the more phycoerythrin it contains in relation to chlorophyll.

Phycology. The study of algae.

Phycomycetes. A class of relatively primitive fungi, many of which are found in water (*e.g.* the water moulds, which may be parasitic on fish) or in damp areas. Many are unicellular but those that form mycelia generally have hyphae lacking cross walls, which distinguishes them from the Ascomycetes and Basidiomycetes.

Phylactocarp. A protective structure, usually a modified hydrocladium, which protects a gonangium in various hydrozoans.

Phyletic. Phylogenetic.

Phyletic Gradualism. Theory holding that macro-evolution is merely the operation of micro-evolution over relatively long periods of time. Thus gradual changes eventually will accumulate to the point at which descendants of an ancestral population diverge into separate species, genera, or higher-level taxa.

Phyllid. A moss or liverwort 'leaf'.

Phyllobranchia pl. **Phyllobranchiae.** A flat, leaflike gill composed of thin plates or lamella, as in certain crustaceans.

Phylloclade. A cladode.

Phyllode. A more or less flattened petiole resembling and performing the functions of a leaf. Vertically expanded petioles are seen in a number of Acacia species. The leaves of many monocotyledons are believed to be of phyllode origin. Compare cladode.

Phyllodium pl. **Phyllodia.** A phyllode.

Phyllody. The transformation of parts of a flower into leaflike structures. This may occur in response to some infections. For example, maize infected with head smut (Sphacelotheca reiliana) develops phyllody of both male and female flowers.

Phyllopodium

1. *bot.* The axis of a leaf.
2. *zool.* A broad, flat appendage in various crustaceans, as the maxilla of a crayfish.

Phyllotaxis (phyllotaxy). The arrangement of leaves on a plant stem. The leaves may be inserted in whorls or pairs at each node or singly up the stem. When arranged in pairs the two leaves arise on opposite sides of the stem and are usually at right angles to the leaf pairs above and below them. Single leaves may be inserted alternately or in a spiral pattern up the stem. Phyllotaxis generally results in the minimum of shading of leaves by those above them.

Phyllozooid. A leaflike or helmet-shaped bract in a siphonophore; hydrophyllium.

Phylogenetic (phyletic). Describing a system of classification of organisms that aims to show their evolutionary history. Compare phenetic.

Phylogeny. The evolutionary history of an organism or group or related organisms. Compare ontogeny.

Phylum pl. **Phyla**. A taxon comprising the largest division of the animal or plant kingdom, consisting of one or more classes. In some plant classifications, the term division is generally used instead of phylum.

Physa. In burrowing anthozoans, the end bulb or base, a constricted portion of the column.

Physoclistous. Applied to the condition in bony fish in which there is no connection or duct between the swim-bladder and the intestinal tract. In physoclists, the gas pressure of the swim-bladder is regulated by special tissues or glands. This condition is found among the 'higher' bony fish, *e.g.* the perch-like fish.

Physiographic Factor. Any of the factors, apart from climatic, biotic, and edaphic factors, that affect the prevailing conditions within a habitat and the distribution of the plants and animals. Such factors include the topography of the area, altitude, drainage conditions, degree of erosion, slope of the land, etc.

Physiological

1. Of or pertaining to physiology.
2. Pertaining to normal processes or activities in contrast to those that are abnormal or pathologic.

Physiological Drought. A drought condition suffered by plants that occurs despite there being sufficient water in the soil. It may occur when the concentration of solutes in the soil water is equal to or higher than that in the root cells so water cannot enter the plant by osmosis. This situation may be found in salt marshes and coastal mud flats. It also occurs during cold spells when there is an increase in the resistance of the root to water movement into the plant. Root resistance increases in response to low temperatures since the permeability of endodermal cells decreases rapidly below 5°C.

Physiological Race (forma specialis). A population that is physiologically distinct but morphologically indistinguishable from other members of the species. Many fungi have large numbers of physiological races, reflecting considerable genetic diversity, even in nonsexual species. Examples are the various races of certain pathogenic fungi, each of which attack different host species or varieties.

Physiological Saline. A liquid medium in which animal tissues may be kept alive for a few hours during experiments without pathological changes or distortion of the cells taking place. Such fluids are salt solutions that are isotonic with and have the same pH as the body fluids of the animal. A well-known example is Ringer's solution, formulated by the British physiologist S. Ringer (1835-1910), which is a mixture of sodium chloride, calcium chloride, sodium bicarbonate, and potassium chloride solutions.

Physiological Specialization. The occurrence within a species of several forms that are identical in appearance but differ in physiology : these are termed physiological races. For example, many pathogenic fungi develop new physiological races in response to the strong selection pressure exerted when disease-resistant crop varieties are sown over large areas.

Physiology

1. The branch of biology which deals with the various processes and activities which occur within a living organism or one of its parts; the study of function.
2. The functioning of an organism or any of its parts.

Physoclistous. Not connected to the alimentary canal by a duct, with reference to swim bladders in fishes.

Physogastric. Having an enlarged abdomen.

Physostomous. Applied to the condition in bony fish in which the swim-bladder is connected to the intestinal tract by a special duct (ductus pneumaticus). In physostome fish, the gas pressure can be regulated by swallowing air or by releasing it via the gut. This condition is found among the somewhat more primitive bony fish, *e.g.* the herrings and their relatives.

Phytic Acid. The hexaphosphoric ester of inositol. It is common as a phosphate storage compound in many seeds in which it exists as the calcium—magnesium salt, phytin.

Phyto-. Prefix denoting plants. For example, phytopathology is the study of plant diseases.

Phytoalexin. A chemical produced by a host plant that inhibits the growth of a pathogenic fungus. For example, the phenolic compound pisatin has been shown to accumulate in pea tissues in the presence of various fungi. Similarly the degree of resistance shown by sweet potato (Ipomoea batatas) to attack by the fungus Ceratostomella has been correlated with the concentration of the terpenoid ipomeamarone in the plant tissue.

Phytobenthos. Benthos.

Phytochrome. Photoreversible pigment, which occurs in every major taxonomic group of plants. It exists in two interchangeable forms with respect to absorption, a red and a far-red form. This phenomenon is utilized in plants as a switch mechanism, linked to environmental light signals, to control many activities in plants. These include flowering, germination, vegetative growth, circadian rhythms, and many more physiological activities.

Phytogeography. The study of the geography of plants, particularly their distribution at different taxonomic levels, *e.g.*

family, genus, and species. Patterns of distribution are interpreted in terms of climatic and anthropogenic influence, but above all in terms of earlier continental configurations and migration routes. This branch of biogeography is also known as floristics.

Phytohormone. A plant hormone.

Phytol. An alcohol containing a chain of 20 carbon atoms which forms the tail of a chlorophyll molecule.

Phytology. The study of plants : Botany.

Phytophagous. Plant-eating or herbivorous, said of animals, especially insects.

Phytoplankton. The plant component of plankton, consisting chiefly microscopic algae, such as diatoms and dinoflagellates. Near the surface of the sea there may be many millions of such plants per cubic metre. Members of the phytoplankton are of great importance as they form the basis of food for all other forms of aquatic life, being the primary produces. Compare zooplankton.

Phytosociology. The description of plant communities, more especially their classification based primarily on floristic rather than life-form or other considerations. The most renowned and extensively used phytosociological scheme is that developed by J. Braun-Blanquet (1927 and later) and his associates at Zurich and Montpellier. A similar, fairly widely applied scheme was developed by G. E. du Rietz (1921 and later) and others at Uppsala.

Phytotron. A large plant growth chamber in which many plants can be raised under strictly controlled conditions of light, photoperiod, temperature, humidity, etc. Often many phytotrons are housed in a specially designed building. Entrance to each unit is by a hermetically sealed door.

Phytotoxin. A toxin produced by a plant, as ricin, croton.

Phytozoan. A biological unit consisting of an animal and plant living in symbiotic mutualism, as a coral polyp and their contained zooxanthellae.

Pia Mater. The innermost of the three membranes (meninges) that surround the brain and spinal cord of vertebrates. The pia moter lies immediately adjacent to the central nervous system, and the choroid plexus, which secretes cerebro-spinal fluid, is an extension of it.

Pickerel. A small, carnivorous, freshwater fish of the pike family, as the chain pickerel (Esox niger).

Picornavirus. One of a group of small RNA-containing viruses (pico=small; hence pico-RNA-virus) commonly present in the alimentary and respiratory tracts of vertebrates. They cause mild infections of these tracts but the group also includes the polioviruses, which attack the central nervous system causing poliomyelitis; and the causal agent of foot and mouth disease in cattle, sheep, and pigs.

Piebald. Spotted; mottled.

Pie Chart. A diagram in which percentages are shown as sectors of a circle. If x per cent of the prey of a carnivore comprises species X, y per cent species Y, and z per cent species Z, a pie chart would show three sectors having central angles $3.6x°$, $3.6y°$, and $3.6z°$.

Pigeon Milk. A nutritious, cheeselike substance produced by the crop glands of pigeons which, when regurgitated, serves as food for the young.

Pigeon Pea. The cajan pea (Cajanus cajan), a food and forage legume.

Pigment. Any coloured compound. Pigments are coloured because they absorb certain types of light. Thus in solution they will have a characteristic absorption spectrum. Because light is a form of energy, pigments that absorb light also absorb energy. The first reaction in photosynthesis is the absorption of energy by accessory and photosynthetic pigments. Pigments also produce the characteristic colours of flowers and fruits.

Pigmentation. The amount and quality of the colouring in animals or plants.

Pigment Cell. A pigment-containing cell, especially a chromatophore.

Pigment Systems I and II. Photosystems I and II.

Pignut. The bitter nut of a hickory (Carya glabra) or the tree that produces it.

Pika. A small mammal of the Order Lagomorpha, as Ocotona princeps, the Rocky Mountain pika of western United States. Also called mouse hare, calling hare.

Pike

1. One of several large, carnivorous fishes of the family Esocidae, as Esox lucius, the Northern pike, a food and game fish.
2. One of a number of similar fishes, as the garpike, walleyed pike.

Pike Perch. The walleyed pike.

Pile. A dense growth of short, fine hairs.

Pileous. Hairy : Pilose.

Pileum. In birds, the entire top of the head; pileus.

Pileus. From the Latin pileus meaning 'cap'

1. (taxon.) The fleshy or leathery structure upon which hymenium-bearing tissue occurs in a fungal fruit body, *e.g.* the cap of an agaric.
2. (meteor.) An accessory cloud occurring as a small cap on or above a cumuliform cloud. Caps may occur one

on top of another. The cloud is associated with cumulus or cumulonimbus.

Pilidium. The free-swimming, helmet-shaped larva of certain nemerteans.

Piliferous Layer. The part of the root epidermis that bears root hairs. It extends over a region about 4-10 mm behind the root tip. Beyond this the piliferous layer is sloughed off to reveal the hypodermis,

Pill

1. A small, rounded mass of medicinal substances which is swallowed whole.
2. One of several oral contraceptive pills containing synthetic hormones which suppress the development of Graafian follicles and the release of ova from the ovary.

Pilose. Having soft long hairs. Compare pubescent.

Piltdown Man. Fossil remains, purported to have been found by Charles Dawson at Piltdown, Sussex, in 1912, that were named Eoanthropus dawsoni and described as a representative of the true ancestors of modern man. The skull resembled that of a man but the jaw was apelike. In 1953 dating techniques showed the specimen to be a fraud.

Pilus (fimbria). A projection from the surface of a bacterium. It is finer than a flagellum aud also differs in having a hollow core. Pili are often found in large numbers and are thought to help attach bacteria to other cells rather than serve a locomotive function. Pilus formation may be initiated by a plasmid, in which case it serves as a conjugation tube for the transmission of a copy of the plasmid to a suitable recipient cell. Plasmids with this ability are termed sex factors or F factors.

Pinacocyte. A flattened, contractile cell in the epidermis of a sponge.

Pincers. A forcipulate organ, as a chela, forceps, or pedicellaria.

Pine. A coniferous tree of the genus Pinus with long needles in groups of two to five; a valuable timber tree, also the source of turpentine, rosin, tar, pitch, and other products.

Pineal Body. The epiphysis cerebri, a small, cone-shaped structure forming a part of the epithalamus.

Pineal Eye. A well-developed parapineal organ which contains photoreceptors, considered a third eye; present in lampreys, tadpoles, lizards.

Pineal Gland. An outgrowth of the fore-brain. In man its functions are obscure, but in other vertebrates it acts as an endocrine gland, secreting hormones that affect reproductive function and behaviour.

Pinfeather. A growing feather just emerging from the skin and still enclosed within its sheath.

Pinion. In birds, the hand bone or the portion of the wing beyond the wrist, exclusive of the feathers.

Pinna (auricle). The visible part of the outer ear, present in some mammals. It is made of cartilage and its function is to channel sound waves into the external auditory meatus. In some species the pinna is movable and aids in detecting the direction from which a sound originates.

Pinnate. Describing a compound leaf in which the leaflets (pinnae) are arranged in two rows, one on each side of the midrib. Such leaves are common in the Leguminosae.

Pinnated. With winglike tufts of feathers along the sides of the neck.

Pinnatifid (pinnatisect). Deeply cut into lobes but not so far as the midrib. Examples are the pinnatifid leaves of the fen sowthistle (Sonchus palustris).

Pinnatisect. Lobed almost to the midrib, said of leaves.

Pinniform. Like a fin, as the wing of a penguin.

Pinniped. An aquatic mammal of the Pinnipedia, a suborder of the Cornivora, which includes the seals, sea lions, and walruses, with limbs modified as flippers.

Pinnule. One of a number of second order leaflets in a compound leaf, such as is typical of many ferns, where the pinnae are themselves divided into leaflets.

Pinocytosis. Process similar to phagocytosis (by which a cell membrane can invaginate and enclose externally derived, solid material within a vacuole, without disrupting the continuity of the cell surface, the vacuole subsequently fusing with a lysosome and its contents being wholly or partly digested), except that the material enclosed is a liquid.

Pinophyta. In certain classifications, a division containing the gymnosperms (Gymnospermae). It is divided into the following subdivisions : Cycadicae (cycadophytes), containing the orders Pteridospermales, Caytoniales, Bennettitales, and Cycadales; Pinicae (coniferophytes), containing the orders Ginkgoales, Cordaitales, Coniferales, and Taxales; and the Gneticae (gnetophytes), containing the orders Ephedrales, Welwitschiales, and the Gnetales. The Cycadicae are differentiated from the Pinicae on the basis that they have palmlike compound leaves, motile antherozoids, radially symmetrical seeds, and loose soft wood. The Pinicae in contrast have simple leaves, nonmotile sperm nuclei (except in Ginkgo biloba), bilaterally symmetrical seeds, and denser wood. The Gneticae resemble the Pinicae in having simple leaves, nonmotile sperm, and flattened seeds. However they differ from both the Pinicae and Cycadicae in possessing ovules with two integuments, rather than one, the inner of which is elongated into a tubular micropyle, and in having compound microstrobili.

Pintail. A surface-feeding duck (Anas acuta).

Pin-tailed. With central tail feathers long and narrow.

Pinus (true pines; family Pinaceae). Genus of resinous, evergreen conifers with the leaves (needles) borne in groups of twos, or fives on short shoots borne along the twigs. There are separate male and female cones, the latter with woody scales; the seeds are winged. Many pines are important for timber, also yielding resin and turpentine. There are some 70 – 100 species, all in the northern hemisphere, occurring mainly in northern temperate regions, extending in America and E. Asia to the seasonal tropics. The common name 'pine' is sometimes used to describe other pine-like tree of different genera, *e.g.* Araucaria araucana (Chile pine or the monkey-puzzle tree), or, loosely, to include all conifers.

Pinule. A ray of a sponge spicule, when covered with spines.

Pinworm. A small nematode (Enterobius vermicularis) parasitic in the intestine of man, especially children. Also called seat worm.

Piperidine Alkaloids. A group of alkaloids, the structures of which are based on the piperidine ring (a six-membered ring with no double bonds and containing one nitrogen atom). Most are derived from the amino acid lysine. An example is nicotine found in many plants, especially Nicotiana tabacum (tobacco) and other Nicotiana species.

Pipit. A small, tail-wagging ground bird of family Motacillidae, as Anthus spinoletta, the American pipit.

Pirana. A voracious, short-toothed fish (Serrasalmus) which operates in schools in Soutn American rivers, noted for its ferocity; also called piranha, caribe.

Pirarucu. A large freshwater fish (Arapaima gigas) of South America.

Pisces. Superclass containing the four classes of fish, including the two extant classes Chondrichthyes (cartilaginous fish, *e.g.* sharks) and Osteichthyes bony fish), the extinct Placodermi and Acanthodii, and also the most primitive of the vertebrates. The first protofish are known from late Cambrian fossils, and the first true fish, an agnathan, has been recorded from earliest Ordovician sediments. Some modern classifications omit the term 'Pisces' regarding it as artificial.

Piscine. Of or pertaining to fishes.

Pistil. A gynoecium or a unit of a gynoecium, the female structure of a flower consisting of an ovary, style, and stigma; a female organ composed of one or more carpels.

Pistillate

1. Having a pistil or pistils but no stamens.
2. Female, with reference to flowers.

Pit

1. A depression or an open cavity.
2. *bot. a.* A thin, depressed area in a cell wall. *b.* The stone of a drupe, as a cherry.
2. *zool.* A depression, as an armpit, facial, or loreal pit, or gastric pit.

Pit Canal. A minute opening in the wall of a sclerid.

Pitch

1. *bot. a.* A resinous exudate of certain conifers, especially the hemlock. *b.* The dark residue resulting from the distillation of coal tar, wood tar, and other substances.
2. *physiol.* The quality of sound which depends upon the frequency of vibrations.

Pitcher Plant. An insect-eating bog plant (Sarracenia purpurea) with a leaf or leaves forming a pitcher-shaped structure which traps insects.

Pit Field. A depression in a primary cell wall in plants.

Pith (medulla). A region of parenchymatous tissue found in the centre of many plant stems to the inside of the stele. A pith is also often seen in the roots of herbaceous plants but rarely in the roots of woodly plants.

Pithecanthropoid. Of or pertaining to Pithecanthropus.

Pit Organ

1. A pit containing sensory cells sensitive to heat located between the eye and the nose in pit vipers and along the margins of the jaws in pythons and boas.
2. A pit in the lateral line system of fishes containing cells sensitive to pressure changes and electrical stimuli.

Pitted. Bearing or marked by minute depressions or pits.

Pitted Thickening. A type of secondary wall patterning in tracheary elements in which the secondary cell wall is more or less continuous, the continuity only broken by pits and perforation plates (if present). The pits may be arranged in an opposite or alternate pattern (illustration at tracheary element) If the pits are greatly elongated transversely and parallel to each other, they are said to be scalariformly pitted. Like reticulate and scalariform thickenings, pitted thickening permits little further extension and is therefore found in tissues that have finished elongating at maturity, such as metaxylem and secondary xylem. Compare annular thickening, spiral thickening.

Pitting. The arrangement and distribution of pits in the cell walls of cells in plant stems.

Pituitary. The pituitary gland or hypophysis cerebri, an endocrine gland attached to the ventral surface of the diencephalon, consisting of an anterior lobe which secretes a number of tropic hormones (somatotrophin, adrenocorticotrophin, thyrotrophin, and several gonadotrophints), and intermediate lobe which secretes a melanocyte-stimulating hormone, and a posterior lobe which stores and releases vasopressin and oxytocin secreted by the hypothalamus.

Pituitary Gland (pituitary body; hypophysis). A pea-sized endocrine gland attached by a thin stalk to the hypothalamus at the base of the brain. It consists of two lobes : the anterior and the posterior. The anterior pituitary secretes such hormones as growth hormone, the gonadotrophins, prolactin, thyroid-stimulating hormone (thyroid gland) and ATCH. Because these hormones regulate the growth and activity of several other endocrine glands, the anterior pituitary is often referred to as the master endocrine gland. Activity of the anterior pituitary itself is regulated by specific hormone-releasing factors (neurosecretions) produced by the hypothalamus (also neuroendocrine system). The posterior pituitary secretes the hormones oxytocin and vasopressin.

Pit Viper. One of several venomous snakes of the family Crotalidae characterized by possession of a pit organ, as the rattlesnake, copperhead, water moccasin, fer-de-lance, and bushmaster.

Placenta

1. The organ in mammals and other viviparous animals by means of which the embryo is attached to the wall of the uterus. It is composed of embryonic and maternal tissues : extensions of the chorion and allantois grow into the uterine wall so that materials (*e.g.*, oxygen, nutrients) can pass between the blood of the embryo and its mother (there is however, no direct connection between the material and embryonic blood). The placenta is eventually expelled as part of the afterbirth.

2. A ridge of tissue on the ovary wall of flowering plants to which the ovules are attached. The arrangement of ovules on the placenta (placentation) is variable, depending on the number of carpels and whether they are free (apocarpy) or fused (syncarpy).

Placental. Of, pertaining to, or having young nourished through a placenta.

Placentate. Having a placenta.

Placentation. The pattern of attachment of an ovule to the ovary wall by the placenta. If there is only one ovule in the ovary then it is usually attached either at the base (basal placentation) or the apex (apical placentation). In a simple ovary the ovules may be attached either along the ventral suture (marginal placentation) or, rarely, all over the inner surface of the ovary wall (laminate placentation). In a compound ovary the ovules may be attached either on a central axis or on the wall along the junctions of the carpels (parietal placentation). Placentation on the central axis is termed axile in a multilocular overy and free-central in a unilocular ovary. It is believed that free-central and parietal placentation are derived from axile placentation. The type of placentation. is an important diagnostic character in many taxa.

Placode. A localized thickening of an epithelium in an embryo which comprises the anlage of a structure, as a lens placode.

Placoid Scale (dermal denticle). Type of scale that comprises the basic unit of the hard skin cover of sharks. It consists of a hard base embedded in the skin and a spiny process (cusp); these are covered by a hard, enamel-like substance (vitrodentine), and the scale projects outwards and backwards. It is these cusps that are responsible for the roughness of the shark's skin. The bulk of the denticle consists of dentin surrounding a central pulp cavity. Unlike the scales of bony fish, placoid scales stop growing after they reach a certain size and new denticles are added instead.

Plagioclimax (biotic climax). 'Plagioclimax' and 'biotic climax' are almost synonymous terms, which are sometimes given different meanings. Generally, they both refer to a stable vegetation community arising from a succession that has been deflected or arrested either directly or indirectly as a result of humaan activities. An important distinction exists between these two cases In a deflected succession. the resulting stable community, even when composed entirely of native species, is one that would not have occurred had the disturbing human intervention not taken place. For example, the lowland heath communities of Britain and W. Europe arose as a consequence of forest clearance and subsequent grazing pressure and controlled burning. Associated changes in the physical environment may mean that even when these pressures are removed succession to the original climax community is no longer possible. In an arrested succession, the stable community is a naturally occurring successional phase: following removal of the disturbing factor, continuation of the natural succession should be possible. For example, the cutting of reed beds arrests the natural succession to alderwood in a hydrosere. Some authors restrict the term 'plagioclimax' to deflected succession; some use 'plagioclimax' where human intervention is more direct, reserving 'biotic climax' for more indirect effects, such as grazing by non-domesticated but introduced animal species, *e.g.* rabbit in Britain. 'Biotic climax' may also be applied to a natural, undisturbed succession in which the final community form is determined by a naturally occcurring biological agent, *e.g.* grasslands on guano-enriched coastal areas.

Plagiotropism. The tendency for a tropism (growth response of a plant) to be orientated at an angle to the line of action of the stimulus concerned. For example, the growth of lateral branches and lateral roots is at an oblique angle to the stimulus of gravity (plagiogeotropism). Compare orthotropism.

Plague

1. In general, any epidemic of a disease in which the death rate is very high.
2. More specifically, and more usually, a disease of humans caused by Yersinia pestis (formerly Pasteurella pestis). The disease occurs in several forms. Bubonic plague is the commonest form. In pneumonic plague the lungs are severely affected and mortality rates are very high. Septicaemic plague involves septicaemia and is also frequently fatal. Y pestis is harboured by rats and is transmitted to humans by fleas.

Plaited. Folded : Plicate.

Plakea. A stage of development of certain algae and protozoans in whch the cells form a hollow ball with flagella directed inward, as in Volvox.

Planarian. Any free-swimming, triclad, turbellarian flatworm, especially those of the genera Planaria, Euplanaria, and Dugesia.

Planetesimal Hypothesis. A cataclysmic theory, propounded early in the twentieth century to explain the origin of the solar system. This was attributed to tidal interactions produced by a close encounter between the Sun and a star. The immense gaseous tides produced in the Sun pulled matter away, in the direction of the star, to form a long, gaseous filament. This then broke into several parts each contracting to form a planet.

Planidium The first in two or more farval stages in an insect undergoing hypermetamorphosis.

Plankter. An individual organism or species of plankton.

Plankton. Minute aquatic organisms that drift with water movements, generally having not locomotive organs. The phytoplankton (plants) comprise mainly diatoms, which carry out photosynthesis and form the basis of the aquatic food-chains. The zooplankton (animals) which feed on the diatoms may sometimes show weak locomotory powers. They include protozoans, small crustaceans, and in early summer the larval stages of many larger organisms. Plankton are sometimes divided into net-plankton (more than 25 μm diameter) and nanoplankton, which are too small to be caught in a plankton net.

Planktonic Geochronology. The use of planktonic organisms, *e.g.*, globigerinid foraminiferids or microscopic algae, to provide a relative dating of sediments deposited in marine waters. Radioactive-decay methods applied to planktonic organisms may also yield an absolute date or information on palaeoclimates.

Plant

1. Any member of the plant kingdom, Planta.
2. A living organism distinguished in general from an animal by the following characteristics: capacity for unlimited growth by persistence of embryonic tissue throughout life; lack of locomotor structures; ability to carry on photosynthesis; slow responses to stimuli cells with cell walls containing cellulose; reproduction involving alternation of an asexual with a sexual generation. Compare animal.

Planta. The sole of the foot.

Plantae. The plant kingdom. In most classifications this is taken to include all the green plants (*i.e.* all organisms containing chlorophyll). In many classifications the fungi and bacteria are also included. Plants are distinguished from members of the animal kingdom (Animalia) by a number of factors. Most are autotrophic, making their food from inorganic starting materials by photosynthesis. Animals by contrast are heterotrophic. However the fungi, most bacteria, and certain parasitic higher plants are also heterotrophic. Plants are usually attached to a substrate and not able to move around freely like animals (this however does not apply to certain flagellate algae and fungi). Plants can generally only respond to external stimuli by growth movements. Response is consequently very slow as compared to animal movements and only occurs if the stimulus is prolonged. Most plant cells are surrounded by cellulose cell walls and starch is a common storage polysaccharide. Animals do not have cellulose cell walls and carbohydrates are commonly stored as glycogen. Perennial plants tend to grow indefinitely while in animals increase in size usually ceases at maturity.

The Plantae has been variously divided into sub-kingdoms and divisions. Some systems recognize two subkingdoms, the Thallophyta and Embryophyta.

Plantain

1. The stemless herb Plantago, a common weed; ribwort.
2. A tropical food plant (Musa paradisiaca) of southern Asia.

Plantar. Of or pertaining to the sole or the under surface of the foot.

Plantar-flexion. Extension of or straightening the foot.

Plant Association (association). Term loosely applied in the classification of vegetation communities and given varying interpretations in different phytosociological traditions, with resulting confusion. The current most widely accepted usage follows the Zurich—Montpellier school. In this, the 'association' is the basic vegetation unit, an abstract entity, floristically defined from field data or releves. Each association has a distinctive faithful species and a group of high-presence or constant species which give the community or association a cohesive structure. Often these companion species of the association form the faithful species of the next and succeeding hierachical levels, alliances, and orders into which similar associations are grouped. In British and American traditions, 'association' has tended to imply a community with physiognomic as well as floristic unity, usually a climax community in which the species dominants are those of the upper vegetation layer. In this tradition an association usually has several codominant species. The term 'consociation' is reserved for single-species dominance.

Plant Breeding. The improvement of plants for agricultural, horticultural, or medical purposes. Probably all cultivated plants are the result of selection practices that originated some 10 000 years ago. Modern breeding techniques include artificial control of pollination, the generation of variability by artificial hybridization and mutation, and selection procedures such as pedigree breeding and backcrossing.

Plant Bug. A hemipterous insect of the family Miridae, also called leaf bug.

Plant Hormone (phytohormone). Compound synthesized by a plant, and not a nutrient, coenzyme, or detoxification product, that regulate growth, differentiation, or other specific physiological processes. It is classically defined as being 'made at one site and functioning at another'; but in fact it is made by various tissues, transported actively or passively, and affects most tissues within the plant.

Plant Geography (phytogeography). The study of the distribution of world vegetation, with particular emphasis on the influence of the environmental factors that determine this distribution.

Plantigrade. Walking on the sole of the foot with heel touching the ground, as man, bears, and certain insectivores.

Planula. The ciliated, free-swimming larva of certain coelenterates, especially hydrozoans and one genus of ctenophorans, Gastrodes, a parasite.

Plaque

1. A small plate or platellke structure.
2. A clear area in a bacterial culture resulting from the action of a bacteriophage.

Plasma

1. The clear fluid portion of blood or lymph.
2. In a general sense, protoplasm.

Plasma Cells. Antibody-producing cells found in the epithelium of the lungs and gut and also in bone-forming tissue. They develop in the lymph nodes, spleen, and bone marrow when antigens stimulate lymphocytes to form the precursor cells that give rise to them.

Plasmagel. The more solid, jellylike, outermost portion of the protoplams of a rhizopod protozoan. Compare a plasmasoal.

Plasmalemma. The plasma membrane cell membrane.

Plasmagene. A game present in any structure other than a chromosome in the nucleus. The term commonly refers to genes present in organellus such as mitochondria and chloroplasts.

Plasma Membrane (plasmalemma). The outer layer of the protoplasm below the cell wall. Like most cell membranes it is formed by the orderly orientation of protein and phosphoglyceride molecules. Plasma membranes range from 7.5 nm to 10 nm in thickness and are composed of approximately 60% protein and 40% phosphoglyceride. Membranes of different species contain characteristic types of polar lipids in proportions that are probably genetically determined.

Davson and Danielli, in 1935, proposed that membranes are made up of a central region consisting of phosphoglycerides and an outer denser region composed of proteins. The phosphoglyceride molecules were believed to be arranged into rows with their hydrophilic polar heads towards the outer edges and their hydrophobic hydrocarbon tails in the centre. Although it is still accepted that the two rows of phosphoglyceride molecules form the backbone of the membrane it is believed that globular proteins, rather than forming a distinct outer layer, actually penetrate the whole width of the membrane in places (diagram). Both the phosphoglyceride molecules and the proteins are thought to be able to move laterally giving the membrane fluid-like properties. This hypothesis of membrane structure is termed the fluid—mosaic model.

Plasma membranes are selectively permeable, controlling the passage of materials into and out of the cell.

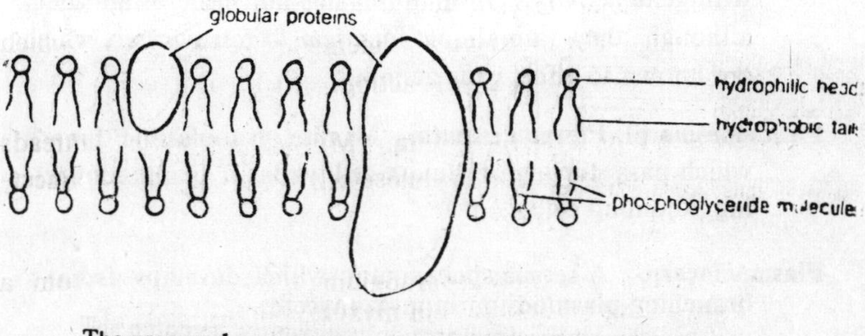

The proposed arrangement of phosphoglyceride and protein molecules in a cell membrane.

The proteins of the membrane include enzymes and compounds of the active transport system. Water and nonpolar molecules that dissolve in the phosphoglyceride layer pass readily through the membrane. The membrane is relatively impermeable to charged ions, which enter the cell by means of the active transport system. Permeability varies in different parts of the plant and at different stages of development. Time-lapse photography of living membranes reveals almost constant movement and it is probable that there is continual replenishment of membrane constituents.

Plasmasol. The specialized inner sol-like cytoplasm of living cells that move by producing pseudopodia. Compare plasmagel.

Plasmid. A structure in cells consisting of DNA that can exist and replicate independently of chromosomes. In bacterial cells plasmids provide genetic instructions for certain cell activities (*e.g.* resistance to antibiotic drugs). They can be transferred from cell to cell in a bacterial colony. Bacterial plasmids are used to produce recombinant DNA in tecniques of genetic engineering. Similar blocks of DNA that appear to move from one chromosome to another have been identified in the cells of a number of other species, including man. In organism (other than man) that have been studied, it appears that they interfere with gene activity. In man this has not been established, although they are almost identical to retroviruses, which are known to affect gene action.

Plasmodesma pl. **Plasmodesmata.** Minute protoplasmic threads which pass through cellulose cell walls of plants connecting adjoining cells.

Plasmodiocarp. A sessile sporangium which develops from a branching plasmodium in myxomycetes.

Plasmodiophoromycetes. A class of the Myxomycota containing fungi that are obligate parasites in the cells of other plants, in which they often induce hyperttrophy. In contains about 35 species in some 10 genera. Two serious parasites of crop plants are Plasmodiophora brassicas, which causes clubrrot in brassicas, and Spongosyora subterranea, which causes powdery or corky scab in potatoes. These fungi are often classified as an other (Plasmodiophorales) of the Myxomycetes, or are sometimes classified with the Mastigomycotina.

Plasmodium (family Plasmodiidae). Genus of parasitic protozoa, which includes some very important disease-causing species : the malarial parasites. The life cycle is complex. Some stages can occur only in a second host, the mosquito vector. The genus includes more than 50 species, of which four (P. vivax, P. falciparum, P. ovale, and P. malariae) cause malaria of differing degrees of severity in humans. Other species infect various other vertebrates, including monkeys, birds, and reptiles.

Plasmogamy. The fusion of the protoplasts of two haploid cells during sexual reproduction. Plasmogamy is usually followed immediately by karyogamy (nuclear fusion), but in some ascomycetes and basidiomycetes the two processes are separated so that binucleate (dikaryotic) mycelia are formed.

Plasmolysis. The shrinking of protoplasm from the cell wall with loss of turgidity as a result of exosmosis. Compare deplasmolysis.

Plasmoptysis. The escape of protoplasm from a cell following rupture of the cell membrane.

Plasmotomy. The division of a multinucleate cell into portions which are still multinucleate, as occurs in certain myxosporidians.

Plastic

1. Capable of being altered or modified.
2. Capable of undergoing change.

3. Concerned with the restoration or building up of tissues.

Plasticity. The capacity of an organism to change its form in response to varying environmental conditions. For example, a plant transferred outside from a warm poorly lit greenhouse may produce smaller paler leaves and shorter internodes. Such changes can only occur in new tissues and the existing mature parts of the plant remain unchanged. In taxonomic work it is important to establish how plastic a particular character can be before placing too much reliance on it. It is also necessary in breeding work to establish what proportion of variation is caused by phenotyic plasticity.

Plastid. Any of a number of self-duplicating bodies present in the cytoplasm of cells, especially plant cells, varying in structure, pigment content, and function. Chloroplast chromoplast, leucoplast, amyloplast, elaioplast, chromatophore.

Plastid Inheritance. Plastome.

Plastocyanin. One of the electron transfer components of chloroplasts, mediating transfer of electrons from photosystem II to photosystem I. It is a blue copper-containing protein, and it is the reduction and oxidation of the copper atom that allows plastocyanin to accept, then donate, electrons The position of plastocyanin in the electron transport chain is thought to be very close to photosystem I, probably between cytochrome *f* and photosystem I.

Plastogene

1. A plasmagene which gives rise to a plastid.
2. A cytoplasmic unit of heredity associated with the development of plastids and responsible for their characteristics.

Plastoglobuli. Droplets of lipid, 10—500 nm in diameter, found singly or in groups in the stroma of chloroplasts. They do not have an enclosing membrane but nevertheless retain their form when isolated from the stroma. Plastoglobuli from chloroplasts of actively photosynthesizing leaves contain various lipid and lipophilic compounds, *e.g.* galactolipids, quinones, and polyisoprenols, but no chlorophylls or carotenoids. As leaves become senescent, chloroplasts change to chromoplasts and changes in the plastogiobuli occur. They accumulate carotenoid pigments and enlarge considerably until they become the dominant features in the chromoplasts.

Plastome. The phenomena by which the primordia of plastids pass through the cytoplasm of the egg and give rise to plastids of the next generation.

Plastoquinone. One of the electron transfer components of chloroplasts, mediating transfer of electrons from photosystem II to photosystem I. It is situated between cytochrome b_3 and cytochrome f and the transfer of electrons by cytochrome f is accompanied by the formation of a molecule of ATP.

Plastron

1. The ventral portion of the shell of a turtle.
2. A thin film of air held by hydroluge hairs or scales of an insect.

Plate

1. *zool.* A thin, flat structure; a lamina, a scute.
2. *microbiol.* A thin, flat, culture dish as a petri dish, which contains a solid medium upon which microorganisms can be grown.

Plate Count. A method employed for estimating the number of bacteria in a substance as milk or water based on introducing a measured amount of the material into a petri dish containing a suitable culture medium, and then, after a period of incubation, counting the number of colonies which develop.

Platelet (thrombocyte). A small disc of red tissue in the blood. Platelets are formed as fragments of larger cells (megakaryocytes) found in red bone marrow; they have no nucleus. They play an important role in blood clotting (also clotting factors) and release serotonin, which causes blood vessels to constricts, so reducing bleeding. There are about 250 000 per cubic millimetre of blood.

Plate Tactonics. The theory that the surface of the earth is made of lithospheric plates, which have moved throughout geological time resulting in the present-day positions of the continents. The theory explains the locations of mountain building as well as earthquakes and volcanoes. The rigid lithospheric plates consist of continental and oceanic crust together with the upper mantle, which lie above the weaker plastic asthenosphere. These plates move relative to each other across the earth. Six major plates (Eurasian, American, African, Pacific, Indian, and Antarctic) are recognized, together with a number of smaller ones. The plate margins coincide with zones of seismic and volcanic activity.

A constructive (or divergent) plate margin occurs when two plates move away from each other. It is marked by a mid-oceanic ridge where basaltic material wells up from the mantle to form new oceanic crust, in a process known as sea-floor spreading. The production of new crust at constructive plate margins is compensated for by the destruction of material along a destructive (or divergent) plate margin. Along these margins, which are also known a subdivision zones and marked by an oceanic trench, one plate (usually oceanic) is forced to plunge down beneath the other (which may be continental or oceanic). The crust becomes partially melted and rises to form a chain of volcanoes in the upper plate parallel to the trench. When two continental plates collide the compression results in the formation of mountain chains. A third type of plate margin—the transform plate margin—occurs where two plates are slipping past each other.

Plating. The cultivation of microorganisms in a petri dish containing a solid nutrient medium, usually nutrient agar.

Platyhelminthes (flatworms). Phylum of acoelomate, bilaterally symmetrical worms in which the internal organs are well developed and metameric segmentation is absent. The gut may be present, but skeletal elements are rare. Morphologically they are quite diverse, and many are parasites. Most are hermaphrodites. The phylum lacks a definite fossil record. From various evolutionary considerations it is probable that platyhelminths were in existence 100-1000 million years ago.

Platyrrhine. With a broad, flat nose.

Plecopteran. An insect of the order Plecoptera comprising the stonefiies.

Platyspermic. Describing the flat bilaterally symmetrical seeds characteristic of the Cordaitales. Compare radiospermic.

Plectenchyma. The hyphae of a fungus when organized into tissues.

Plectenchyma. A form of 'tissue', commonly found among the higher fungi, composed of a mass of interwoven anastomosing hyphae. It is termed prosenchyma when formed from long fused hyphae and pseudoparenchyma when it has a cellular appearance due to regular divisions in the hyphae. Pseudoparenchymatous tissue is also seen in the thalli of certain red algae.

Plectomycetes. A class of the Ascomycotina containing those ascomycetes that produce a cleistothecium. It numbers about 2300 species in some 160 genera. It is not a natural class as it contains both fungi with single-walled asci and others with double-walled asci. Also some are primitive while others are regressive. It contains the orders Ascophaerales, Eurotiales, Microascales, Erysiphales, and Meliolales.

Plectostele. A protostele in which the xylem consists (in transverse section) of several plates of tissue surrounded by phloem. This type of stele is exhibited in some species of Lycopodium and is thought to have evolved from an actinostele.

Plectrum

1. The stapes in anurans, reptiles, and birds.
2. The rasping part of a stridulatory organ.

Pleiomerous. Having more than the normal number of floral parts, as petals or sepals.

Pleiotropism. A condition in which there are multiple effects produced by a single gene.

Pleistocene. The first of two epochs of the Quaternary, preceded by the Pliocene. It is held conventionally to have lasted from approximately 1.8 million years ago until the beginning of the Holocene, about 10 000 years ago, but recent evidence from deep-sea cores may necessitate a revision of the earlier date. The epoch is marked by several glacial and interglacial episodes in the northern hemisphere.

Pleomorphic. Having more than one form during a life cycle, as in certain bacteria and fungi.

Pleiomorphism. The existence of distinctly different forms during the life cycle of an individual, *e.g.* the caterpillar, pupa, and winged adult of a butterfly.

Pleon

1. The abdomen of a crustacean.
2. The telson of a king crab.

Pleopod. A slender, biramous abdominal appendage of a malacostracan crustacean.

Plerocercoid. The wormlike, second, larval stage of a fish tapeworm which develops in a fish following ingestion of a procercoid.

Plerocercus. The larval stage of a tapeworm consisting of a solid, globular body containing the invaginated head or scolex.

Plerome. Meristem tissue comprising the central portion of a growing root or stem.

Plesiomorphy. A primitive character state whose origin can be traced back to a remote ancestor. Plesiomorphies shared by different taxa (symplesiomorphies) are not used in the construction of cladograms or phylogenies. Compare apomorphy.

Pleura. The double membrane that lines the thoracic cavity and covers the exterior surface of the lungs. It is serious membrane forming a closed sac, with a small space (the pleural cavity) between the two layers.

Pleural. Of or pertaining to the pleura or a pleuron.

Pleurapophysis. A lateral process of a vertebra with which a rib fuses.

Pleurite. A sclerite of a pleuron.

Pleurobranch. A gill borne on the side of a thorax.

Pleurocarpous. Describing mosses in which the reproductive organs are produced laterally and the main axis is usually creeping. Compare acrocarpous.

Pleurocentrum. A lateral element in the centrum of a vertebra of certain fishes and amphibians.

Pleuron pl. Pleura. The lateral portion of the body wall of a segment of an arthropod.

Pleuston. A mass of free-floating organisms, especially a mat of algae.

Plexus. A compact branching network of nerves or blood vessels, such as the branchial plexus—a network of spinal nerves that supply branches to the forelimbs in vertebrates.

Plica pl. **Plicae.** A fold.

Plicae Circulares. Circular folds on the inner surface of the intestine.

Plicate. Arranged in or having folds as, for example, the mesophyll cells of many gymnosperms and certain angiosperms, which have inward foldings of the cell wall.

Pliocene. The fifth and final epoch of the Tertiary period. Preceded by the Miocene and followed by the Pleistocene, it began about 7 million years ago and lasted for about 5 million years. Mammals similar to modern forms existed during the epoch and the australopithecines early forerunners of man, appeared.

Pliomorphic (pleomorphic, pleiomorphic). Describing organisms that exhibit two or more different forms in their life cycle. For example, many ascomycetes have two conidial states.

Pliody. genetics. A condition in which the chromosome number is a multiple of the haploid number.

Plotless Sampling. Sampling without the use of quadrats. Individual pin-frame records may be regarded as plotless samples. Plotless sampling is most often used for surveys of forest vegetation, especially where a rapid inventory is needed. Various approaches have been developed, *e.g.* the nearest-neighbour sampling method.

Plover. A shorebird of the family Charadriidae, as the golden plover (Pluvialis dominica).

Pluck. The heart, liver, and lungs of an animal.

Plum. The fruit, a drupe, from the plum tree (Prunus).

Plumage. The entire covering of feathers of a bird.

Plumelet. A small plume.

Plumose

1. Like a plume or feather.
2. Covered with fine hairs, as the stigma of many grasses.
3. Having fine hairs or bristle resembling a plume.

Plurilocular Sporangium. A sporangium that is divided by septa into many compartments. Plurilocular sporangia are seen, for example, on lateral branches of the diploid generation in the brown alga Ectocarpus. Compare unilocular sporangium.

PMS. Pregnant mare's serum gonado trophin with effects similar to FSH and LH.

Pneumatic

1. Pertaining to air or gas.
2. Operated by air pressure.
3. Conducting or containing air.

Pneumatic Duct. The duct which connects the swim bladder of a fish with the pharynx or esophagus.

Pneumatic Sinus. An air sinus in a cranial bone; a paranasal sinus.

Pneumatocyst. An air-containing cavity, as *a.* the swim bladder of a fish; *b.* the air bladder or float of various algae, as rock-weeds.

Pneumatophore. Specialized 'breathing' root developed in some plant species that grow in waterlogged or strongly compacted soils, *e.g.* mangroves. The aerial part of the root contains many pores, enabling gas exchange with the atmosphere. Internally a well-developed system of intercellular spaces allows gases to diffuse throughout the submerged portion of the roots.

Pneumonia. A disease of the lungs characterized by inflammation and consolidation, usually due to a bacterial or virus infection.

Pneumostome. The external opening of the respiratory chamber in arachnids and pulmonate snails.

Pneumothorax. Air or gas in the pleural cavity.

Poacher. A marine fish of the family Agonidae.

Poad. A meadow plant.

Pocket. A pouch or diverticulum.

Pood

1. *bot.* A dry, dehiscent fruit, splitting along two sutures, as that of a legume, as a bean or pea.
2. *zool. a.* A number of animals clustered together, as a school of fishes, flock of birds, or a group of whales or porpoises. *b.* A mass of insect eggs cemented together.

Podetium. A specialized spore-bearing structure that develops on the thalli of certain lichens, *e.g.* the erect cylindrical podetia of Cladonia.

Podex. The rump or anal region.

Podical Plate. One of two platelike structures representing the eleventh segment of the abdomen in certain insects, as the grasshopper.

Podium pl. **Podia.** The tube foot of an echinoderm.

Podobranchium pl. **Podobranchia.** A gill borne on a thoracic appendage of a decapod crustacean.

Podocyst. A chitinous cyst containing a ciliated larva present in the basal disk of certain coelenterates; pedal cyst.

Podocyte. A cell with numerous cytoplasmic processes which come in contact with the capillaries of a renal corpuscle.

Podsol (podzol). A type of zonal acid infertile soil (a pedalfer) found in regions of heavy rainfall and long cool or cold winters. The soils of the northern coniferous forest zone of North America and Eurasia are typical examples. The soil is heavily leached, by the sudden snow-melt in the spring that washes out lime and iron compounds. Thus beneath the humus layer in the A horizon there is a bleached horizon composed of quartz sand. Iron compounds accumulate in the B horizon, which stains brown and has a clayey texture. These compounds may form an impermeable hard pan that, if developed sufficiently, can stop water percolating from above, resulting in the A horizon becoming waterlogged. Such soils may be termed gley podsols. The leaf litter is such regions also tends to be highly acid and maintains the acidity of the soil.

Poikilotherm (exotherm). Organism that regulates its body temperature by behavioural means, *e.g.* by basking or burrowing. Such animals are often termed 'cold-blooded', although when active their body temperature is little different from that of homoiothermic ('warm-blooded') animals. Poikilothermy is characteristic of lower vertebrates (fish, amphibians, and reptiles), but not of birds and mammals. Compare homoiotherm.

Poikilothermous

1. Having a body temperature which varies with the environment.
2. Cold-blooded, said of animals as amphibians and reptiles.

Poikilothermy (cold-bloodedness). The passive variation in the internal body temperature of an animal, which depends on the temperature of the environment. All animals except birds and mammals are cold-blooded. Although unable to maintain a constant body temperature, they can respond to compensate for very low or very high temperatures. For example, the tissue composition (especially cell osmotic pressure) can change to regulate the blood flow to peripheral tissues (and thus increase heat loss or heat absorption), and the animals can actively seek sun or shade. Seasonal changes in metabolism are usually under hormonal control. In particularly hot climates, cold-blooded animals may undergo aestivation to escape the heat. Compare homoiothermy.

Poison

1. A substance which, upon contact with or being introduced into an organism, impairs or prevents normal metabolic processes from taking place, thus altering the normal functioning of organs or tissues.
2. An agent with an injurious or deadly effect.

Poison Claw

1. A clawlike fang on the tip of a chelicera of a spider.
2. The maxilliped of a centipede.

Poison Gland. A gland which secretes a poisonous substance.

Poison Hemlock. A poisonous plant (Conium maculatum) of the family Umbelliferae.

Poison Ivy. A climbing, three-leafed vine (Rhus radicans) which produces a volatile oil capable of causing a severe dermatitis.

Poison Oak. A shrub (Rhus toxicodendron) which causes a contact dermatitis similar to poison ivy.

Poisonous

1. Having the properties of or producing the effects of a poison.
2. Containing a poison, as a poisonous plant or animal.
3. Venomous, toxic.

Poisonous Snake. A venom-producing snake, including those of the following families : Elapidae (cobra, krait, coral snake); Hydrophiidae (sea snakes); Viperidae (Old World vipers); Crotalidae (pit vipers).

Poison Sac. A sac for storing poison, as that of the sting of a honeybee.

Poison Sumac. A poisonous shrub (Rhus vernix), also called poison dogwood or poison elder.

Polar Bear. A large white bear (Thalarctos maritimus) of the polar regions.

Polar Body. A polocyte, a minute cell produced during oogenesis.

Polar Capsule. A special cell which develops within sporoblasts of various sporozoans, as myxosporidians.

Polarity. The condition that results from the establishment of a definite orientation during the differentiation of a cell, tissue, or organ. Polarity is evident in the early growth of plants, as in the bipolar development of an embryo from the zygote. In later growth it is evidenced in the separate development of roots and shoots, as well as various phenomena at the cellular level.

Polarization

1. The state or condition of being polarized.
2. *physiol.* The existence of opposite charges on the two sides of a cell membrane, as in a nerve fiber.

Polarizing Microscope. A microscope that uses polarized light to illuminate the specimen. Certain crystalline molecules transmit polarized light in a way that depends on the orientation of the molecules in the crystal. The technique has been used, for example, to investigate the arrangement of cellulose molecules in plant cell walls.

Polar Nuclei. In angiosperms, the two nuclei in the midregion of the embryo sac, which, when fertilized, develop into the triploid endosperm.

Pole. Either of the two extemities of a structure which exhibits polarity, as an ovum.

Polian Vesicle. One of several stalked sacs attached to the ring canal of the water-vascular system in echinoderms.

Poliomyelitis. An acute, febrile disease caused by a virus in which motor neurons in the spinal cord are affected; also called infantile paralysis.

Pollard

1. A hornless ruminant.
2. A stage which has shed its antlers.
3. *bot.* A tree that has had its crown removed in order to promote growth of numerous branches.

Pollarding. A severe form of pruning in which all the younger branches of a tree are cut back virtually to the trunk. It encourages new bushy growth and is often performed on urban avenues of trees to provide summer shade. The tips of the branches of pollarded trees are characteristically club shaped due to the growth of wound wood. Compare stooling.

Polled. Lacking horns, with reference to cattle; lacking antlers, with reference to deer.

Pollen. The mass of grains containing the male gametes of seed plants, which are produced in large numbers in the pollen sacs. The pollen gains of insect-pollinated plants may be spiny or pitted and are usually larger than those of wind-pollinated plants, which are usually smooth and light. The pollen grain represents the male gametophyte generation. The wall of the mature pollen grain consists of the tough outer wall (exine) and the more delicate narrower intine. The latter gives rise to the pollen tube.

Pollen Analysis. Polynology.

Pollen Basket. A concave depression on the outer surface of the tibia of the third leg of a honeybee, its anterior margin bearing recurved hairs.

Potten Brush. A group of stiff hairs on the first tarsal segment of the first and second pairs of legs in the honeybee or on the abdomen of certain bees; also called scopa.

Pollen Chamber. A cavity at the micropylar end of the nucellus in some gymnosperms in which pollen grains lodge after pollination. The pollen may be immature at this stage but it ripens in the pollen chamber prior to germination and fertilization of the egg.

Pollen Comb. A series of rows of stiff bristles on the inner surface of the metatarsus of the third leg of a honeybee.

Pollen Flower. One which produces pollen but no nectar.

Pollen Grain

1. A microspore produced in the pollen sac of angiosperms or the microsporangium of gymnosperms.
2. A haploid cell containing two nuclei, a tube nucleus and a generative nucleus.

Pollen Mother Cell (PMC). A somatic cell that, after meiosis, forms a tetrad of pollen grains. Many are found closly packed within the pollen sacs of angiosperms and gymnosperms. In angiosperms the pollen mother cell and the resulting pollen grains have been shown to obtain proteins and their precursors from the disintegrating tapetum that surrounds them. Compare megaspore mother cell.

Pollen Packer. A structure in the honeybee for compressing pollen into a compact mass consisting of a pecten and auricle located at the joints between tibia and metatarsus of the hind leg.

Pollen Sac. The structure in seed plants in which pollen is produced. In angiosperms there are usually four pollen sacs in each anther. In gymnosperms variable numbers of pollen sacs are borne on the microsporophylls that make up the male cone.

Pollen Stratigraphy. The study of pollen present in successive layers of sediment deposited in bogs or lakes.

Pollen Tube. Tube formed from a germinating pollen grain, and down which the two male gametes (sperm nuclei pass to the ovum. In flowering plants each pollen tube penetrates tissues of stigma and style into the ovary where it grows towards an ovule, passing down the micropyle to the nuclellus and finally penetrating into the embryo sac. Here the tip of the tube rupeures releasing the two male gametes : one of these fuses with the nucleus of the ovum; the other fuses with the two polar nuclei to give rise eventually to the endosperm.

Pollen Diagram. Standardized pictorial summary of the pollen record for a particular location. The vertical axis represents depth, and the proportions or absolute amounts of the various pollen types occurring at different levels are shown by bar histograms or by points on a continuous curve. Conventionally, similar patterns are grouped together on the diagram with arborcal types shown first followed in turn by shrubs, herbs, and spores.

Pollen Zone (pollen assemblage zone). Characteristic pollen-and-spore assemblage classically considered indicative of a particular type of climate, which was assumed to be typical of a fairly extensive geographic region. Changes from one group of pollens to another characteristic assemblage are used to define pollen-zone boundaries. The standard British (Godwin, 1940) and very similar European post-glacial (*i.e.* late Devensian and Flandrian) chronology recognizes eight major pollen zones : zones

I-III being the characteristic late glacial sequence : order Dryas (I), Allerod (II), younger Drays (III). More recently, based on N. American work, the importance of regional variation in the typical zone floras has been acknowledged, and a moreflexible approach to pollen-zone definition applied. Pollen assemblage zones are defined in terms of their pollen and spore profiles alone for a particular site, and initially without reference to or matching with the standard zone models with their strong climatic links. This has enabled local changes, often man-induced rather than climatic, to be elucidated more clearly.

Pollex. The innermost digit on the forelimb of a tetrapod vertebrate. It contains two phalanges (pentadactyl limb) and in man and higher primates it is the thumb, which is opposable (*i.e.* capable of facing and touching the other digits) and gives the hand greater manipulating ability. In some mammals a pollex is absent. Compare hallux.

Pollinate. To perform the act of pollination.

Pollination. The transfer of pollen grains from the another (part of the androecium) to the stigma (part of the gynoecium) of a flowering plant. This process facilitates contact between male gemetes and the female ovum, leading to fertilization, development of seed and thence a new plant. In gymnosperms, the pollen tube containing a pollen grain grows down and penetrates the neck of the archegonium, facilitating contact between the sperm cells (male gametes) and the ova. Most archegonia contain many ova, so that multiple fertilization can occur, although only one sperm can fertilize an egg. Unlike angiosperms, which do not possess archegonia, pollen cones and seed cones mature at different times within a season, so that there is usually a long interval between pollination and fertilization.

Pollination Drop. A drop of sugary fluid that is secreted through the micropyle in gymnosperms. Wind blown or insect transported pollen falls into the pollination drop and is drawn through the micropyle to the ovule as the drop is reabsorbed.

Polliniferous. Bearing or producing pollen.

Pollinium. The structure formed when individual pollen grains remain massed together and are transported as a unit during pollination. They may be held together only by sticky secretions or they may be retained within the pollen sac wall, as in many orchids. When several pollen sacs remain together and are transported as a pollination unit they are called a pollinarium.

Pollutant. Substance that enters the environment or becomes concentrated within it, and that has, or may have, a detrimental biological effect. Pollutants may occur naturally (*e.g.* sulphur dioxide and dust from volcanic eruptions), or be introduced by human activity (*e.g.* organochlorine pesticides such at DDT).

Pollution. An undesirable change in the physical, chemical, or biological characteristics of the natural environment, brought about by man's activities. It may be harmful to human or nonhuman life. Pollution may affect the soil, rivers, seas, or the atmosphere. There are two main classes of pollutants : those that are biodegradable (*e.g.* sewage), *i.e.* can be rendered harmless by natural processes and need therefore cause no permanent harm if adequately dispersed or treated; and those that are nonbiodegradable (*e.g.* heavy metals (such as lead) and DDT), which eventually accumulate in the environment and may be concentrated in food chains. Other forms of pollution in the environment include noise (*e.g.* from jet aircraft, traffic, and industrial processes) and thermal pollution (*e.g.* the release of excessive waste heat into lakes or rivers causing harm to wildlife). Recent pollution problems include the disposal of radioactive waste; acid rain resulting from industrial emissions of sulphates; increasing levels of human waste; and high levels of carbon dioxide in the atmosphere. Attemps to contain or prevent pollution include strict regulations concerning factory emissions, the use of smokeless fuels, and the banning of certain pesticides.

Polyadelphous. Describing stamen filaments that are fused into many groups.

Polyandrous. Having separate stamens freely inserted on the receptacle. Compare adelphous.

Polyandry. The mating of a female with more than one male at one time (usually taken to be during the course of a single breeding season). Simultaneous polyandry occurs where the female mates with more than one male to produce a clutch of eggs or brood of young bearing genes from each male. Successive polyandry occurs where the female mates with one male, lays eggs or gives birth to the young but plays little part in their parental care (usually cared for by this first male), instead moving off to mate with another male. The existence of the former situation is usually difficult to prove, and polyandry appears to be mainly of the latter type. Examples are a number of arctic species of wading birds, such as the Temminck's stint and grey phalarope. Polyandry is generally much rarer than polygyny, presumably because the mother is usually not sexually receptive following successful mating, and since she bears the young, she is more involved with their care and less able to seek another mate. Promiscurity is a form of polygyny or polyandry in which a member of one sex mates with more than one member of the other sex, but each relationship is an ephemeral one and terminates after mating, whereas in the other cases a bond of some kind forms.

Polycarpellary. Fruit.

Polychaeta (bristleworms; phylum Annelida). Class of annelid wroms which possess distinct metameric segmentation. All have bristly parapodia on each body segment. Eyes may be present. Males and females occur. Most are marine, although some occur in fresh water and on land. The group first appeared in the Cambrian and it contains more than 5000 species.

Polycyclic Stele. A stele in which the meristeles or vascular bundles are arranged in concentric rings. Polycyclic steles are present in some ferns.

Polydactile. Having extra fingers or toes or both.

Polydisc. Designating a multiple disc scyphistoma consisting of several ephyrae.

Polyembryony

1. The formation of more than one embryo in a plant seed. Often one embroy develops from the fertilized egg cell, while the others have formed asexually from other tissues in the ovule.

2. The formation of mor than one embryo from a single animal zygote. Identical twins are produced in this way.

Polyestrous. Having more than one estrous cycle per year, as in rats, rabbits.

Polygamous

1. *bot.* Bearing staminate, pistillate, and hermaphroditic flowers at the same time.

2. *zool.* Having more than one mate at one time.

Polygene. Any of a group of genes influencing a quantitative characteristic, *e g.* height in man.

Polygenic. Due to many genes, said of hereditary traits of a quantitative character.

Polymer. A substance having large molecules consisting of repeated units (the monomers). There are a number of natural polymers, such as polysaccharides.

Polymorphism

1. In genetics, the existence of two or more forms that are genetically distinct from one another but contained within the same interbreeding population. The polymorphism may be transient or it may persist over many generations, when it is said to be balanced. Classical examples of polymorphisms are the presence or absence of banding in Cepaea snails, the number of spots on the wings of ladybirds, and eye colour in humans. All these are visible polymorphisms that can readily be seen in nature. Some polymorphisms, however, are cryptic and require biochemical techniques to identify phenotypic differences. Such techniques include gel electrophoresis of enzymes and other proteins, and the fragmentation of the DNA molecule by restriction enzymes (which allows the sequencing of nucleotides), both of which operate nearer to the level of the genotype.

2. In social insects, the presence of different castes within the same sex.

Polymorphonuclear. Having a nucleus consisting of two or more lobes joined together by slender strands, as in graenlar leukocytes.

Polymyarian. Having numerous muscle cells in each quadrant of the body wall, as in certain nematodes. Compare meromyarian.

Polyp. The sedentary stage in the life cycle of the Coelenterata, consisting of a cylindrical body fixed at one end to a firm base and having a mouth surrounded by a ring of tentacles at the other. Some polyps (*e.g.* Hydra) are single; others (*e.g.*, the corals and Obelia) form colonies. Polyps typically reproduce asexually by budding to form either new polyps or medusal. The latter reproduce sexually giving rise to new polyps. Sea anemones are solitary polyps that reproduc e sexually to form new polyps.

Polypeptide. A peptide chain containing a large number of amino acid residues (most polypeptides have a molecular weight greater than 5000). Proteins are made up of one or more polypeptides.

The amino acid sequence of a polypeptide chain determines the three-dimensional conformation of that molecule under physiological conditions. This conformation can be disrupted by heating or extremes of pH (denaturation).

Polypetalous. Having separate petals freely inserted on the receptacle. Compare gamopetalous.

Polyphagous. Subsisting on many kinds of foods.

Polyphyletism. The occurrence in taxa of members that have descended via different ancestral lineages. True polyphyletism has traditionally been distinguished from errors of classification, especially at the higher taxonomic levels, where organisms, as a result of convergent or parallel evolution, have been placed wrongly in the same natural group; but modern phyletic taxonomists would hold that any taxon found to be polyphyletic is unnatural, and so an 'error', and must be disbanded.

Polyphyletic. Denoting any group of organisms the members of which have originated from several different ancestors. An example is the group including all insectivorous animals. Polyphyletic groups are not natural groups and do not have any place in natural classifications. Compare monophyletic.

Polyphyodont. Describing a type of dentition in which the teeth are continuously shed and replaced during the lifetime of the animal. Sharks and frogs have a polyphyodont dentition. Compare diphyodont; monophyodont.

Polyploid. Describing a nucleus that contains more than two sets of chromosomes (diploid) or a cell or organism containing such nuclei. For example, triploid plants have three sets of chromosomes and tetraploid plants have four. Polyploidy is far more common in plants than in animals; many crops, in particular, are polyploid (bread wheat, for example, is hexaploid, *i.e.*, $6n$).

Polyploidy. The condition in which an individual possesses one or more sets of homologous chromosomes in excess of the normal two sets found in diploid organisms. It is caused by the replication within a nucleus of complete chromosome sets without subsequent nuclear division. Examples are triploidy ($3n$), tetraploidy ($4n$), hexaploidy ($6n$), and octoploidy ($8n$).

Polypod. Having many legs or feet, with reference to insect larvae.

Polypoid. Polyplike in appearance or structure.

Polyribosome (polysome). A string of ribosomes attached together by a single molecule of messenger RNA. The strings may be folded or coiled into complex configurations, often spirals. The ribosomes move along the mRNA and as they pass each base triplet a transfer RNA molecule adds the corresponding amino acid to the base of a growing polypeptide chain. When a ribosome move off the end of the mRNA it releases its completed polypeptide chain and is ready to start at the beginning again. This enables the code to be used highly efficiently.

Polysaccharide. Any of a group of carbohydrates comprising long chains of monosaccharide (simple sugar) molecules. Homopolysaccharides consist of only one type of monosaccharide; heteropolysaccharides contain two or more different types. Polysaccharides may have molecular weights of up to several million and are often highly branched. Some important examples are starch, glycogen, and cellulose.

Polysaprobic. Capable of living in waters of low oxygen content containing much decomposing organic material.

Polysepalous. Having separate sepals freely inserted on the receptacle. Compare gamosepalous.

Polysome. Polyribosome.

Polysomy. The presence of several additional copies of one particular chromosome in a cell or organism.

Polyspermia. Excessive production of spermatozoa or semen.

Polyspermy. The entry of several sperms into the egg during fertilization although only one sperm nucleus actually fuses with the egg nucleus. Polyspermy occurs in animals with yolky eggs (*e.g.* birds).

Polystachyous. Bearing many spikes.

Polystely. The condition of having a number of independent steles. For example, the aerial axes of many Selaginella species have several protosteles ascending the stem, separated by the cortex.

Polystichous. Arranged in many ranks or rows.

Polystomatous. Having many or multiple pores, mouths, openings, or suckers.

Polytene Chromosome. A chromosome with multistranded DNA due to repeated replication of the DNA without subsequent separation. The resulting giant chromosomes are valuable in cytological and genetical research. They are seen in the salivary glands of the larvae of dipteran insects, *e.g.* Drosophila (fruit flies).

Polytrophic

1. Utilizing various kinds of foods.
2. Having nutritive cells alternating with oocytes, with reference to insect ovarioles.

Polytypic. Consisting of more than one subspecies.

Polyuria. Production of an excessive quantity of urine.

Polytocous. Producing more than one at birth.

Polyxenous. Having many possible hosts, with reference to parasites.

Polyzoa (Bryozoa). A phylum of aquatic, mainly marine, invertebrates the moss animals. They live in colonies, 50 cm or more across, which are attached to rocks, seaweeds, or shells. The individuals making up the colonies are about 1 mm long and superficially resemble coelenterate polyps, with a mouth surrounded by ciliated tentacles that trap minute particles of organic matter in the water. Some have a horny or calcareous outer skeleton into which the body can be withdrawn.

Pome. A type of fruit characteristic of apples and pears. The flesh of the fruit develops from the receptacle of the flower, which completely encloses the fused carpels. After fertilization the carpels from the 'core' of the fruit, which contains the seeds.

Pomegranate. A bush or low tree (Punica granatum) of its fruit, a large, thick-rinded berry.

Pongid. Any anthropoid ape of the family Pongidae.

Pons (pons Varolii). A thick tract of nerve fibres in the brain that links the medulla oblongata to the midbrain. Its function is to relay impulses between different parts of the brain. The pons is named after its discoveser, the Italian anatomist C, Varoli (1543-75).

Poppy. A plant of the genus Papaver, family Papaveraceae, with showy, regular flowers, capsular fruits, and a milky juice, especially P. somniferum, the opium poppy.

Population. A local community of potentially interbreeding organisms. In asexual organisms, the term normally refers to a local community of physiologically or morphologically similar individuals of the same species.

Population Dynamics. The study of factors that influence the size, form, and fluctuations of individual species or genus populations. Emphasis is placed on change, energy flow, and nutrient cycling, with particular reference to homoeostatic controls. Key factors for study are those influencing natality, mortality, immigration, and emigration.

Population Explosion (population eruption) Sudden rapid increase in size of the population of a spceies or genus. The most violent explosions occur when a species is introduced into a new locality where it finds unexploited resources of suitable food, shelter, etc., and a lack of negative controls such as predators or parasites. Examples include the population explosions of the rabbit and prickly pear when these were first introduced into Australia. The situation may be stabilized by the introduction of controls, *e.g.*, the use of myxomatosis to control rabbit numbers. Alternatively, once food supplies become exhausted the population may crash, and even become locally extinct once more.

Population Genetics. The study of inherited variation in populations of organisms, and its modulation in time and space. Population genetics relates the heritable changes in populations to the underlying individual processes of inheritance and development. Such studies generally involve the estimation of gene frequencies and the influences of selection, mutation, and migration upon these frequencies in natural (and experimental) populations.

Porate. Having pores, with reference to the exine of a pollen grain.

Porbeagle. A medium-sized, voracious sharx (Lamnia nasus) of northern waters.

Porcine. Of or pertaining to swine.

Porcupine. One of a number of large, stout-bodied rodents with barbed, erectile quills, comprising two families, Erethizontidae (New World porcupines), as Erethizon dorsatum, the Canadian porcupine, and Hystricidae (Old World porcupines), as Hystrix cristata, the crested porcupine.

Pore (porus). A circular or slightly elliptic germinal aperture in a pollen grain. Compare colpus.

Porifera (Spongiaria, sponges). Phylum of aquatic Metazoa, most of which are marine. They lack definite tissues and organs, but have a filter-feeding system composed of flagellate cells, pores, and canals. Most are covered externally by a cortex or dermis. The soft body is supported by a skeleton composed of siliceous or calcareous spicules, and some forms may possess organic fibres as well. Larvae are motile and produced by sexual reproduction. The phylum ranges from the Cambrian to Recent.

Porogamy. The condition in plants in which the pollen tube gains entrance to the ovule through the micropyle. Compare aporogamy.

Porometer. An apparatus designed to measure the resistance to the flow of air through a leaf in different external conditions. An example is Meidner's porometer, which consists of a Perspex clamp attached to a bulb pipette.

The bulb is squeezed flat and the leaf is inserted into, and covered by, the clamp. The time taken for the air to pass through the leaf and inflate the bulb is proportional to the resistance of the leaf and gives an estimate of the degree of opening of the stomata.

Porose. Porous.

Porous. Possessing openings or pores : Porose.

Porphyrin. Any of a group of related organic compounds characterized by the possession of a cyclic group of four linked nitrogen-containing rings (a pyrrole nucleus). Porphyrins differ in the nature of their side-chain groups. They include the chlorophylls and the haem groups of haemoglobin, myoglobin, and the cytochromes.

Porrect. Extended outward and forward.

Portal. An entryway, especially the hilus of an organ.

Portal Heart. A contractile portion of the portal vein in cyclostomes.

Portal of Entry. The avenue through which an infectious organism gains entrance to the body.

Portal System. A vein with a capillary network at each end, as the hepatic, hypophyseal, or renal portal systems.

Portal Vein (portal circulation; portal system). Any vein that collects blood from one network of capillaries and transports it directly to a second capillary network in another region of the body, without returning to the heart.

Portuguese Man-of-war. A polymorphic, colonial hydrozoan (Physalia pelagica) with a large float from which numerous elongated processes are suspended.

Position Effect

1. A modification in the normal expression of a gene due to a change in its position on the chromosome following an inversion.

2. The determination of the appearance of an organism according to whether two nonallelic mutations of a single gene are in the *cis* arrangement or the trans arrangement. The position effect is the basis of the *cis-trans* test.

Positive

1. Numerically, anything greater than zero.

2. *biol.* *a.* Directed toward a stimulus, as a positive tropism or taxis. *b.* Designating increased or favorable activity, as a positive reaction.

3. *chem.* *a.* Having less than the normal number of electrons, as a positive ion, *b.* Yielding electrons, as a positive valence.

Positive Feedback. Feedback.

Possum. The shortened form of opossum.

Postabdomen

1. In primitive arachnids, the posterior portion of the abdomen.

2. In various crustaceans, the recurved tip of the abdomen, as in cladocerans.

Postaxial

1. Located or situated behind an axis.

2. Designating the posterior side of a vertebrate limb.

Postcardinal. Posterior to the heart.

Postcava. The posterior or inferior vena cava.

Post-climax. In the mono-climax model of climax vegetation development, the term given to communities differing from the climatic climax due to cooler and/or moister conditions than are characteristic of the regional climate. Such conditions occur typically at higher elevations, especially on the windward slopes of mountain ranges.

Posterior

1. Designating the part of an animal that is to the rear, *i e.* that follows when the animal is moving. In man and bipedal animals (*e.g.* kangaroos) the posterior surface is equivalent to the dorsal surface.
2. Designating the side of a flower or axillary bud that faces towards the flower stalk or main stem, respectively. Compare anterior.

Postganglionic Fibers. Fibers of the autonomic nervous system whose cell bodies are located outside the central nervous system in autonomic ganglia.

Postlarva. In crustaceans, the final stage in development in which the individual resembles, in general, the adult but still differs significantly in a number of features.

Postmortem. An examination of a body after death; an autopsy.

Post-transcriptional Processing. Messenger RNA.

Posture. The attitude or position assumed by a body.

Potamoplankton. The plankton of running waters; rheoplankton.

Potash. Potassium Carbonate.

Potassium (K). Element, required for healthy plant growth. Potassium ions neutralize anionic macromolecules and organic acids and thus control the water potential of cells. They pass readily through membranes and are important in the movements of leaves and guard cells. Deficiency leads to reduced growth and to dark or blue-green coloration in the leaves, which may also develop a purple-brown pigment.

Potassium-argon Method (K-Ar method). Geological dating technique based on the radioactive decay of potassium (^{40}K) to argon (^{40}Ar). This potassium isotope has a half-life of 1.3 billion (10^9) years, making this a valuable dating method for long time-scales. The minimum age limit for this dating method is about 250 000 years.

Potato. The edible tuber of the plant Solanum tuberosum or the plant which produces it; the white or Irish potato.

Potato Blight. One of a number of diseases of the white potato, especially the late blight, caused by a fungus (Phytophthora infestans), a downy mildew.

Potency

1. *physiol.* The ability of a male to perform the sexual act.
2. *embryol.* The extent to which an egg, blastomere, or a part of the embryo is capable of developing under a certain set of conditions.
3. *phar.* The power or effectiveness of a drug.

Potential Instability (convective instability). Atmospheric condition in which otherwise stable air would become unstable if forced to rise, *e.g.* over high ground, thereby reaching its saturation point. Large cumulus with much precipitation often results from the forced uplifting of such air.

Potentiation. Increasing the effectiveness of a drug by combining it with another.

Potometer. An apparatus designed to measure the rate of water uptake by a cut leafy shoot or whole plant and hence, indirectly, the rate of transpiration. One version consists of a glass tube that bends upwards at one end and supports the plant. The other end of the tube is connected to a capillary tube with an attached scale. The whole apparatus is filled with water from a reservoir joined via a tap to the tube and then made airtight. The plant takes up water and the flow of water is measured by observing the progress of an air bubble along the capillary tube. If the diameter of the capillary tube is known the volume of water taken up by the plant can also be measured. The apparatus is usually used to compare the rate of water uptake when the plant is subjected to certain changes in the external conditions, such as moving air, different light intensities, differences in humidity, etc. It may also be used to compare the rate of water uptake by different plants in the same conditions. An atmometer is a similar apparatus and is used to measure the rate of evaporation from a non-living wet surface, such as a porous pot. By comparing water loss from a potometer with that from an atmometer under similar conditions, the rate of water evaporation from a leaf, which is controlled by the leaf to some extent, can be compared to the rate of uncontrolled evaporation.

Pouch

1. A sac or receptacle, as *a.* the marsupial pouch of the Metatheria; *b.* the cheek pouch of a rodent; *c.* the buccal food pouch or gular pouch of a bird; *d.* the brood pouch of a bivalve.
2. *anat.* A pocketlike cavity, as the rectouterine pouch.
3. *embryol.* An outpocketing, as a pharyngeal pouch.

Poult. The young of domesticated fowl, especially a young chicken or turkey; also the young of game birds.

Poultry. Domesticated birds raised for the production of eggs or meat, as chickens, turkeys, ducks, geese.

Pout. One of several freshwater catfishes, especially Ameiurus nebulosus, the horned pout.

Powdery Mildew. Either a fungus of the family Erysiphaceae or a plant disease caused by such a fungus. The leaves, fruit, etc. of an infected plant bear characteristic powdery white patches of conidium-bearing mycelium; tiny black perithecia may also be visible. Many types of plant may be affected, usually each by its own particular species or strain of fungus.

Poxvirus. One of a group of DNA-containing viruses, often enclosed in an outer membrane, that typically produce skin lesions in vertebrates. They include those viruses causing smallpox (variola), cowpox (vaccinia), and myxomatosis. Some poxviruses produce tumours.

P-P Factor. The pellagra-preventative factor.

P_{fr}. The inactive form of toe plant pigment phytochrome that has a peak of light absorption in the red part of the spectrum, *i.e.* at about 655-665 nm. It is interchangeable with the P_{fr} form.

Prairie. A large, treeless area of level or rolling land covered with grass.

Prawn. One of a number of edible, shrimplike, decapod crustaceans, especially those of the genera Penaeus and Palaemonetes.

Preadaptation. The possession of a trait or traits which are not necessarily and often not advantageous to an organism in its present environment but would be advantageous in a different environment.

Preaxial

1. Located or situated in front of an axis.
2. Pertaining to or located on the anterior side of a vertebrate limb.

Pre-boreal. The first Flandrian (Holocene, or post-glacial) stage, a time of rapid forest spread, from about 10 300 to 9600 BP. 'Pre-Boreal' refers to climatic conditions and in vegetational terms is equivalent to Pollen Zone IV of the standard British and European post-glacial pollen chronology.

Precambrian. The longest period of geological time, which began with the consolidation of the Earta's crust and ended with the beginning of the Cambrian Period 570 million years ago. The Precambrian lasted approximately 4000 million years; the rocks of this period of geological time are usually altered and few fossils with hard parts or skeletons have been found within them. Precambrian rocks outcrop extensively in shield areas such as northern Canada and the Baltic Sea. In many texts the Precambrian is subdivided into the Archaean and Proterozoic.

Precaval Vein. Vena cava.

Precipitin. Any antibody that combines with its specific soluble antigen to form a precipitate. The term is sometimes applied to the precipitate itself.

Pre-climax. In the mono-climax model of climax vegetation development, the term given to communities differing from the climatic climax due to hotter and/or drier environmental conditions than are characteristic of the regional climate. Such conditions typically occur in rain-shadow areas in the lee of mountain ranges.

Precocial. Designating birds whose young, upon hatching, are covered with down, are active and able to move about and feed themselves. Compare altricial.

Precocious

1. *zool.* More fully developed than usual; prematurely developed.
2. *bot.* Ripening or fruiting before the usual time.

Precursor. That which gives rise to something else; something essential for the development of something more complex.

Precystic. Preceding the formation of a cyst.

Predacious or **Predaceous.** Predatory; preying upon other animals.

Predation. Interaction between species populations in which one organism, the predator, obtains energy (as food) by consuming, usually killing, another, the prey. Most typically, a predator is an animal that catches, kills, and eats its prey; but predation also includes feeding by insectivorous plants and grazing interactions, *e.g.* the complete consumption of unicellular phytoplankton by zooplankton. Predation is analogous to parasitism in being both a means of feeding and a cause of immediate harm, but differs in that predators are usually larger than prey organisms and the prey is usually wholly consumed. The distinction is not clear-cut, especially for insect populations. In detail, a continuous gradation of interactions is found from predation to parasitism.

Predation Analysis. The mathematical modelling of predator-prey relationships as, for example, in the Lotka-Volterra equations. Using these models, computer simulations of predator and prey behaviour can be made and tested against field results. This gives a useful insight into the development of community structure, and more particularly into the behaviour of pest organisms and other species that are important commercially or in conservation.

Predator. A predatory organism; a beast of prey.

Predatory. Predacious; living by killing and eating other animals.

Preformation. *embryol.* A formerly held theory that an individual exists preformed within the ovum or spermatozoan and that development results from the unfolding and growth of previously developed parts. Compare epigenesis.

Preganglionic Fibers. Fibers of the autonomic nervous system whose cell bodies are located in the brain or spinal cord.

Preganglionic Neuron. The first of two neurons in the efferent pathway of impulses from the brain or spinal cord to a visceral effector organ (gland, smooth muscle, cardiac muscle).

Pregnant. The condition of being with child or bearing young : Gravid.

Prehallux. A rudimentary digit on the tibial side of the tarsus in frogs and other salientians; calcar.

Prehensile. Adapted for grasping or clasping, especially by wrapping around, as the prehensile tail of a monkey.

Prehensor. An appendage bearing a poison claw on the first trunk segment of a centipede; a maxilliped.

Prementum. In insects, the distal portion of the labium usually bearing the ligula and labial palps.

Premolar. A broad ridged tooth in mammals that is situated behind the canine teeth (when present) and in front of the molars. Premolars are adapted for grinding and chewing food and are present in both the deciduous and permanent dentitions.

Premunition. A state or condition in certain parasitic infections in which the host is immune to reinfection as long as the parasites remain within the body.

Prenatal. Existing before birth.

Prepubis. One of a pair of bones in monotremes and marsupials which extend forward from the pubis serving to support the ventral body wall and marsupium; a marsupial bone.

Prepuce. The foreskin, a fold of skin which covers the glans penis or glans clitoridis.

Prepupa. A pharate pupa; a pupa which is retained within the old larval skin.

Presbyopia. A loss of accommodation that normally develops in human eyes over the age of 45-50 years. Vision of distant objects remains unchanged but accommodation of the eye to near objects is reduced as a result of loss of ealsticity in the lens of the eye. The defect is corrected by reading glasses using weak converging lenses.

Pressoreceptor. A receptor which responds to an increase in blood pressure, as those located in the carotid sinus or arch of the aorta : Baroreceptor.

Pressure gradient Force (PGF). The force acting on air due to pressure differences. Horizontal variations in pressure create a tendency for movement from higher to lower pressure : this is only one component of the forces acting on the actual wind, though, so air does not normally flow at right angles across the isobars. Other forces are associated with the rotation of the Earth underneath the moving wind and a centrifugal force where the path of the wind is curved. In practice the air moves nearly along the isobars above the friction layer.

Pressure Potential (turgor potential). A component of water potential, represented by the symbol ψ_p. Pressure potentials may be negative, in which case they represent tensions. Tensions arise as a result of transpiration and are caused by resistance of the tissues to water flow. In extreme conditions very low (—150 bar) pressure potentials can develop. Pressure potential gradient are responsible for the upward movement of water in the xylem (cohesion theory). Positive pressure potentials are termed hydrostatic pressures.

Presumptive. *embryol.* A term applied to tissues or cells before differentiation indicating that, in the course of normal development, the embryonic structure would follow a certain predetermined course, as designating certain blastomeres as presumptive ectoderm.

Presumptice. Describing embryonic tissue that is not yet determined but which will eventually develop into a certain kind of tissues by virtue of its position in the embryo.

Prevailing Climax. The most common undisturbed, stable community that occurs in a region. In any given area various stable communities are found in response to local differences in habitat. Gradual transitions from one stable type to another occur as environmental controls change. The steady-state community occupying the largest number of non-extreme habitats in the area is the prevailing climax. This approximates to the climatic climax communities for the area. Unlike mono-climax, prevailing climax does not involve consideration of possible long-term climatic changes, or associated habitat changes due to weathering and erosion. Thus it is a more practicable and readily applied concept.

Prevernal. Of the early spring, with reference to flowering.

[1]Prey. An animal that is seized by another and eaten.

[2]Prey. To engage in predaceous activity, seizing and killing other animals.

Prezygapophysis. The anterior or superior zygapophysis of a vertebra; the anterior articular process.

Pricket. A male deer in its second year.

Prickle. A hard sharp protective outgrowth, many of which may cover the surface of a plant. In contains cortical and vascular tissue and is not regarded as as epidermal outgrowth. Compare spine; thorn.

Prickly Pear. A cactus of the genus Opuntia or the fruit it produces.

Prim. The common privet.

Primary. One of the outer flight feathers of birds, which originate from the hand or manus. Most non-passerines have ten primaries. Ciconiidae (storks), Phoenicopteridae (flamingos), and Podicipediae (grebes) have 12; Ardeidae (herons), Anatidae (ducks, geese, etc.), and some other groups have 11. Most passerines have nine functional primaries, the tenth being reduced.

Primary Endosperm Nucleus. The triploid nucleus that results from fusion of the polar nuclei or definitive nucleus of the embryo sac with one of the male gametes released from the pollen tube. It develops into the endosperm.

Primary Growth. The increase in size of shoots and roots of plants that results from the activity of the apical (tip) meristems and subsequent expansion of the cells produced. The tissues thus produced are called primary tissues and the resultant plant parts constitute the primary plant body. Compare secondary growth.

Primary Phloem. Phloem derived from the procambium in the primary plant body. In nonwoody plants the primary phloem, consisting of the protophloem and metaphloem, is the only food-conducting tissue, whereas mature plants exhibiting secondary growth this function is usually performed by the secondary phloem.

Primary Pit Field. An area of greatly reduced thickness in the primary wall of a plant cell, often penetrated by plasmodesmata. Primary pit fields enable relatively easy transfer of materials between eells, thus having a similar function to pits. Cells lacking secondary walls can possess only primary pit fields, whereas those possessing secondary walls may also possess pits, which are often, but not always, positioned directly over the primary pit fields.

Primary Productivity (primary production). The rate at which energy is stored by photosynthetic and chemosynthetic autotrophs (mainly green plants) in the form of organic substances that may be used as food materials. Gross primary productivity (GPP) is the total rate of photosynthesis and chemosynthesis, including that portion of the organic material produced that is used in respiration during the measurement period. Net primary productivity (NPP) is the rate of production of surplus organic material after some has been lost to plant respiration during the measurement period. Net community productivity is the rate of accumulation of organic material, allowing for both plant respiration and heterotrophic predation during the measurement period. Rates of storage at higher trophic levels are termed secondary productivities. Strictly, the primary production of an ecosystem (as distinct from its productivity) is the amount of organic material accumulated. It is usual to indicate a period of time, however, since otherwise such data have limited value. Thus in practice the terms 'production' and 'productivity' are often used interchangeably. It is also vital to indicate whether production figures relate to net primary or net community productivity, or to some portion of these, as with a harvested crop.

Primary Thickening Meristem. A meristem that is found in certain monocotyledons, such as palms, below the leaf primordia at the apex. It serves to increase the width of the stem behind the apex by cutting off rows of cells by periclinal divisions. Prolonged primary growth, due to the activity of this meristem, allows some monocotyledons to attain considerable stature.

Primary Tissue. Tissue formed from a primary meristem, such as the procambium, protoderm, or ground meristem. In woody plants primary tissue is formed before secondary tissue (secondary growth). In herbaceous plants that possess no secondary meristems, all tissues are primary The primary xylem and primary phloem are examples of primary vascular tissues.

Primary Xylem (primary wood). Xylem derived from procambium in the primary plant body. In nonwoody plants the primary xylem, consisting of the protoxylem and metaxylem, is the only water-conducting vascular tissue, whereas in mature plants exhibiting secondary growth this function is performed largely by the secondary xylem. As well as differing from secondary xylem in origin, the primary xylem usually also has longer tracheary elements, which are often arranged in a random fashion, although these differences are not always reliable. Primary xylem also consists of an axial system only and therefore does not contain rays, although rays may be present between the vascular bundles.

Primates. An order of mammals that includes the monkeys, apes, and man. Primates evolved from arboreal insectivores 130 million years ago. They are characterized by thumbs and big toes that are opposable (*i.e.* capable of facing and touching the other digits), which permits manual dexterity, and forward-facing eyes allowing binocular vision. The brain, particularly the cerebrum, is relatively large and well-developed, accounting for the intelligence and quick reactions of these mammals. The young are usually produced singly and undergo a long period of growth and development to the adult form.

Primipara. A woman who is giving birth or has given birth to a child for the first time.

Primite. The anterior of two sporadins.

Primitive

1. Occurring early in evolutionary development; simple, unspecialized; primordial.
2. Occurring early in development; simple; elemental.
3. Uncivilized; undeveloped.

Primitive Streak. A longitudinal thickening on the dorsal surface of the embryo in birds and mammals where involution of the chordamesoderm occurs, considered homologous to the blastopore of amphibians.

Primocane. The first year's cane in a bramble.

Primordium. A group of cells that represents the initial stages in development of a plant organ. Root and shoot primordia are present in a young plant embryo while leaf primordia (or leaf buttresses) are seen as small bulges just below the shoot apex.

Prison Flower. A flower that traps insects.

Probable Mutation Effect. The idea that, as most mutations act to produce failures of development, a non-essential organ will eventually be reduced simply by repeated mutations accumulating in a population. This idea has been used to explain the loss of hind limbs in whales, etc.

Proboscidea. The order of mammals that comprises the elephants. They are herbivorous, with a muscular trunk (proboscis) used for drinking, bathing, and collecting food. The tusks are continuously growing upper incisors and the enormous ridged molar teeth are produced in sequence to replace worn teeth throughout life. The order, which evolved in the Eocene epoch, was formerly much larger and more widespread than it is today and included the extinct mammoths. There are only two species of modern elephants: the African and Indian species.

Proboscis

1. The trunk of an elephant: a muscular and very flexible elongation of the nose, which has a finger-like extremity and is capable of picking up and moving objects, taking in water, collecting food, etc.
2. The elongated mouthparts of certain invertebrates, such at the two-winged flies (Diptera).

Proboscis Worm. A nemertean.

Procambium. A plant tissue formed by the apical meristems of shoots and roots. It consists of cells elongated parallel to the long axis of the plant. The procambium subsequently gives rise to the primary vascular tissue.

Procarp. A specialized branch in red algae from which a carpogonium develops.

Procaryote. Prokaryote.

Procaryotic. Pertaining to cells in which the nucleus is not separated from the cytoplasm by a nuclear membrane and hereditary material is not organized into chromosomes. Compare eucaryotic.

Procercoid. The first larval stage of certain tapeworms, as the fish tapeworm, which develops, in copepods following ingestion of a ciliated coracidium.

Process

1. A series of related activities, as the process of digestion.
2. A series of phenomena exhibiting continuous change, as the process of growth.
3. A prominence, outgrowth, or projecting part.

Prochordate. A protochordate.

Procoelous. Concave at the anterior end, with reference to the centra of vertebrae.

Proconsul. A genus of extinct apes known from fossil remains, 50 million years old, found mostly in Kenya and assigned to the species P. africanus. A find made in 1948 was the first discovery of a skull of Miocene ape. It is believed that Proconsul was similar and possibly closely related to the genus Dryopithecus.

Proctodeum

1. *embroyl.* An ectodermal pit in the anal region which gives rise to the anal canal of vertebrates or the hind intestine of an insect.
2. The cloaca or the terminal portion of the intestine in vertebrates.

Proctodone. In insects, a hormone produced by epithelial cells of the hindgut which activates the neurosecretory cells of the brain.

Proctostome. Term proposed for the single opening of a gastrovascular cavity which serves both as a mouth and anus, as in coelenterates.

Procumbent. Describing a plant or parts of a plant that trail loosely along the ground. An example of a procumbent plant is the heath bedstraw (Galium saxatile). Compare decumbent, prostrate.

Producer. An organism considered as a source of energy for those above it in a food chain (*i.e.* at the next trophic). levle

Green plants, which convert energy from sunlight into chemical energy, are primary producers; herbivores are secondary producers, as they utilize energy from green plants and supply energy for carnivores.

Productivity (in ecology). The rate at which an organism, population, or community assimilates energy (grass productivity) or maeks energy potentially available (as body tissue) to an animal that feeds on it (net productivity). The difference between these two rates is due to the rate at which energy is lost through excretion and respiration. Thus gross primary productivity is the rate at which plants assimilate light energy, and net primary productivity is the rate at which energy is incorporated as plant tissue. In terrestrial plants, much of the net productivity is not actually available to consumers, *e.g.* tree roots are not eaten by herbivores.

Proembryo. The young plant individual after fertilization but before tissue differentiation into embryo and suspensor tissue.

Proenzyme. The zymogen or inactive form of an enzyme.

Proestrus. The period preceding estrus.

Profile. The outline of a structure as seen from the side, especially the face.

Profundal. Occurring in or designating the deep-water zone of an inland lake. Light intensity, oxygen concentration, and (during summer and autumn) temperature are markedly lower than in the surface layer. Compare littoral; sublittoral.

Progametangium. The fertile tip of a conjugating hypha before the formation of a gametangium, as in molds of the genus Mucor.

Progenetic. Becoming sexually mature before reaching the final host, with reference to the metacercariae of certain flukes.

Progency. Offspring; descendants.

Progestational. Preceding gestation or pregnancy.

Progesterone. A hormone, produced primarily by the corpus luteum of the ovary but also by the placenta, that prepares the inner lining of the uterus for implantation of a fertilized egg cell. If implantation fails, the corpus luteum degenerates and progesterone production ceases accordingly. If implantation occurs, the cropus luteum continues to secrete progesterone, under the influence of luteinizing hormone and prolactin, for several months of pregnancy, by which time the placenta has taken over this function. During pregnancy, progesterone maintains the constitution of the uterus and prevents further release of eggs from the ovary. Small amounts of progesterone are produced by the testes.

Progestogen. One of a group of naturally occurring or synthetic hormones that maintain the normal course of pregnancy. The best known is progesterone. In high doses progestogens inhibit secretion of luteinizing hormone, thereby preventing ovulation, and alter the consistency of mucus in the vegina so that conception tends not to occur. They are therefore used as major constituents of oral contraceptives.

Proglottid. One of the segments comprising the oody (strobila) of a tapeworm.

Prognathous

1. Having an upper jaw which protects beyond the facial profile.
2. *entomol.* Having a head with its long axis horizontal and mouth parts located anteriorly. Compare hypognathous.

Prognosis. The prediction or forecast of the course of a disease, its duration, effects, and prospects of recovery.

Progoneate. Having the genital opening located anteriorly, as in millipedes.

Progravid. Before pregnancy; progestational.

Progressive Evolution. Steady, long-term improvement of evolutionary grade, which has allowed plants and animals to become ever more independent of the aquatic environment in which they first evolved. For example, the sequence bryophyte, pteridophyte, gymnosperm, angiosperm represents a progressive evolutionary trend.

Progressive Feeding. The provision of larval food by female wasps and bees at regular intervals throughout the period of larval growth. It is practised by all the social vespid wasps and the honeybees (Apis species). It is uncommon in solitary (non-social) species, though it is found in some sphecid and nyssonid wasps.

Progressive Succession. The normal sequential development of communities, from simple communities with few species and low productivity to the optimum sustainable in a given environment. It is contrasted with retrogressive successional change (retrogression).

Progymnosperm. Any of certain plants of the Devonian period that shows various characteristics apparently intermediate between nonseed-bearing and seedbearing vascular plants. They have heterosporous reproduction, and certain anatomical features such as woody fibres in the cortex and secondary phloem, that are also found in the early gymnosperms.

Projection. *physiol.* The mental process by which sensations are referred to the point of stimulation, or in case of exteroceptors, to the source of the stimulating agent outside the body, as in visual sensations.

Prokaryote (procaryote). An organism in which the genetic material is not enclosed in a cell nucleus. Bacteria and blue-green algae are prokaryotes. It is belived that eukaryotic cells (eukaryote) probably evolved as symbiotic associations of prokaryotes.

Prokaryotic (procaryotic). Describing cells in which the nuclear material is not separated from the rest of the protoplasm by a nuclear membrane. The terms also refers to those organisms, namely the bacteria and blue-green algae, that are based on this type of organization. The term is not used of viruses.

As well as lacking a defined nucleus, prokaryotes also lack nucleoli, plastids, mitochondria, vacuoles, golgi apparatus, and endoplasmic reticulum. Ribosomes are present but are smaller (70S) than those of eukaryotes (80S) though similar in size to those of chloroplasts and mitochondria. This observation has led to speculation that eukaryotes may have evolved as symbiotic associations of prokaryotic organisms (serial endosymbiotic theory). The cells themselves are also much smaller (about 1 μm in diameter) than eukaryotic cells (about 20 μm in diameter) and cytoplasmic streaming is not apparent. The genetic material is a circular strand of DNA, which, unlike that of eukaryotes, is not complexed with histone proteins. Cell division is amitotic.

The biochemistry of prokaryotes is essentially similar to that of eukaryotes. However sterols are conspicuous in their absence from prokaryotes and prokaryotic cell walls characteristically contain muramic acid, a sugar acid not found among eukaryotes. Some unusual amino acids, *e.g.* diaminopimelic acid, are also associated with the cell wall structure and certain familiar amino acids, *e.g.* alanine and aspartic acid, occur as their D-isomers. Peptides containing D-amino acids are resistant to hydrolysis by peptidase enzymes though lysis of gram-positive bacteria can be brought about by lysozyme enzymes.

The basic differences between prokaryotes and eukaryotes have led many taxonomists to place the prokaryotes in a separate kingdom, Prokaryota.

Prolactin (lactogenic hormone; luteotrophic hormone; luteotrophin). A hormone produced by the anterior pituitary gland. In mammals it stimulates the mammary glands to produce milk (lactation) and the corpus luteum of the ovary to secrete the hormone progesterone. Secretion of prolactin is increased by suckling. In birds prolactin stimulates secretion of crop milk by the crop glands.

Prolamellar Body. A three-dimensional regular lattice found in etioplasts. It is composed of a continuous system of tubules but when exposed to light the symmetrical arrangement is rapidly lost as tubules become pinched off into two-dimensional sections of lattice. These form perforated sheets of membrane that move apart, extend and increase, finally establishing the typical granal and intergranal lamellae of the mature chloroplast. Plastoglobuli in the etioplasts are dispersed as their lipid contents are utilized in membrane formation.

Prolamine. Any of a group of simple plant proteins that are soluble in 70-90% alcohol but insoluble in water and absolute alcohol. Prolamines contain a high proportion of proline and glutamic acid but only small amounts of basic amino acids. Examples are gliadin, hordein, and zein, found as storage proteins in wheat, barley, and maize respectively. Compare glutelin.

Prolegs (false legs). Unjointed, fleshy protuberances found on the abdomen of certain insect larvae, in contrast with true legs, which are jointed and found on the thorax. In Lepidoptera, prolegs, which usually bear sclerotized hooks called 'crochets', are usually found on segments 3-6 and 10, but some or all may be absent.

Proliferation. Multiplication; an increase, usually rapid, as in *a.* the number of cells in a developing embryo; *b.* the number of parts, as proglottids in a tapeworm; *c.* the number of individuals, as in a colony.

Proliferous

1. *bot.* Reproducing by buds, bulbils, gemmae, or other vegetative structures.
2. *zool.* Proliferating, as production of numerous branchlets by corals.

Prolific. Fruitful; productive of numerous offspring.

Proline. A nonpolar imino acid, formula C_4H_8NCOOH (illustration at amino acid). Synthesis of proline is from glutamic acid, while breakdown occurs by reversal of the synthetic pathway. Cell walls are rich in 4-hydroxyproline, a derivative of proline.

Promeristem. The primordial or embryonic meristem which contains the initials or foundation cells of new organs or tissues.

Promoter. Nucleotide sequence within an operon, lying between the operator and the structural gene or genes, that serves as a recognition site and point of attachment for the RNA polymerase. It is the starting point for transcription of the structural gene or genes in the operon, but is not itself transcribed.

Promycelium. The basidium of the Uredinales and Ustilaginales. It is formed on germination of the resting spores of these fungi and is usually divided by cross walls into a number of cells.

Pronation. Rotation of the lower forearm so that the hand faces backwards or downwards with the radius and ulna crossed. Compare supination.

Pronephros. The head kidney, the most anterior of a series of embryonic excretory structures occurring in the embryos of all amniotes, and becoming the functional kidney in cyclostomes and some teleost fishes.

Prong. A slender, pointed structure, especially one of the tips of an antler.

Pronghorn. A swift-running ruminant (Antilocapra americana) formerly abundant throughout the western United States; the pronghorn antelope.

Pronotum. The dorsal portion of the prothorax in an insect.

Pronucleus. Either of the two haploid nuclei (male or female) of a fertilized ovum.

Pronymph. A first stage nymph which has just emerged from its egg case.

Propagate

1. To cause to increase or multiply; to breed.
2. To disseminate or spread about.

Propagation. The act of propagating.

Propagule. A propagulum.

Propagulum. A propagable shoot, especially a short, flat branch of certain algae which becomes detached and gives rise to a new plant; a propagule.

Propalinal. Pertaining to the forward and backward movement of the jaws in mastication.

Properdin. A euglobulin in mammalian blood which serves as a nonspecific immune substance.

Prophage. A bacteriophage that has become integrated in the bacterial DNA and is replicated along with it when the bacterium divides. In this state it is quiescent but it may excise itself from the DNA at any time and, following replication, cause lysis of the host bacterial cell.

Prophase. The first phase of mitosis and meiosis, during which the chromosomes become visible within the nucleus, coiling up to produce a series of compact spirals. In meiosis they also undergo pairing during this phase, the phase then being divided into five successive stages; leptotene, zygotene, pachytene, diplotene, and diakinesis.

Prophylaxis

1. The prevention of disease.
2. The use of drugs or other agents to prevent infection.

Propionibacteriaceae. Family of Gram-positive bacteria in which the cells are variable in shape, forming branched or unbranched, regular or irregular rods or filaments. They are chemo-organotrophic; most strains grow only in the absence of air. There are two genera, found in dairy products, in soil, on skin, and in the respiratory and intestinal tracts of animals. Some species can cause disease.

Proplastid. A small plastid, less than 1.0 μm in diameter, with rudimentary internal structure. The inner of the two surrounding membranes is often extended into finger-like projections. Small membrane-bound vesicles and a few starch grains and plastoglobuli may be present in the matrix. Proplastids are present in the cells of meristematic tissue and are thought to differentiate into mature plastids.

Propodium. The anterior portion of the foot in certain burrowing gastropods.

Proprioceptive Sense. The sense of position or movement; the kinesthetic or muscle sense.

Proprioceptor. Any receptor that is sensitive to movement, pressure, or stretching within the body. Proprioceptors occurring in muscles, tendons, and ligaments are important for the coordination of muscular activity and the maintenance of balance and posture.

Prop Root. Any of the modified roots that arise from the stem of certain plants and provide extra support. Such stems are usually tall and slender and the prop roots develop at successively higher levels as the stem elongates, as in the maize plant. Buttress roots, which develop at the base of the trunks of many tropical trees, are similar but tend to have a more flattened appearance. Stilt roots are stouter than prop roots. Those formed at the base of the mangrove tree provide firm anchorage in the soft mud of the swamps.

Prosencephalon. The forebrain.

Prosenchyma

1. Any tissue composed of more or less elongated cells with tapering ends. The component cells are called stereids. Prosenchyma is an obsolete term, sometimes used in contrast with the more or less isodiametric parenchyma cells.

2. Plectenchyma.

Prosodus. A narrow canal between the incurrent channel and a flagellated chamber, as in certain leuconoid sponges.

Prosoma. The cephalothorax of an arthropod.

Prosopyle. In a sponge, the opening between an incurrent and radial canal.

Prostaglandin. One of a number of biologically active lipids present in seminal, menstrual, and amniotic fluids and various mammalian tissues. They stimulate smooth muscle contraction, inhibit lipolysis, platelet aggregation, and gastric secretion.

Prostal. A spicule which projects from the surface of a sponge.

Prostate Gland. A gland in male mammals that surrounds and opens into the urethra where it leaves the bladder. During ejaculation it secretes a fluid into the semen that activates the sperms and prevents them from sicking together.

Prostheca. A fringed plate on the inner surface of the mandible of certain insects.

Prostnetic Group. A coenzyme that is tightly bound to the enzyme with which it acts. An exampie is the biocytin coenzyme of acetyl CoA carboxylase, an enzyme of fatty acid synthesis. The biocytin has a terminal CH (NH_2) COOH group, which covalently binds to the protein as part of the peptide.

Prostomium. The portion of the head which projects forward and overhangs the mouth, as in various annelids.

Prostrate. Describing a plant that grows closely along the ground, such as the white stonecrop (Sedum album).

Protamine. Any of a group of proteins of relatively low molecular weight found in associated with the chromosomal DNA of vertebrate made germ cells. They contain a single polypeptide chain comprising about 67% arginine. Protamines are thought to protect and support the chromosomes.

Protandry. The maturation of the male reproductive organs before those of the female. For example, in many members, of the Compositae and Leguminosae the pollen is released from the anthers before the stigma in the same flower is receptive. Protandry is a consequence of the normal centripetal development of the floral parts and is the most frequently encountered form of dichogamy Compare protogyny.

Protaspis Larva. An early larval stage of a triobitel.

[1]Protean. Variable; assuming various forms and shapes.

[2]Protean. A derived protein, resulting from the action of water, dilute acids, or enzymes on proteins, as fibrin from fibrinogen.

Protease (peptidase; proteolytic enzyme) Any enzyme that catalyses the splitting of proteins into smaller peptide fractions and amino acids, a process known as proteolysis. Examples are pepsin and trypsin. Several proteases, acting sequentially, are normally required for the complete digestion of a protein to its constituent amino acids.

Protein. Name given to polymers with high relative molecular mass of L-amino acids : they occupy a central position in the architecture and functioning of living matter. Structurally they are divided into two groups, globular and fibrous proteins; and they are often found associated with a non-protein component, forming so-called conjugated proteins. Functionally they act variously as enzymes, as structural elements (*e.g.* hair and collagen), as hormones, as respiratory pigment, as contractile elements, as antibodies, and as hereditary factors.

Proteinase. A proteolytic enzyme; an enzyme which acts on proteins, especially native proteins, as pepsin, trypsin.

Protein Synthesis. The process by which living cells manufacture proteins from their constituent amino acids, in accordance with the genetic information carried in the DNA of the chromosome. This information is encoded in messenger RNA, which is transcribed from DNA in the nucleus of the cell (genetic code; transcription) : the sequence of amino acids in a particular proteins in is determined by the sequence of nucleotides in messenger RNA. At the ribosomes the information carried by messenger RNA is translated into the sequence of amino acids of the protein in the process of translation.

Protelean. Designating parasitism by the embryonic or larval stages of an organism, as by the larvae of ichneumon flies.

Proteolysis. The breakdown of the proteins to their constituent amino acids by proteolytic enzymes. Much information about the action of specific proteases and peptidases has been gained from studies on animal digestive tracts, but little is known of the mechanisms by which proteins are broken down within the cell. Radioactive tracer studies have shown that turnover of proteins within the cell is extremely rapid, indicating that intracellular proteolysis is a very efficient process.

Proteolytic Enzyme. An enzyme that hydrolyses proteins.

Proteose. One of a group of derived proteins resulting from the hydrolysis of proteins. They are intermediate between proteins and peptones

Proteroglyph. Any snake of the group Proteroglypha, venomous snakes with fixed fangs located anteriorly in the upper jaw. Includes the families Hydrophiidae and Elapidae.

Proterozoic Era. The second geologic era characterized by the coming into existence of simple multicellular plants and animals.

Prothallial. Of or pertaining to a prothallus.

Prothallial Cell. The smaller sterile cell formed along with the antheridial cell by the first division of the microspore in certion pteridophytes, *e.g.* Selaginella, and in gymnosperms. The prothallial cell does not usually undergo any further division and represents the only vegetative tissue of the gametophyte generation.

Prothallus. A small flattened multicellular structure that represents the independent gametophyte generation of pteriodophytes. In some pteridophytes a single prothallus bears both male and female sex organs. In others there are separate male and female prothalli.

Prothoracic Gland. A gland in insects which secretes ecdysone, the molting hormone.

Prothorax. The most anterior of the three divisions of the thorax of an insect.

Prothrombin. A substance present in blood plasma which is essential for clotting.

Protist. Any organism of the Protista, a major taxonomic group comprising all algae except the blue-greens, fungi, slime molds, and protozoa, characterized by possession of a true nucleus and chromosomes and usually unicellular reproductive structures.

Protista. Kingdom (is some classifications ranked as a super-phylum or phylum) of relatively simple, undifferentiated, unicellular or multicellular organisms, including algae, bacteria, fungi, and protozoans. May be used to include only the bacteria, protozoans, unicellular fungi, and unicellular or simple colonial algae. In most modern classifications bacteria are placed in the kingdon Procary-otae, such as the term 'Protista' is considered outdated. Groups suuh as the foraminifera and radiolarians have a well-established fossil record. The multicellular organisms arose from the protists by various independent routes, possibly as many as 17. They were already a diverse group 1000 million years ago.

Protobiont (coacervate). An aggregate of large complex organic compounds bounded by an organic membrane. It is suggested in certain theories on the origin of life that such aggregates were the precursors of living organisms. It is thought that the membrane selected molecules that could be added to the aggregate and that gradually the chemical component become more efficient and coordinated. Possibly polymeric molecules resembling RNA and DNA developed and became associated with the protobiont, thus enabling it to store and transfer information, a major step in the development of life.

Protocaryotic. Procaryotic.

Protocercal Tail. A primitive type of tail, as that in cyclostomes, in which notochord extends to the tip and dorsal and ventral portions are approximately equal.

Protochlorophyll. The precursor of chlorophyll, present in dark-grown seedlings.

Protochordate. Any chordate of the group Acrania; a tunicate or lancelet.

Protocneme. One of the six pairs of primary septa or mesenteries of an anthozoan coelenterate.

Protocoel. The coelomic cavity of a protosome.

Protoconch

1. The first shell formed by a larval gastropod.
2. A calcareous chamber in the first-formed portion of the shell of an ammonite.

Protocone

1. The single cusp of a primitive reptilian tooth.
2. The inner of three-cusps of an upper molar tooth.

Protoderm. The outermost layer of the apical meristem, the derivatives of which give rise to the epidermis and sometimes also to associated subepidermal tissues. Compare procambium, ground meristem.

Protogyny

1. The condition in which the fame reproductive organs (carpels) of a flower mature before the male ones (stamens), thereby ensuring that self-fertilization does not occur. Examples of protogynous flowers are plantain and figwort. Compare protandry; homogamy.
2. The condition in hermaphrodite or colonial invertebrates in which the female gonads or individuals are sexually mature before the male ones. Compare protandry.

Protomerite. The anterior portion of a gregarine.

Protonema. Early stage in the development of a moss or liverwort. A protonema is produced when a moss or livewort spore germinates. In mosses it usually consists of green, branching filament, but it is thalloid (a flat sheet or disc. of cells) in Sphagnum and Andreaea, for example, and in many liverworts. The familiar moss or livewort plant (the gametophyte) arises from buds which develop on the protonema.

Protonephridium. A primitive type of excretory tubule which opens externally by a nephridiopore but terminates internally in a flame bulb or solenocyte, as in flatworms, rotifers, and some nemerteans.

Protonymph. The first of three developmental stages in mites, ticks, and pseudoscorpons. Compare deutonymph tritonymph.

Protonymphon. The larval stage of a pycnogonid, with three pairs of legs.

Protophloem. Early primary phloem. The sieve elements of the protophloem, which often lack companion cells, are functional for a brief period only and are usually later obliterated, being unable to keep pace with the elongation of the surrounding cells. These obliterated cells often differentiate into fibres.

Protophyte. Any member of the division Protophyta, comprising bacteria and viruses.

Protoplasm. The granular material comprising the living contents of a cell, *i.e.* all the substances in a cell except large vacuolses and material recently ingested or to be excreted. It consists of a nucleus embedded in a jelly-like cytoplasm.

Protoplast (energid). The living unit (protoplasm) of a cell, consisting of the nucleus and tytoplasm bounded by the cell membrane. Protoplasts of bacterial and plant cells can be prepared by removing the cell wall; they are used to study the processes involved in a cell metabolism and reproduction.

Protoplast Fusion. The induction of the fusion of naked (wall-less) plant cells under culture conductions. Such cells or protoplasts can be produced by enzymatic digestion of cell walls, osmotic shock, etc. The technique has potential use for hybridizing unrelated or incompatible species.

Protopodite. The basal portion of a crustacean appendage consisting typically of two parts, a coxopodite and basipodite.

Protostele. A stele consisting of a cylinder of phloem and pericycle surrounding a central core of xylem and lacking a central pith. This type of stele is regarded as being the most primitive both ontogenetically and phylogenetically. The haplostele, actinostele, plectostele, and medullated protostele are all forms of protostele. Compare siphonostele.

Protostome Any member of the Protostomia, a large group of coelomate animals in which the mouth, and sometimes the anus, develops from the region of the embryonic blastopore, as in annelids, mollusks, and arthropods. Compare deuterostome.

Prototheria. A subclass of mammals—the monotremes—that lay large yolky eggs. It contains only the duckbilled platypus and the spiny anteater. After hatching, the young feed on milk from simple mammary glands inside a maternal abdominal pouch. In the anteater the eggs are also incubated in this pouch, while the platypus builds an underground nest. Adult monotremes have no true teeth. Their skeleton resembles that of reptile, and although they are warmblooded the body temperature is somewhat variable. They are believed to have originated at least 150 million years ago.

Prototherian. A mammal of the subclass Prototheria comprising a single order, the Monotremata, which includes the egg-laying mammals.

Prototroch

1. A band or several bands of ciliated cells which encircle a trochophore larva just above its equator.

2. A similar band in the pilidium larva of nemerteans.

Protoxylem. Early primary xylem. The protoxylem matures before the organ completes its longitudinal growth and is thus often distorted or destroyed as the surrounding tissues elongate. In higher plants, the protoxylem of the stem occurs at the innermost edge of the vascular bundles whereas in the root it occurs external to the metaxylem as protoxylem poles. The protoxylem is composed mostly of parenchyma cells with a relatively small number of tracheary elements of the protoxylem usually possess spiral, annular, or sometimes reticulate thickening and nonpitted secondary cell walls. Compare metaxylem, protophloem.

Protozoa. Phylum (division) of eukaryotic, single-celled micro-organisms which show a wide variety of forms. The phylum includes free-living, commensal, mutualistic, and parasitic species, and some important disease-causing organisms. In some classifications the Protozoa are grouped with other simple eukaryotic organisms in the phylum Protista.

Protozoan. Any member of the phylum Protozoa comprising all unicellular or acellular animals, some forming colonies but lacking differentiation of tissues. It includes rhizopods, flagellates, sporozoadss, and ciliates.

Protozoea Larva. A stage in the development of certain crustar ceans which follows the nauplius stage, as in shrimps and prawns.

Protozoology. The study of protozoans.

Protozoon pl. **Protozoa.** A protozoan.

Protraction. The act of drawing out, protruding, or extending. Compare retract.

Protractor. A muscle which causes a part to be protruded, as the protractor muscle of a bivalve.

Protrusible Mouth (protractile mouth). In fish, a structural arrangement of the jaws that enables the animal to protrude (extend) or withdraw the mouth at will. When fully protruded, the cavity of the mouth is enlarged to form a funnel-like space facilitating the uptake of food, *e.g.* in the family Zeidae (dories).

Proturan. Any insect of the order Protura which includes the telsontails, primitive insects with simple metamorphosis.

Proventriculus

1. The anterior part of the stomach of a bird, where digestive enzymes are secreted. Food passes from the proventriculus to the gizzard.
2. Gastric mill.

Provitamin

1. A substance which, when activated or chemically changed, becomes an active vitamin.
2. The precursor of a vitamin, as carotene which is converted in the liver to vitamin A.

Proximal. Denoting the part of an organ that is nearest to the organ's point of attachment. For example, the knuckles are at the proximal end of the fingers. Compare distal.

[1]Prune A plum with high sugar content which can be dried without fermentation occurring.

[2]Prune. To cut off surplus branches of trees or shrubs.

Pruinose. Having a whitish bloom, *e.g.* the fruits of the Oregon grape (Mahonia aquifolium).

Pruning. The cutting back of some or all of the branches of a woody plant. Pruning may be necessary for a number of reasons, *e.g.* the removal of dead or diseased wood or to train the plant into a special shape. Usually however pruning is performed to promote the vigour of a plant and, in the case of fruit trees, to maintain a balance between vegetative growth and fruit production. The time or pruning depends on whether the plant flowers early in the season on the previous season's wood, in which case pruning is carried out after flowering, or in the summer on the current season's wood, in which case pruning should be done in early spring to encourage new growth. Examples of the first group of plants are Prunus species and winter jasmine (Jasminum nudiflorum) and of the second group butterfly bush (Buddleia davidii) and lemon-scented verbena (Lippia citriodora).

Psammon. The organisms that live between the sand particles on a lake or sea shore. Diatoms and other algae provide food for the bacteria, protozoans, and other heterotrophic organisms of the psammon.

Psammophyte. A plant which grows in sand or on sandy soils.

Pseudoalleles. Two or more mutations having similar effects on the phenotype but occurring in different parts of the same gene. Being in the same cistron they will be closely linked and recovery of recombinants from heterozygotes will be rare.

Pseudoallelism. A condition in which groups of alleles show recombination with each other, that is, two or more genes (duplicate genes) act on the same trait and occupy closely adjacent loci.

Pseudobranch. A structure which is not a true gill but functions as one, as that on the side of the foot in pulmonate gastropods.

Pseudocarp (false fruit). A fruit that incorporates, in addition to the ovary wall, other parts of the flower, such as the receptacle. For example, the fleshy part of the strawberry is formed from the receptacle and the 'pips' on the surface are the true fruits.

Pseudocoel. The body space of an invertebrate, differing from a true coelom in that it lacks a peritoneal lining.

Pseudocoelomate. An invertebrate of the group Pseudocoelomata, comprising the phyla Entoprocta, Aschelminthes, and Acanthocephala characterized by possession of a pseudocoel.

Pseudocolony. A group of individuals united by tubes or stalks of dead material but not organically connected, as certain protozoans.

Pseudocopulation. The attempt by a male insect to mate with a flower, or parts of a flower, which it mistakes, because of the colouring, shape, or scent of the flower, for a female of the same species. During pseudocopulation pollination of the flower is achieved. This pollination mechanism can be observed frequently in the orchid family.

Pseudoendosperm

1. The development of an endosperm without fusion of the polar nuclei or definitive nucleus with a male gamete. It may arise spontaneously from the definitive nucleus or from somatic tissue and is therefore usually diploid.
2. In gymnosperms, the tissues of the female gametophyte, which nourish the embryo. It is not homologous with the endosperm of angiosperms, being haploid rather than triploid.

Pseudogamy. A form of apomixis in which a diploid embryo forms without fertilization though a stimulus from the male gamete is required and thus pollination is necessary.

Pseudohermaphrodite. An individual whose external genitalia resemble those of one sex but whose gonads are those of the opposite sex.

Pseudomonadales. An order mainly containing gram-negative rod-shaped bacteria with, in the motile forms, polar flagella. They do not form spores. Many species are pathogenic to plants, *e.g.* Pseudomonas tabaci and P. angulata, which cause wildfire and angular leaf spot of tobacco, and Xanthosomonas, which is responsible for various blights and cankers. The order also contains the nitrifying bacteria Nitrobacter and Nitrosomonas and the photosynthetic bacteria.

Pseudomonas (family Pseudomonadaceae). Genus of Gram-negative, rod-shaped bacteria which are typically motile with polar flagella. Species are capable of breaking down a wide range of organic compounds and are important agents of mineralization. There are many species. They are common is soils, and in fresh and marine waters. Some can be pathogenic, for example P. aeruginosa can cause infection of burns, P. mallei causes glanders, and P. solanacearum can cause wilt in a variety of plants.

Pseudoparenchyma. A plant tissue that superficially resembles parenchyma but is made up of an interwoven mass of hyphae (in fungi) or filaments (in algae). Examples of pseudoparenchymatous structures are the fruiting bodies (mushrooms, toadstools, etc.) of certain fungi and the thalli of certain red and brown algae.

Pseudoperianth. A relatively late-developing membranes sheath surrounding the young sporophyte in certain liverworts, *e.g.* Fossombronia. It is sometimes termed a perigynium.

Pseudoplasmodium. A small sluglike aggregation of myxamoebae that acts as a unit but within which each myxamoeba remains distinct. The fruiting structure is a sorocarp, which is sometimes borne on a slender cellulose stalk, the sorophore. This type of organization is found in the Acrasiomycetes.

Pseudopodium. A temporary outgrowth of the cell of some protozoans (*e.g.* Amoeba) which serves as a feeding and locomotory organ. Pseudopodia may be blunt or thread-like, form a branching network, or be stiffened with an internal supporting rod. White blood cells also form pseudopodia to engulf invading bacteria.

Pseudopregnancy. A state resembling pregnancy that may occur in some mammals in which many of the phenomena of pregnancy are present but there is no fetus developing in the uterus.

Pseudothecium. The type of ascocarp characteristic of the Loculoascomycetes. Pseudothecia are superficially similar to perithecia but contain two-walled asci and also differ in the way they develop. They are often loosely called perithecia.

Psilopsida. A subdivision or class of vascular plants containing two living genera, Psilotum and Tmesipteris; that together constitute the order Psilotales. The fossil forms, which are known chiefly from rocks of the Devonian period, are placed in the order Psilophytales. These fossils include Psilophyton and, from the Rhynie chert, Rhynia. The living psilopsids are considered the most primitive of the vascular plants. The sporophyte is dichotomously branching and bears rhizoids rather than true roots. Small leaflike appendages are often present and the vascular tissue consists of tracheids and poorly defined phloem. The spores, which are homosporous, give rise to a subterranean gametophyte. Fertilization of the gametes relies on the presence of a film of water and embryogeny is exoscopic. In some classifications the living and fossil forms are separated into two subdivisions or classes, the Psilotopsida and Psilophytopsida respectively.

Psocid. Any insect of the order Psocoptera (Corrodentia) which includes the bark lice and book lice.

Psoroptid. Of, pertaining to, or caused by mites of the genus Psoroptes.

Psorosis. A virus-caused disease of citrus trees characterized by formation of concavities and blind pockets on trunks and larger limbs.

Psychrophil. An organism which grows best at a low temperature, as certain bacteria, fungi, and algae whose optimum temperature range is from 5° to 10°C.

Psychrophilic. Describing microorganisms that require temperatures below 20°C for optimal growth, *e.g.* the fungus Cladosporium herbarum. Compare mesophilic, thermophilic.

Pteridophyte. Any plant of the Pteridophyta, formerly a division of vascular plants which included the ferns, horsetails, and club mosses.

Pteridophyta. A division of the plant kingdom that includes the ferns, horsetails, and clubmosses. Pteridophytes possess true stems, leaves, and roots, and have an organized vascular system. They have a wide (mainly terrestrial) distribution with the maximum development in the tropics. Many genera are now extinct, having formed prominent plant groups in the Carboniferous period. There is a marked alternation of generations between gamete-bearing forms (gametophytes) and spore-bearing forms (sporophytes). Unlike the bryophytes, the generations are often independent and the sporophyte is the dominant generation. Pteridophytes differ from gymnosperms and angiosperms in not producing seeds. The division includes the classes Lycopsida, Pteropsida, and Sphenopsida. In some classification schemes these classes are regarded as subdivisions of the Tracheophyta.

Pteridospermales (Cycadofilicales, seed ferns). An extinct order of gymnosperms known from fossils of the Devonian to Triassic periods. Although they had fernlike fronds, similar to those of the fern order Marattiales, their stems show secondary thickening and more significantly there is evidence of seed formation. The ovules were not borne in strobili but developed along the margins or on the surface of megasporophylls, similar to the foliage leaves. Their seeds were characteristically radially symmetrical, a feature shared by the Cycadales, Bennettitales, and Caytoniales, and thought to indicate that these orders possibly originated from the Pteridospermales.

Pterocaulous. With a winged stem.

Pterodactyl. A flying reptile of the Mesozoic era.

Pteropod. An opisthobranch gastropod of the order Thecosomata, with winglike muscular flaps (parapodia) along the sides of the foot; a sea butterfly.

Pteropsida. A subdivision of the Tracheophyta containing the ferns (Filicinae) and seed plants (Gymnospermae; Angiospermae), or a class of the Pteridophyta containing only the ferns.

Pterosauria. An extinct order of flying reptiles—the pterodactyls—that lived in the Jurassic and Cretaceous periods (180-70 million years ago). Pterodactyls had beaked jaws and an elongated fourth finger that supported a membranous wing. They had long jointed tails, no feathers, and could probably only fly by soaring.

Pterospermous. With winged seeds.

Pterygium

1. The limb of a vertebrate.
2. A lateral lobe at the tip of the snout in certain beetles.

[1]Pterygoid. Winglike, as the pterygoid process of the sphenoid bone.

[2]Pterygoid. A dermal bone in lower vertebrates forming a part of the upper jaw and roof of the mouth.

Pterygopodial Gland. A mucous gland located at the base of the clasping organ in skates and rays.

Pteryla. A feather tract, an area on the skin of a bird from which contour feathers arise. Compare apterium.

Ptilopaedic. Covered with down at hatching, with reference to birds.

Ptilosis. The plumage of birds.

Ptyalin. An enzyme that digests carbohydrates (amylase). It is present in mammalian saliva and is responsible for the initial stages of starch digestion.

Ptyxis. Vernation.

PU. Pregnancy urine, a source of hormones (estrogens and chorionic gonadotrophins).

Puberty. The period in life when sexual maturity is attained, that is, when functional sperm and ova begin to be produced and, in the female, menstrual cycles occur.

Pubes

1. The hair covering the pubic region in man.
2. The pubic region.

Pubescence

1. The state of being pubescent.
2. The fine hairy covering of *a. bot.* the leaves and/or stems of plants; *b. zool.* the bodies of certain animals, as insects.

Pubescent

1. Covered with fine hair or down.
2. Having reached the age of puberty.

Pubic Symphysis. The ventral union of the two pubic bones.

Pubis. One of the three bones that make up each half of the pelvic girdle. It is the most anterior of the three pelvic bones. In mammals and many reptiles the pubes are united at a slightly movable joint, the pubic symphysis.

Puccinia (family Pucciniaceae). Genus of rust fungi, which form two-celled teliospores. They parasitize monocotyledonous and dicotyledonous plants throughout the world. Many species cause diseases of economic importance : for example, P. graminis causes black-stem rust of wheat, P. menthae causes mint rust. There are about 3000 species.

Pudendum. The vulva or external genitalia of a female.

Puerperal. Of or pertaining to childbirth or labor.

[1]Pulmonate Possessing lungs or lunglike organs.

[2]Pulmonate. Any mollusk of the Pulmonata, a subclass or order of the class Gastropoda which includes freshwater and terrestrial snails and slugs in which the mantle cavity functions as a respiratory chamber.

Pulp

1. *zool.* A soft, spongy tissue, as that which *a.* fills the pulp cavity of a tooth; *b.* forms the central substance of an intervertebral disk; *c.* forms the substance of the spleen.
2. *bot.* *a.* The soft, succulent portion of a fruit. *b.* The pith of certain stems. *c.* A mixture of plant fibers from which paper is made.

Pulp Cavity. The central region of a tooth, which is connected by a narrow channel at the tip of the root with the surrounding tissues. The pulp cavity contains the pulp—

connective tissue in which blood vessels and nerve fibres are embedded, and it is lined with odontoblasts, which produce the dentine.

Pulse (in physiology). A series of waves of dilation that pass along the arteries, caused by pressure of blood pumped from the heart through contractions of the left ventricle. In man it can be felt easily where arteries pass close to the skin surface, *e.g.* at the wrist.

Pulse Labelling. Technique using radioisotopes for the measurement of the rates of synthesis of compounds within living cells. A suspension of cells or organelles is exposed to a small quantity of isotope for a brief period (seconds or minutes), hence the term 'pulse'. This is achieved through the addition to the suspension of a much larger quantity of the stable (unlabelled) isotope of the same compound following the required period of exposure to the radioisotope. The effect of competition between the two isotopes is to reduce to a negligible level the further uptake of the latter. Measurement of the levels of activity in samples under various experimental conditions can yield useful information regarding the factors influencing the uptake and metabolism of compounds.

Pulveraceous. Covered with dust or powder.

Pulverulent

1. Of a powdery nature.
2. Appearing as though covered by dust or powder.

Pulvinus. A group of cells at ths base of a leaf or leaflet in certain plauts that, by rapidly losing water, brings about changes in the position of the leaves. In the sensitive plant (Mimosa pudica), the pulvinus is responsible for the folding of the leaves that occurs at nightfall or when the plant is touched or injured.

Pulmonary Artery. The artery that conveys deoxygenated blood from the right ventricle of the heart to the lungs, where it receives oxygen.

Pulmonary Vein. The vein that conveys oxygenated blood from the lungs to the left atrium of the heart.

Pumpkin. A vine (Cucurbita pepo) or the large, orange-colored gourdlike fruit it produces.

Punctate. Marked by or bearing minute dots, depressions, pits, or punctures.

Punctiform. Having the form of a point or dot, with reference to colonies of bacteria.

Punctuated Equilibrium. A theory proposing that plant and animal species usually arise very quickly in terms of geological time (in less than 100 000 years) and seldom through a process of gradual change. It thus questions the traditional Darwinian theory of evolution, citing as evidence the discontinuities observed in the fossil records of certain animal groups (*e.g.* the ammonites).

Punctuated Equilibrium. Comparatively recent theory of macro-evolution which stands in opposition to the classical interpretation of phyletic gradualism. It argues that the anagenetic component in evolution is small, and that the speciational component is overwhelmingly more important. According to this view, most lineages are characterized by stasis for the greater part of their existence, the key changes being compressed into geologically very short periods of time.

Punicaceae. Family of one genus of plants, related to the Lythraceae, in which the leaves are simple, spiral, and without stipules. The flowers are perigynous, with 5-8 sepals and petals, many stamens, and many carpels which are adnate to the receptacle. The fruit is seated on the persistent calyx, with a leathery rind, and numerous seeds with partly fleshy leaves.

Punnaet Square. A chequerboard diagram, attributed to the geneticist R.C. Punnet, used to illustrate how the gametes involved in a particular cross result in various genotypes in various frequencies.

Pupa. The third stage of development in the life cycle of some insects. During the pupal stage locomotion and feeding cease and metamorphosis from the larva to the adult form takes place. There are three types of pupa. The commonest is the exarate or free pupa, in which the wings and other appendages are visible and movable. In the obtect type the wings are stuck to the body and immovable, as in the chrysalis of a butterfly or moth; and in the coarctate type an exarate pupa develops within a hard barrel-shaped puparium, as in the housefly and other Diptera.

Pupate. To transform into a pupa.

Pupil. The opening in the iris of the eye through which light enters.

Pure. Free from impurities or contamination.

Pure Culture. A culture which contains organisms of only one species.

Pure Line (pure strain). A succession of generations recognized by their ability to produce genotypically identical offspring when selfed or crossed between themselves. The members of a pure line are said to breed true. By inference, such individuals are deemed to be homozygous.

Purine. An organic nitrogenous base, sparingly soluble in water, that gives rise to a group of biologically important derivatives, notably adenine and guanine, which occur in nucleotides and nucleic acids (DNA and RNA).

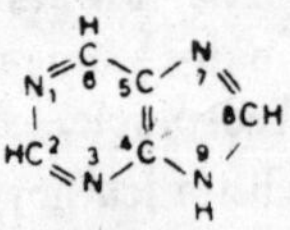

Purine

Purkinje Cells. Specialized neurons of the cerebellar cortex with a flaskshaped body and dendrites showing extensive arborization.

Pus. A semifluid, yellowish substance consisting principally of serum, leukocytes, bacteria, and tissue debris usually the result of inflammatory processes.

Pustular

1. *med.* Resembling or of the nature of pustules.
2. *bot.* Having small elevations resembling blisters.

Pustule. A small elevation of the skin containing pus; a pimple.

Putrid. Rotten; decomposed; having a foul odor resulting from decomposition and decay.

Pycnidium

1. (pycnium, spermogonium). A flasklike structure produced by certain fungi (*e.g.* Puccinia and Leptosphaeria) in which asexual pycnospores (spermatia) are formed.
2. A spore-producing body formed by the fungal component of certain lichens, *e.g.* Parmelia physodes. It is a flask-shaped structure sunken in the thallus and opens to the surface by a pore. Inside the pycnidium are a number of conidiophores, which produce pycnoconidia. The functions of the pycnoconidia are uncertain though it appears that in some species they may, by behaving as male gametes, initiate ascocarp formation.

Pycniospore

1. A spore produced by a pycnium, as in the wheat rust.
2. A spermatium, a gamete of either plus or minus strain.

Pycnium. A flask-shaped fruiting body in certain rusts which produces pycniospores; a spermagonium.

Pycnogonid. An arthropod of the class Pycnogonida (Pantopoda) which includes the sea spiders.

Pycnosis. The shrinkage and condensation of nuclear material into a dense, structureless mass, as occurs in degenerating or dying cells; pyknosis.

Pygal. Of or pertaining to the posterior portion of the back.

Pygal Plate. The most posterior plate in the carapace of a turtle.

Pygidium. The caudal, posterior portion of the body in various invertebrates, as the tagma of a trilobite, the terminal tergite of an insect, and the terminal segment of an annelid.

Pyogenic. Of or pertaining to the formation of pus.

Pyramid. A cone-shaped structure, as *a.* the pyramids of the medulla oblongata containing efferent fibers from the cerebral cortex; *b.* the pyramids of the kidney containing collecting ducts; *c.* one of the five calcareous plates comprising an Aristotle's lantern.

Pyramidal. Having the form of a pyramid.

Pyramid of Biomass. Diagrammatic expression of biomass at different trophic levels in an ecosystem, usually plotted as dry matter or calorific value per unit area or volume. Typically this gives a gradually sloping pyramid, except where the sizes of organisms vary dramatically from one trophic level to another. In this case, the higher metabolic rate of the smaller organisms may result in a greater biomass of consumers than of producers, giving an inverted pyramid. Aquatic communities in winter typically show inverted biomass pyramids. Compare pyramid of energy; and pyramid of numbers.

Pyramid of Energy. Diagrammatic expression of the rates of flow of energy through the different trophic levels of an ecosystem. It reflects the rates of photosynthesis, respiration, etc. (and not the standing crop as in the pyramid of biomass), and can never be inverted since energy is dissipated through the ecosystem. It is the most fundamental and most useful of the three ecological pyramids. Compare pyramid of biomass; and pyramid of numbers.

Pyramid of Numbers. The numbers of animals found in an area at ascending trophic levels of a food chain. Because only a small proportion of the energy taken in by an organism is converted to tissue and is thus available to consumers at the next trophic level, the number of organisms that can be supported at each level is generally much less than the number at the level that supplies its food (*i.e.* the level below). A pyramid of biomass, representing the biomass of animals at ascending trophic levels, shows a smaller decrease at each trophic level since the animals at the higher levels are generally larger (although fewer) than those at the lower levels.

Pyranose Ring. A six-membered ring containing five carbon atoms and an oxygen atom. Pyranose rings are formed by any aldose sugars with five or more carbon atoms. In solution the aldehyde group at the first carbon atom reacts with the hydroxyl group on the fifth carbon atom. This reaction renders the first carbon atom asymmetric. The pyranose forms of aldoses can thus exist in two isomeric forms. For example, D-glucose in solution forms both α-D-glucopyranose and β-D glucopyranose. These isomers differ in a number of properties, *e.g.* optical activity, solubility in water, and melting point. Compare furanose ring.

Pyrene. A nutlet, especially the stone of a drupelet, as that of the fruit of the huckleberry.

Pyrenoid. A spherical protein body found in the chloroplasts of many algae. Pyrenoids are associated with the storage of starch : layers of starch are often found around them.

Pyrenomycetes. A class of the Ascomycotina containing those ascomycetes that produce a perithecium. With over 6000 species and some 640 genera it is the largest group of ascomycetes and contains the orders Hypocreales, Clavicipitales, Sphaeriales, Coronophorales, Coryneliales, and Pyrenulales.

Pyridine Alkaloids. A group of alkaloids, the structures of which are based on the pyridine nucleus (a six-membered ring containing five carbon atoms and a nitrogen atom, and with three double bonds). They include the hemlock alkaloids, *e.g.* coniine, which is present in Conium maculatum (hemlock).

Pyridoxine (vitamin B_6). A pyridine derivative, essential in its activated forms, pyridoxal phosphate and pyridoxanine, as a coenzyme in various transamination reactions.

Pyriform. Pear-shaped.

Pyrimidine. A nitrogen-containing organic base composed of a single heterocyclic ring (diagram), synthesized mainly from amino acids. Two pyrimidines, cytosine and thymine, are constituents of DNA, while uracil replaces thymine in RNA. Thiamin (vitamin B_1) is also partly constructed from a pyrimidine.

Pyrimidine Base. A nitrogenous base present in nucleotides, as cystosine, urosil, thymine.

Pyruvic Acid. Three-carbon keto acid that occupies a central position in cell metabolism. It represents the final product of glycolysis in aerobic respiration : it subsequently undergoes oxidation to carbon dioxide and acetyl coenzyme A. During anaerobic respiration it is reversibly converted to lactic acid in animal cells and irreversibly to ethyl alcohol in those of plants. It may also be variously converted into alanine, malic acid, and oxaloacetic acid.

Python. One of a number on nonvenomous constrictors of the Old World of the genus Python, family Pythonidae; includes the largest of living snakes, some reaching a length of 30 feet.

Q

Q_{10}. The ratio of the velocity of a reaction at a given temperature to that of the same reaction at a temperature by 10 °C lower. This ratio is approximately 2.0 for most biological reactions.

Q Fever. Acute disease caused by Coviella burnetii. A wide range of animals can be infected, including domestic livestock; humans are commonly infected from domestic animals *e.g.* via contaminated milk or on inhalation of contaminated dust. Symptoms are typically respiratory, with fever, headache, and prostration; the disease is rarely fatal.

Q Technique. Method for analysing data, in which observations (N) form the columns and the variables or attributes (*n*) form the rows in a table or matrix. Compare R technique.

Quadrat. Basic sampling unit of vegetation surveys. Traditionally 1 m^2 quadrats were used to sample short, non-woody communities such as grasslands and heathlands. More recently circular and rectangular quadrats have been used as well as squares of all sizes depending on the purpose of the survey, *e.g.* 10 m^2 and 20 m^2 quadrats are commonly used in woodland studies.

Quadrat. An ecological sampling unit consisting of a small square area of ground within which all species of interest are noted or measurements taken. Quadrats may be spaced over a larger area to form an overall view when a total survey would be impracticable, or they may be used to sample along a transect.

Quadrate. A paired bone in the upper jaw of bony fishes, amphibians, reptiles, and birds that articulates with the lower jawbone. It is absent in mammals, being reduced to a small bone (the incus) in the middle ear.

Quadrate Bone. In most vertebrates, the ossified posterior end of the pterygoquadrate cartilage of the skull with which the lower jaw articulates. In mammals, it gives rise to the incus.

Quadriceps Femoris. In man, the large muscle comprising the rectus femoris, vastus lateralis, vastus medialis, and vastus intermedius which forms the anterior portion of the thigh. It extends the leg and flexes the femur.

Quadrivalent. The structure formed by the pairing of four homologous chromosomes in a tetraploid during prophase and metaphase of the first division of meiosis. Compare bivalent.

Quadruped. A four-footed animal.

Quadruplet. One of a set or group of four of a kind, especially one of four individuals which develop from a single pregnancy.

Quaking Grass. Several species of grass found throughout Europe. The most common species are the small quaking grass, pearl grass and the widespread common quaking grass. They are named after their rounded spikelets of tiny flowers which quiver or quake in the wind. The grasses are often planted for ornamental purposes.

Qualitative Inheritance. Inheritance of a character that differs markedly in its expression amongst individuals of a species : variation in that species is discontinuous. Such characters are usually under the control of major genes. A principal example is gender. Compare quantitative inheritance.

Qualitative Variation (discontinuous variation). The expression of a characteristic in perceptibly different ways by different individuals in a population. Examples include the tall and short forms of garden pea used by Gregor Mendel. Qualitative variation is most obvious in characteristics determined by only one or two genes whose expression is not greatly affected by environmental factors. Such variation may be due either to recurrent mutation or to the existence of a balanced polymorphism. Compare quantitative variation.

Quantasome. Particle, approximately 1.8 nm long, embedded in a paracrystalline array on the surface of thylakoid discs in chloroplasts. Quantasomes are composed equally of lipids and proteins, which include various photosynthetic pigments and redox carriers. For this reason they are considered to be the centre of the light reaction in photosynthesis.

Quantitative Inheritance. Inheritance of a character that depends upon the cumulative action of many genes, each of which produces only a small effect. Examples of such quantitative characters include clutch size in birds, milk production in cattle, and weight and skin pigmentation in humans. Usually the character shows continuous variation, *i.e.* a gradation from one extreme to the other. Compare qualitative inheritance.

Quantitative Variation (continuous variation). The type of variation shown by a characteristic that is exhibited to a greater or lesser extent by all members of a population or species. Often the characteristic has an average value, about which individuals in the population are distributed. An example would be the size of ears from a cereal crop. Continuous variation is common in characteristics that are strongly affected by environmental influences, and in characteristics determined by many genes, each with a small effect. Compare qualitative variation.

Quantum Evolution. Sudden spurt of diversification in an evolutionary lineage. Typically it results when a population shifts into another adaptive zone. Initially the number of individuals will be small and rapid genetic and phenotypic change is feasible in such circumstances, particularly if the new niche is unoccupied. The concept of quantum evolution has been given special significance in the theory of punctuated equilibrium.

Quantum Speciation. Traditionally, the rapid speciation that can occur in small populations isolated from the large, ancestral population, and that are therefore subject to the founder effect and to gentic drift. More recently the term has been assigned a central role in the theory of punctuated equilibrium.

Quaternary. The second period of the Cenozoic era, which began about 2 million years ago, following the Tertiary period, and includes the present. It is subdivided into two epochs—the Pleistocene and Holocene. The beginning of the Quaternary is usually based on the onset of a world-wide cooling. During the period four principal glacical phases occurred in Europe and North America, in which ice advanced towards the equator, separated by interglacials during which conditions became warmer and the ice sheets and glaciers retreated. The last glacial ended about 10 000 years ago. Man became the dominant terrestrial species during the Quaternary. Among the fauna adapted to the cold conditions were the mammoth and the woolly rhinoceros.

Quaternary. Period of geological time that covers the last 1.8 million years approximately. The Quaternary comprises the Pleistocene and Holocene Epochs and is noted for numerous major ice-sheet advances in the northern hemisphere. By the Pleistocene most of the faunas and floras had a modern appearance. The Quaternary is often termed 'the Age of Man'.

Quaternary Structure. The structure of a protein that results from the interaction of two or more individual polypeptides to give larger functional molecules. Compare primary structure; secondary structure; and tertiary structure.

Quaternary. The second period of the Cenozoic era from two million years ago to the present day. It is divided into the Pleistocene and Holocene (Recent) epochs. At its commencement, the climate was cool and temperate and there were four glacial periods, the evidence for which is borne out by the distribution of fossils. Many plants and animals became extinct. In the Holocene epoch, beginning about 10 000 years ago, the rise of civilization saw the origin of crop plants and their associated weeds.

Queen. The fully developed, egg-laying female of a social insect.

Quercus (oak; family Fagaceae). Genus of deciduous and evergreen trees and shrubs of the beech family. The wood has distinctive, broad, compound rays. The buds are scaly. The leaves have small stipules, and are entire, toothed or rarely crenate. Male flowers are borne in catkins, female flowers are solitary. The fruit is one nut seated in a woody cupule, the acorn. Many species are important for timber, tanning (the bark) cork (Q. suber), or as ornamentals. There are about :00 species, found in the northern-hemisphere temperate zone, subtropical and tropical Asia, and the Andes.

Quiescent Centre. The region in the apical meristem of a root where little or on cell division occurs. The cells in the queiscent centre are capable of assuming meristematic activity if the initials in the meristem are damaged, and thus act as a reservoir of potential initials, protected from damage by their relative inactivity. The quiescent centre may also be a site of another synthesis.

Quill

1. The proximal, hollow portion of the shaft of a feather; calamus.
2. A feather, especially one of the large feathers of the wing or tail.
3. A stiff spine of a hedgehog or porcupine.

Quilled. Designating a ligulate floret which has become tubular.

Quillwort. A lycopod of the order Isoetales.

Quinary. In fives; quintuple.

Quinate. Arranged in groups or sets of five.

Quince. A rosaceous tree (Cydona oblonga) or the large, round, acid fruit it produces.

Quinine. A bitter alkaloid obtained from the bark of the cinchona tree (Cinchona), used medicinally as an anti-malarial agent.

Quinone. p-dioxybenzene or a derivative thereof; many quinones act as electron carriers in mitochondria and chloroplasts.

Quinone Fungicide. Any fungicide developed from chlorinated quinones, such as chloranil, which is used as a seed dressing, and dichlone, which is used as a foliar fungicide.

Quinsy. Advanced stage of tonsillitis in which abscesses develop around the tonsils. The causal agent is a bacterium, usually Streptococcus pyogenes.

Quintan. Occurring every fifth day, as a fever.

R

Rabies An acute, infectious disease of animals, especially carnivores, caused by a neurotropic virus, transmissible to man. Also called hydrophobia.

Rabbit. The rabbit can be distinguished from the hare by its shorter ears and limbs. Rabbits live in extensive burrows or warrens with several emergency exists. Their diet consists of a wide variety of plant food including grass and many important crops. During the summer the female may have a number of the litters at intervals of 5-6 weeks. Rabbits seem to have spread through Europe from Spain. They have also been introduced into other continents. In Australia rabbits have destroyed vast areas of grassland. There are over 50 races of domesticated rabbits.

Rabies. Disease which affects mainly terrestrial carnivores, although almost any homoiothermic animal can be infected. Symptoms vary among animals. In dogs and humans there is initially an excited stage with excessive salivation, and this is followed by depression, hydrophobia and paralysis. It is almost always fatal in all species. The disease is usually transmitted by bites; saliva of infected animals is highly infectious. It is caused by a rhabdovirus.

Race. Interbreeding group of individuals all of whom are genetically distinct from the members of other such groups of the same species. Usually these groups are geographically isolated from one another, so there are barriers to gene flow. Examples are island races of birds and mammals such as the Skomer vole and the St Kilda wren.

Raceme. A simple, elongated, indeterminate inflorescence in which stalked flowers are borne on a central axis, the lowermost having longer pedicels and maturing before those nearest the apex, as the mustard flower.

Racemose

1. *bot.* Pertaining to or of the nature of a raceme.
2. *anat.* Resembling a bunch of grapes, as a racemose gland.

Racemose Inflorescence (indefinite inflorescence). An inflorescence in which meristematic activity continues at the apex of the main stem and primary laterals and flowers are developed from the axillary meristems. The inflorescence is often pyramidal in shape with older flowers at the base or, in the case of a flat-topped arrangement, on the outside. Different types of racemose inflorescence include the capitulum, corymb, panicle, raceme, spadix, spike, and umbel (diagram). Compare cymose inflorescence.

Racer. A group of non-venomous snakes with slender bodies and large heads found in the warmer, drier parts of the world. The largests is the black racer, over one metre long.

Rachilla (rhachilla)

1. The secondary axis of a pinnately compound leaf, such as that of a fern.
2. The main axis of a sedge or grass spikelet. Compare rachis.

Rachis (rhachis)

1. The main axis of compound leaf or an inflorescence.
2. The shaft of a feather.
3. The backbone.

Radial

1. Describing a longitudinal section that passes through the centre of a cylindrical organ (*i.e.* along a radius or diameter). In a radial section down a woody stem the growth rings appear parallel and flecks of rays may be seen. Compare tangential.
2. anticlinal.

Radial Canal

1. A canal extending outward from a central cavity, as in sponges or medusae.
2. In sea stars, a canal of the water-vascular system which extends peripherally in each ray.

Radiale. A cartilage or bone of the carpus which articulates with radius; in man, the navicular bone.

Radial Symmetry. The arrangement of parts in an organ or organism such that cutting through the centre of the structure in any direction produces two halves that are mirror images of each other. The stems and roots of plants usually show radial symmetry, while all animals belonging to the Coelenterata (*e.g.* jellyfish) and Echinodermata (*e.g.* star fish) are radially symmetrial—and typically sessile—in their adult form. The term actinomorphy is used to describe radial symmetry in flowers (*e.g.* a buttercup flower). Compare bilateral symmetry.

Radiant

1. Shining, brilliant, glowing.
2. Emitting rays or electromagnetic waves.
3. *bot.* Diverging from a central axis.

Radiate

1. To emit rays, as heat or light rays; to shine.
2. To diverge from a central point or region.

3. Bearing ray flowers, as in composites.

Radiation. The act or process of radiating.

Radiation Damage. Harmful changes that occur to inanimate materials and living organisms as a result of exposure to energetic electrons, nucleons, fission fragments, or high-energy electromagnetic radiation. In organisms this can cause changes to cells that alter their genetic structure, interfere with their division, or kill them. In humans, these changes can lead to radiation sickness, radiation burns (from large doses of radiation), or to long-term damage of several kinds, the most serious of which result in various forms of cancer (especially leukaemia).

Radiation Ecology. The branch of ecology concerned with the effects of radioactive materials on living systems and on the pathways by which they are dispersed through ecosystems, including their dispersal through the abiotic environment. The term is used especially with regard to those materials released through human agency.

Radiation Fog. Condensation effect over land surfaces on clear nights with light breezes, due to surface radiation cooling. Favoured initial conditions are very humid air, with wet and cold surfaces, *e.g.* marshes. The fog, most common in winter, is generally cleared by the Sun's warmth in the morning, but thick fog over wet surfaces in winter may persists much longer, particularly if an upper cloud layer screens the Sun.

Radiation Units. Units of measurement used to express the activity of a radionuclide and the dose of ionizing radiation. The units curie, roentgen, rad, and rem are not coherent with SI units but their temporary use with SI units has been approved while the derived SI units becquerel, gray, and sievert become familiar.

The becquerel (Eq), the SI unit of activity, is the activitiy of a radionuclide decaying at a rate, on average, of one spontaneous nuclear transition per second. Thus 1 $Bq=1s^{-1}$. The former unit, the curie (Ci), is equal to $3.7\times10^{10}Bq$. The curie was originally chosen to approximate the activity of 1 gram of radium—226.

The gray (Gy), the SI unit of absorbed dose, is the absorbed dose when the energy per unit mass imparted to matter by ionizing radiation is 1 jule per kilogram. The former unit, the rad (rq), is equal to 10^{-2} Gy.

The sievert (Sv), the SI unit of dose equivalent, is the dose equivalent when the absorbed dose of ionizing radiation multiplied by the stipulated dimensionless factors is 1 J kg^{-1}. As different types of radiation cause different effects in biological tissue a weighted absorbed dose, called the dose equivalent, is used in which the absorbed dose is modified by multiplying it by dimensionless factors stipulated by the International Commission on Radiological Protection. The former unit of dose equivalent, the rem (originally an acronym for roentgen equivalent man), is equal to 10^{-2} Sv.

In SI units, exposure to ionizing radiation is expressed in coulombs per kilogram, the quantity of X-or gamma-radiation that produces ion pairs carrying 1 coulomb of charge of either sign in 1 kilogram of pure dry air. The former unit, the roentgen (R), equal to 2.58×10^{-4} Ckg^{-1}.

Radical. Describing leaves arising close together at the base of the stem, as in a rosette plant.

Radicle. The embryonic root, which in the seed is directed towards the micropyle. It is normally the first organ to emerge from the testa on germination. The radicle may persist to form a taproot. Alternatively it may be replaced either by lateral or adventitious roots.

Radioactive Age. The age of an archaeological or geological specimen as determined by a process that depends on a radioactive decay.

Radioactive Carbon. Carbon 14 (Cl^{14}), present in the atmosphere in small amounts and incorporated into carbon compounds in photosynthesis. On the basis of its half life of 5568 years, the age of a substance containing it can be estimated, hence it is referred to as a "carbon clock".

Radioactive Tracer. Radioactive isotope, whose movement can be monitored, that is used to trace the pathway by which individual substances move through an organism, a living system, the abiotic environment, etc. Non-radioactive chemical analogues of certain substances may be used for the same purpose if their movement can be monitored, *e g.* caesium, which can be substituted for potassium.

Radioautograph. A photograph taken by radiation from a radioactive substance, used in determining the presence and location of radioactive substances in tissues. Also called autoradiograph.

Radiobiology. The branch of biology concerned with the effects of radioactive substances on living organisms and the use of radioactive tracers to study metabolic processes.

Radioactive Waste (nuclear waste). Any waste material that contains radionuclides (radioactive atomic nuclei). These wastes are produced in the mining of radioactive ores, the normal running of nuclear power stations and other reactores, the manufacture of nuclear weapons, and in research laboratories. Because high-level radioactive wastes can be extremely dangerous to all living matter and because they may contain radionuclides having half-lives of many thousands of years, their disposal has to be controlled with great stringency.

The first stage in disposal involves extensive reprocessing to retrieve usable material and reduce the activity of the waste. Subsequent final disposal, usually of solid material in strong metal canisters, involves burial of the material. The two currently favoured categories of sites for burial are deep (600 metres) mined cavities in stable geological formations on land and in red clay some 50-100 metres below the seabed away from tectonic plate margins and where the currents at the bottom of the sea are weak.

Radio-carbon Dating (^{14}C dating). A dating method for organic material that is applicable to about the last 70 000 years. It relies on the assumed constancy over time of atmospheric ^{14}C : ^{12}C ratios (now known not to be valid), and the known rate of decay of radioactive carbon, of which half is lost in a period—the 'half-life'—of every 5730 years ±30 years. (The earlier 'Libby standard', 5568 years, is still widely used.) In principle, since plants and animals exchange carbon dioxide with the atmosphere constantly, the ^{14}C content of their bodies when alive is a function of the radiocarbon content of the atmosphere. When an organism dies, this exchange ceases and the radiocarbon fixed in the organism decays at the known half-life rate. Comparison of residual ^{14}C activity in fossil organic material with modern standards enables the calculation of the age of the samples Since the method was first devised it has been realized that the atmospheric ^{14}C content varies, as the cosmic-ray bombardment of the outer atmosphere that generates the ^{14}C varies. Correction for these fluctuations is possible for about the last 8000 years by reference to the ^{14}C contents of long tree-ring series, *e.g.* those for bristlecone pine.

Radiography The process or technique of producing images of an opaque object on photographic film or on a fluorescent screen by means of radiation (either particles or electromagnetic waves of short wavelength, such as X-rays and gamma-rays) The photograph produced is called a radiograph. The process is widely used in diagnostic radiology, using X-rays.

Radioisotope (radioactive isotope). An isotope of an element that is radioactive.

Radiolarian. A marine protozoan of the order Radiolaria (Radiolarida) with a body consisting of a central capsule and possessing a skeleton of silica or stranium sulfate; many possess axopodia.

Radiolarian Ooze. A soft deposit covering vast areas of the ocean floor, consisting principally of the skeletons of radiolarians.

Radiole. A pinnate process on the crown of certain polychaetes, as fanworms.

Radiology. The study and use of X-rays, radioactive materials, and other ionizing radiations for medical purposes, especially for diagnosis (diagnostic radiology) and the treatment of cancer and allied diseases (radiotherapy).

Radiometric Dating (radioactive dating). The most precise method of dating rocks, in which the relative percentages of 'parent' and 'daughter' isotopes of a given radioactive element are estimated. Early methods relied on uranium and thorium minerals, but potassium argon, rubidium/strontium, and carbon 14 are now of considerable importance. Of these the uranium 238/lead 206 parent and daughter isotopes have a half-life of 4.5 billion (10^9) years, rubidium 87/strontium 87 a half-life of 50.0 billion years, and potassium 40/argon 40 one of 1.5 billion years. For carbon 14 the half-life is a mere 5730 ± 30 years (radiocarbon dating), and beyond about 70 000 years the amount of carbon 14 remaining in organic matter is beyond accurate measurement.

Radio-opaque. Describing a medium that is opaque to X-rays and gamma rays. Examples are barium salts, used in diagnostic radiology of the digestive tract.

Radioreceptor. A receptor which is stimulated by radiant energy, as the eye.

Radiospermic. Describing the radially symmetrical seeds of the Pteridospermales, Cycadales, Bennettitales, Caytoniales, and Angiospermae. Compare platyspermic.

Radioulna. The fused radius and ulna, as in the frog.

Radish. A small annual herb related to Mustard. It has small, rough leaves and white flowers. It produces large spherical or cylindrical red or white spicy roots, which are eaten in salads.

Radix pl. **Radices**. A root, as *a*. the root of a plant; *b*. the root of a hair.

Radius (in anatomy). The smaller of the two bones in the lower section of the forelimb of a tetrapod vertebrate (compare ulna). The radius articulates with some carpal bones and the ulna at the wrist and with the humerus at the elbow. This sophisticated articulation of the radius enables man (and some other animals) to twist the forearm.

Radula. A tonguelike organ of molluscs, consisting of a horny strip whose surface is studded with rows of horny teeth for rasping food. In some species it is modified for scraping or boring.

Radula Sac. A ventral diverticulum of the buccal cavity in gastropods in which rows of radular teeth are formed, replacing those which are lost.

Radulla Tooth. A long, hollow tooth of the radula of certain gastropods which functions as a poisonous, harpoonlike structure, as in cone shells.

Raffinose. A common plant trisaccharide found particularly in cotton seed and sugar beet. It is a tasteless non-reducing sugar composed of galactose, glucose, and fructose units.

Rafflesia. Any of six Malaysian plants which have no stems or leaves. They are parasitic on climbing shrubs and consist mainly of slender threads which spread through the host plant. Huge flowers spring from the base of the host plant from which the threads have drawn all their nourishment. The flowers, measuring up to 90 cm across, smell like rotting meat and are pollinated by small flies.

Ragi. A tall grass (Eleusine corocana), an important food crop of southeast Asia; raggee, raggi, raggy. Also called korakan, finger millet, African millet.

Ragweed. One of several composites of the genus Ambrosia, its pollen being an important antigen and a common cause of hay fever.

Ragwort. A perennial herb of the daisy family, native to Eurasia. It has stems up to 1.2 metres tall, ragged leaves, and bright yellow flowers.

Raisin. A special type of dried grape with a high sugar content.

Ramapithecus. A genus of extinct primates that lived between 8 and 14 million years ago. Fossil remains of ramapithecines have been found in India and Pakistan, the Near East, and East Africa. Jaw fragments suggest that they chewed from side to side and had fairly short muzzles, both of which are humanoid features. They were possibly the earliest representatives of the hominid line after this split from the pongids (apes) during the Miocene.

Ramentum. Any of the small brown scales that cover the young fronds of a fern. The ramenta are shed as the frond unfurls but some persist on the rachis.

Ramet. Any individual belonging to a known clone. Studies of phenotypic plasticity in relation to environmental factors are more quantifiable if ramets are used rather than genetically mixed individuals.

Ramose, Ramous. Branched; having many branches.

Ramus

1. A branch of an artery, vein, or nerve.
2. A portion of a bone which projects from the body, as the ramus of the mandible.

Randomization. The allocation of experimental units to completely random positions in an experiment, normally by using tables of random numbers. This form of experimental design is used when the units are very similar and they are being observed under particularly controlled conditions as, for example, a pure line of plants in a growth chamber. It has the advantage over randomized block and Latin square designs in that it increases the number of degrees of freedom, which consequently reduces the error variance. If, however, the experimental units or the environment are variable then a completely random design is less likely to pick up significant differences between treatments.

Randomized Block. A type of experimental design in which each block contains one representative of each treatment, the treatments being allocated to random positions in the block. Each block is thus a complete replication but allocation of treatments to columns is random. The columns are therefore not complete replication since they may contain two or more representatives of one treatment and none of another. Randomized blocks may be used, for example, when dealing with identifiable inherent variation. Compare Latin square.

Range Management. The use of extensive, open grasslands for cattle production or, where appropriate, for the exploitation for human use of semi-domesticated or wild grazing animals (*e.g.* game cropping on the African savannah) by methods that maintain the ecosystem. These require the determination of the optimum stocking density that will permit long-term cropping of the grassland without deterioration of the pasture.

Rank (category). The position or status of a taxon in a classification hierarchy. Examples of ranks are the family, genus, and species.

Ranunculaceae. A large family of dicotyledonous plants commonly known as the buttercup family. It is cosmopolitan in distribution through best represented in temperate and cold latitudes. There are some 50 genera and over 1800 species, most of which are herbaceous. The leaves are often divided or lobed and usually arise either from the base of toe stem or in an alternate arrangement.

The flowers may be solitary, *e.g.* Anemone, or borne in a raceme or cyme. The flowers are usually actinomorphic with the parts arranged spirally or, less commonly, in whorls. There are numerous stamens and normally five prominent petals. Some genera, *e.g.* Consolida (larkspurs), Aconitum (monkshoods, wolf-banes) and Aquilegia (columbines), have zygomorphic flowers. The family contains many ornamentals, *e.g.* Clematis, Caltha, and Nigella, but there are no important food crops.

Raphe

1. A longitunidal ridge on the outer integument or seed coat in anatropous ovules where the funiculus becomes fused with the integument.
2. The longitudinal fissure in the cell wall of motile bilaterally symmetrical diatoms. It is believed to play a part in the movement of such organisms by allowing contact between the cytoplasm and external medium.

Raphide. A needle-shaped crystal, often of calcium oxalate, found in clusters in plant cells. The presence and form of raphide clusters are sometimes useful as diagnostic characters. For example, the subfamily Rubioideae of the Rubiaceae is distinguished from the other two subfamilies, Cinchonoideae and Guettardoideae, by the presence of raphides in the leaves.

Raphides sing. **Raphid.** Minute crystals, usually of calcium oxalate, formed within plant cells, considered to be metabolic waste products.

Raptorial

1. Living on prey, with special reference to certain birds.
2. Pertaining to birds of prey, adapted for seizing prey.

3. Having feet adapted for seizing and tearing prey.

Rasorial. Scratching the ground in search of food, as by gallinaceous birds.

Raspberry. A berry (drupelet) produced by a rosaceous shıub (Rubus) or the shrub which produces it.

Rastellus. A row of short spines on the basal segment of the chelicera of a burrowing spider.

Rat

1. One of a number of long-tailed rodents of the genus Rattus and related genera of the family Muridae, as R, norvegicus, the brown or Norway rate.
2. One of a number of similar rodents, as the cotton rat, muskrat, wood rat.

Rat-bite Fever (soduku). Disease which may occur following the bite of a rat; the causal agent is usually either Streptobacillus moniliformis or Spirillum minor, bacteria normally present in the mouth of a rat. Symptoms include fever and prostration, and the disease may be fatal.

Rathke's Pouch. A dorsal outpocketing of the stomodeum which gives rise to the anterior and intermediate lobes of the hypophysis.

Ratite

1. Having a flat, keelless sternum. Compare carinate.
2. One of several flightless birds with poorly developed wings and an unkeeled sternum, as the ostrich, rhea, cassowary, emu, and the extinct moas.

Ratoon. A secondary shoot which sprouts from the root of a perennial plant, as in the second year's growth of sugar cane.

Rat-tailed Maggot. The aquatic larva of flies of the genus Eristalis, family Syrphidae, which possess a long, extensible breathing tube.

Rattan. A climbing palm of the genus Calamus or material obtained from its stem, used extensively in wickerwork.

Rattle. A sound-producing structure on the end of the tail of a rattlesnake, composed of several loosely interlocking segments.

Rattler. A rattlesnake.

Rattlesnake. One of a number of sluggish, thick-bodied, venomous snakes of the family Crotalidae, characterized by possessing of a rattle. They comprise two genera : Sistrurus (massasaugas and ground rattlers) and Crotalus (the timber, diamondback, and priairie rattlesnakes).

Raunkiaer System of Classification. A method of plant classification devised by the Danish botanist, C. Raunkiaer, Plants are divided into groups depending on the position of perennating buds and the degree of protection that they give in cold conditions or drought (diagram). Generally the closer the buds are to the ground the more protected they are. It is particularly useful for dividing glven areas of vegetation into groups and comparing the occurrence of these groups in different climatic regions. Chamaephyte, cryptophyte, hemicryptophyte, therophyte.

Ratitae. A group comprising the fightless birds, including the ostrich, kiwi, and emu. They have long legs, heavy bones, small wings, a flat breastbone, and curly feathers. These birds are thought to have descended from a varietv of flying birds and are not representatives of a single homologous group.

Raven. A crowlike bird (Corvus corax) of the Northern Hemisphere.

Ray (secondary ray). A radial line of parenchyma cells in the secondary xylem and phloem, derived from the ray initials of the vascular cambium. The ray system of gymnosperms often also contains tracheids, distinguished from the ray parenchyma by their bordered pits and lack of protoplast. Rays may be uniseriate (one cell thick in tangential longitudinal section) or multiseriate (several cells thick in tangential longitudinal section). Compare medullary ray.

Ray Flower

1. An outer or marginal flower or floret in the head of a composite. Compare disk flower.
2. An entire head which lacks disk flowers.

Ray Initials. More or less cubical initials in the vascular cambium that give rise to the components of the ray (radial) system of the secondary xylem and secondary phloem (*e.g.* ray parenchyma cells). Compare fusiform initials.

Reaction Time (latent period). The period of time between the detection of a stimulus at a sensory receptor and the performance of the appropriate response by the effector organ. This delay is caused by the time taken for the impulse to travel across the synapses of adjacent neurones. The reaction time for a reflex response, involving only a single-linking synapse, is very short.

Reaction Wood. Structurally abnormal wood formed in response to various stresses. In gymnosperms it is termed compression wood and tends to form on the lower side of branches. Compression wood is dense in structure due to the heavy lignification of tracheid walls. Tension wood forms in angiosperms on the upper side of the branches and the fibers tend to be gelatinous rather than lignified.

Reading-frame Shift (genetics). In the normal transcription of a cistron, nucleotides are read in threes, the 'reading frame' being determined by the starting-point. Each triplet codes a specific amino acid; the sequence of codons therefore dictates the amino acids and their order in a given protein. Certain mutagens (*e.g.* acridine dyes), which incorporate themselves between the complementary strands of the DNA, may cause errors in replication such that the daughter DNA gains or loses a nucleotide. When the daughter DNA is transcribed, the nucleotides will be read in the correct triplets up to the point of mutation, but the extra or missing nucleotide will cause a shift in the reading frame (to left or right) thereafter, such that all subsequent nucleotides will be read in wrong triplets. The result might be a protein with the wrong amino acids—often it is terminated early—but in any case it is dysfunctional.

Realm. One of the six major faunal areas of the globe, namely Nearctic, Neotropical, Palearctic, Ethiopian, Oriental, and Australian.

Recalcitrant Seed. A seed that loses its viability if stored for any length of time, even under conditions that are normally conductive to seed longevity, *i.e.* low moisture content and low temperatures. Many tropical plants, *e.g.* coconut, rubber, and tea, have recalcitrant seeds. Such seeds can often only be kept for a year or less.

Recapitulation. *biol.* The appearance in the development of an individual of transitory or temporary structures which resemble or correspond to functional structures possessed by ancestors.

Recapitulation Theory. A theory formulated by Ernst Haeckel that proposed that ontogeny is a short recapitulation of phylogeny, *i.e.* an organism in its development goes through a series of stages that resemble the adult forms of its ancestors in evolutionary sequence. The theory has since been discarded.

Recent. Quaternary.

Recent Epoch. An epoch in the Quaternary period following the Pleistocene extending from the end of the last ice age; the Age of Man.

Receptacle

1. (thalamus or torus). The tip of a flower stalk, which bears the petals, sepals, stamens, and carpels. The way the receptacle develops determines the position of the flower parts. It can be dilated and dome-shaped, saucer-shaped, or hollow and enclosing the gynaecium. In some plants it may become part of the fruit.
2. A swollen part of the thallus of some algae *e.g.* Fucus, that bears the conceptacles in which the sex organs sre situated.

Receptor. A sense organ : one that responds to a stimulus by producing nerve impulses which are carried to the central nervous system by sensory nerves. Different receptors respond to different stimuli, such as light, heat, pressure and smell, and enable an organism to monitor its external and internal environment. Receptors may be single cells or they may be complicated structures such as the eye.

Recess. A depression, fossa, cleft, or cavity.

Recessive. Describing an allele that is only expressed when homozygous. Recessive alleles are in most cases considered to be the mutant form of dominant alleles. They are often rarer in the population and usually lower the fitness of the individual. Their effect is often due to their failure to produce a normal functional protein. They are masked (*i.e.* recessive) in a heterozygote because the normal (dominant) allel will produce a normal protein and hence a normal phenotype.

Recessive Character. In genetics, a trait which, in the presence of a dominant gene, fails, to express itself; one which appears only in a homozygous individual or one lacking the dominant gene.

Recessive Gene. One which can produce its effects only in a homozygous individual or in the absence of a dominant gene.

Recipient. An individual who receives tissues or organs of the body from another (the donor).

Reciprocal Cross. In genetics, one of a pair of crosses in which the two opposite mating types (or sexes) are each coupled with each of two different genotypes and mated with the reciprocal combination, *e.g.* male of genotype A × female of genotype B (first cross), and male of genotype B × female of genotype A (the reciprocal cross). Such crosses are used to detect sex linkage, maternal inheritance, or cytoplasmic inheritance.

Reciprocal Genes. Non-allelic genes that reciprocate or complement one another.

Reciprocal Translocation. Translocation.

Reclinate. Bent downward.

Reclining. *bot.* Bending down; turning away from the perpendicular.

Recombinant DNA. DNA that contains genes from different sources that have been combined by the techniques of genetic engineering rather than by breeding experiments. Genetic engineering is therefore also known as recombinant DNA technology.

Recombination. The formation of new combinations of genes during meiosis by crossing over and by reassortment of whole chromosomes into new sets. As a result of recombination, the gametes that an organism produces differ from the gametes from which it arose. Consequently the offspring will vary genetically and hence phenotypically from the parents. Recombination is a major source of variation.

Recon. Gene.

Recreatability (salvageability). Term used by conservationists to denote a community or ecosystem that could be readily re-established following disturbance—by motorway building, open-cast mining, etc.—without any noticeable change. Certain long-established communities (*e.g.* in Britain primary woodlands) are thought not to be recreatable since they would take many hundreds of years to re-establish their present detailed structure and composition and it is virtually impossible to reconstruct the same long-term environmental influences as fashioned their present form.

Rectal. Of or pertaining to the rectum.

Rectal Gills. Tracheal gills located on the internal surface of the rectum, as in the nymphs of dragonflies.

Rectrix pl. **Rectrices.** An elongated tail feather of a bird.

Rectum. The portion of the alimentary canal between the colon and the anus. Its main function is the storage of faeces prior to elimination.

Recurrent Parent. Backcrossing.

Red/Far-red Effects. Those physiological responses exhibited by many plants as a result of being illuminated by either red or far-red light. Usually a period of red light will reverse the effect of a period of far-red light and *vice versa.* Thus the response elicited in the plant depends on which treatment was given most recently.

Red Algae. Algae of the division Rhodophyta (Rhodophyceae) with accessory phycobilins in addition to caretenoids and chlorophyll and food reserves in the form of floridian starch.

Red-and-yellow Forest Soil. A type of zonal acid soil (a pedalfer) formed in wet subtropical regions. Leaching results in the accumulation of salts in the B horizon. The red colour is due to iron oxides in the A horizon though if the soil is sandy, it tends to be yellow. Such soils contain little humus and are soon exhausted of nutrients when cultivated. They can be easily eroded.

Red Blood Cell. Erythrocyte.

Red Body. A vascular body in the inner surface of the swim bladder of certain fishes, as the eel.

Redbud. The Judas tree (Cercis canadensis), a legume.

Red Bug. A harvest mite or chigger.

Red Corpuscle. An erythrocyte.

Redd. A spawning area or nest prepared by certain fishes for the deposition of eggs.

Red Deer

1. The common deer of Europe (Cervus elaphus).
2. The white-tailed deer in its summer coat.

Red Desert Soil. A type of coarse zonal soil rich in salts and lime (a pedocal) but poor in humus. They are formed in hot deserts and can be cultivated under irrigation.

Redia. The second larval stage in the development of a digenetic trematode found in snails or bivalves. Redia arise from sporocysts and in turn give rise to daughter rediae or cercariae.

Red Light. Electromagnetic radiation of approximately 630 nm wavelength. Light in this part of the spectrum is the most effective in initiating various light-dependent reactions in plants. For example, short-day plants are prevented from flowering if given a short burst of red light during the dark period. Similarly red light is best for promoting germination in light-sensitive seeds and for reversing etiolation. Compare far-red light.

Redox Potential. Scale indicating the reduction (addition of electrons) and oxidation (removal of electrons) for a given material. The position on the scale is expressed as an electric potential in millivolts, normally in the range 0 – 1300 or 0—1400 mV. The pH of the sample must be known since this can alter the reading.

Redox Reaction. Reaction involving the transfer of electrons from a donor molecule, the reducing agent, to an acceptor molecule, the oxidizing agent. In some biological oxidations this reaction manifests itself in the removal of hydrogen from a molecule.

Red Tide. The recurrence of enormous numbers of dinoflagellates, especially Gonyaulax and Gymnodinium, in waters off the coasts of Florida and California, resulting in reddish hue of waters by day and luminescence by night.

Red Tropical Soil. A type of zonal soil formed in rain forests, and in savanna with alternating dry and wet seasons. It is heavily leached but a balance is maintained between the nutrients produced by decomposition and those taken up by the plants. The red colour is due to the presence of iron, magnesium, and aluminium oxides. Some red tropical soils may form a hard crust of chemicals on the surface.

Reducing Sugar. A sugar capable of reducing an oxidizing agent. To do this it must have a potentially active aldehyde or ketone group. All monosaccharides have such a group and consequently they are all reducing sugars. For a disaccharide to be reducing one of the reducing groups of either of the two component monosaccharides must be left intact. Maltose, which consists of two glucose units linked by an α(1—4) glycosidic linkage, is reducing because the second glucose residue can undergo oxidation, having an aldehyde at carbon five. Sucrose however is nonreducing because the component glucose and fructose units are linked by their aldehyde (carbon one of glucose) and ketone (carbon two of fructose) groups. Various solutions, *e g.* Benedict's and Fehling's, are used to detect reducing sugars.

Reduction Division. Meiosis.

Reductase. An enzyme which catalyzes a reduction reaction.

Reduction

1. *biol.* The reduction in number of chromosomes from diploid to haploid number, as occurs in meiosis.
2. *chem.* A chemical reaction in which one or more electrons are gained by the substance reduced; the

addition of hydrogen atoms or the loss of oxygen atoms. Compare oxidation.

Red Water

1. Water containing large numbers of organisms containing a red pigment.
2. Urine containing blood; hematuria.

Red Water Fever. Texas Fever.

Reed. One of a number of tall, bamboolike grasses or their slender, jointed stems.

Reedbuck. An African antelope of the genus Redunca.

Reef. A ridge of rocks, coral, or sand close to the surface of water.

Reflex. An automatic and innate response to a particular stimulus, such as withdrawal of the hand from a painful stimulus (such as fire). A reflex response is extremely rapid. This is because it is mediated by a simple nervous circuit called a reflex arc, which at its simplest involves only a receptor linked to a sensory neurone, which synapses with a motor neurone (supplying the effector) in the spinal cord or brain.

Reflex Action. An involuntary, stereotyped, and usually purposeful response or reaction resulting from nervous impulses initiated by a stimulus, as the knee jerk.

Reflex Arc. The nervous pathway from point of stimulation to responding organ, comprising a receptor, afferent neuron, reflex center in brain or spinal cord, efferent neuron, and an effector organ.

Reflexed. Describing a structure that is bent sharply backwards, such as the petals of Cyclamen.

Reforest. To reestablish forests on land form which timber has been removed, as by fire or cutting.

Refract. To bend; to subject to refraction as light rays.

Refractory

1. Obstinate; intractable; tending to resist the effects of; incapable of responding to stimuli.
2. *med.* Failing to respond to treatment.

Refractory Period. The period following stimulation during which a muscle or nerve fiber is incapable of responding.

Refugium pl. **Refugia.** An area, usually more or less isolated, which, with respect to fauna and flora, has remained relatively unchanged in contrast to surrounding areas which have been markedly affected by environmental changes; a refuge.

Regeneration. The ability to replace parts of the body that have been lost through accident. All animals and plants are capable of it to some extent but, as a general rule, the more hightly evolved an animal is, the less are its powers of regeneration. Human beings, for example, are able to regenerate skin and bone tissue to mend wounds and fractures. But some animals (*e g.* lizards and crabs) are able to regenerate new limbs while others, such as flatworms, can grow complete bodies—including the head—from a small portion of the original body.

Region. A division of a zoological realm characterized by a distinctive type of fauna or flora.

Regma. A dry fruit that is characteristic of the geranium family. It is similar to the carcerulus but breaks up into one-seeded parts, each of which splits open to release a seed.

Regress. To go backward; to return to a former state or condition.

Regulator Gene. In the operon theory of gene regulation, a gene that is involved in switching on or off the transcription of structural genes. When transcribed, the regulator gene produces a repressor protein, which switches off an operator gene and hence the operon that this controls. The regulator gene is not part of the operon, and may even be on a different chromosome.

Regular

1. According to custom, habit, or rule.
2. Uniform in size, shape, or structure.
3. *bot.* Having members of a floral whorl, especially the corolla, of similar shape and equally spaced about the center of the flower.

Regulative Development. That which occurs in eggs with indeterminate cleavage in which loss of one or more blastomers does not adversely affect the development of the embryo, organspecific regions being established fairly late, as in mammalian ova.

Regurgitation

1. The casting out of undigested or partially digested food from the stomach.
2. The backward flow of blood through a defective heart valve.

Reinforcement (in animal behaviouea). Increasing (or decresing) the frequency of a particular behaviour through conditioning, by arranging for some biologically important event (the reinforcer) always to follow another event. In instrumental conditioning an appetitive reinforcer, or reward (*e g.* food), given after a response made by the animal, increases that response; an aversive reinforcer, or punishment (*e.g.* an electric shock) decreases the response.

Rejuvenation. The restoration of youth, strength, and vigor; making young again.

Relative Humidity. The water-vapour centent of air at a given temperature, expressed as a ratio (the percentage) of the vapour content that would be required for saturation.

Generally the relative humidity decreases during the day, with increase of temperature, and increases at night as the temperature falls.

Relaxin. An ovarian hormone which, in certain pregnant mammals, relaxes joints of the pelvic girdle and dilates the uterine cervix.

Release Factor. A substance produced by neurosecretory cells of the hypothalamus which regulates the production and release of hormones by the anterior pituitary.

Relic. A survivor or vestige; a relict.

Relict. Applied to organisms that have survived while other related ones have become extinct. Often the term refers to species that have survived periods of unfavourable conditions (*e.g.* glacial periods or land submergence) by existing in regions called refugia, while becoming extinct elsewhere (*e.g.* some arctic-alpine plants). It may also refer to a surviving species of a group the other species of which have become extinct (*e.g.* coelacanth fish).

Relict Community. Community that formely had a much wider distribution but that now occurs only very locally. Such contraction can be caused by various factors including climatic change, *e.g.* glaciation. Communities widespread during glacial times may now be restricted to mountain tops, *e.g.* Upper Teesdale (England) contains isolated flora characteristic of much of lowland Britain during glacial periods.

Relict Species. Species that formerly had a much wider distribution but that now occur only very locally, often because of climatic change. They may be part of a relict community, *e.g.* Dryas octapetala (mountain avens) in Britain, which was widespread during glacial times but is now mainly restricted to a few mountain tops.

Remex pl. **Remiges.** A flight feather of a bird, including primaries, those attached to the manus, and secondaries, those attached to the ulna.

Remicle. The reduced outermost primary.

Remiges. Plural of Remex.

Remora. A shark sucker or suckerfish with a modified dorsal fin by which it attaches itself to sharks and other fishes. Common genera are Remora and Echeneis of the order Discocephali.

Renal. Of or pertaining to the kidney.

Renal Corpuscle. A filtering structure in the kidney of amniotes, consisting of a glomerulus surrounded by Bowman's capsule; Malpighian corpuscle.

Renal Portal Vein. A vein which carries blood from the posterior portion of the body to the kidney, as in fishes, amphibians, reptiles, and birds.

Renal Tubule. A nephron.

Renaturation. Denaturation.

Rendzina (calcisol). A type of shallow intrazonal soil rich in lime (calcimorphic) formed from the underlying limestone or chalk rocks. The A horizon is brown or black and rich in humus. The B horizon, if one is distinguishable, is grey or yellowish with limestone fragments. Brown earths develop in similar climatic conditions from other parent rocks. Compare terra rossa.

Reniform. Shaped like a kidney.

Rennet

1. A substance containing rennin, obtained from the lining of a calf's stomach.
2. The abomasum, the fourth chamber in the stomach of a ruminant.

Rennin. An enzyme secreted by cells lining the stomach in mammals that is responsible for clotting milk. It acts on a soluble milk protein (caseingen), which it converts to the insoluble form casein. This ensures that milk remains in the stomach long enough to be acted on by protein-digesting enzymes.

Reovirus. One of a group of orphan viruses found in the respiratory and digestive tracts of man.

Repair Synthesis. The enzymatic excision and replacement of regions of damaged DNA. The defective single-stranded segments of DNA are cut out, correct bases are inserted using the comple mentary strand as a template, and these are interlocked by a DNA polymerase. A polynucleotide ligase joins the two ends of the broken strand to complete the repair. An example is the removal by a nuclease enzyme of a thymine dimer that has been included by UV radiation of the DNA molecule.

Repand. Having a wrinkled, wavy, or undulated margin, as a leaf or bacterial colony.

Repeated Sequence. Any long base-pair sequence found at many different places throughout the chromosomes. This excludes DNA coding for structural genes, which with few exceptions are present as single copies. Repeated sequences account for more than 50% of all the DNA present and fall into three categories.

Repetitive DNA usually consists of widely scattered sequences about 300 base pairs long, which are often adjacent to structural genes. It has been proposed that these sequences are functionally equivalent to the operator genes of bacteria. Suppose that sequence A is adjacent to three unlinked genes X, Y, and Z, and that A′ is an inducer of A. The presence of A′ in the cell would 'switch on' all genes to which A was adjacent, in this case X, Y, and Z. An appropriate mix of repeated sequences, say A, B, C, and D next to structural gene X would make possible an elaborate transcriptional control system as demanded in a complex organism.

Highly repetitive or satellite DNA is often about 20 base pairs long and is usually found near the centromere. Palindromes, which are often a few hundred base pairs long, are scattered throughout the chromosomes. Such sequences read the same in both directions, *i.e.* are palindromic. The functions of satellite DNA and palindromic DNA are uncertain.

Repellent. An agent used to repel noxious organisms as insects, ticks, and mites.

Repent. Creeping, prostrate, with roots at the internodes.

Repetitive DNA. Repeated sequence.

Repletum. A fruit whose valves remain attached together by threads following dehiscence, as in orchids.

Replica Plating. A technique used in electron microscopy to examine the surfaces of specimens that are too electron dense, too delicate, or too robust for sectioning. The specimen surface is coated with a thin film of material, such as carbon, in order to make a cast or replica. This is removed by soaking the specimen in 10% sodium hydroxide solution. It may be subjected to shadowing procedures before examination. The development of the scanning electron microscope has tended to make replica plating redundant, although it is still used in freeze fracturing.

[1]**Replicate.** To duplicate or reproduce.

[2]**Replicate.** Folded over backwards upon itself.

Replication. The formation of exact copies (replicas). The term has been applied both to DNA and asexual organisms, both of which produce essentially identical copies/offspring.

Replum. The framework of the placenta which remains after the valves fall away in dehiscence, as in plants of the mustard family.

Repressor. A protein product of a regulator gene that prevents transcription of other genes by binding to the DNA and blocking attachment of messenger RNA polymerase.

Reproduce

1. To produce again.

2. To bring into existence another of the same kind or an individual that will give rise to one of the same kind.

Reproduction. A term which simply means producing more of the same kind. Nothing lives for ever, and if plants and animals could not reproduce, their species would soon die out. There are two main methods of reproduction—sexual and asexual.

Sexual reproduction always involves the joining together of two special cells called Gametes to form the new generation. The joining together is called fertilization. In some simple plants and animals the gametes are all alike, but most organisms produce two very different kinds of gametes, known as male and female. The male gamete is usually very small and active, and it generally seeks out the larger and often immobile female gemete. Both kinds of gametes may be produced by one organism, especially among the plants, and these organisms are said to be bisexual or Hermaphrodite. Most animals, however, are unisexual : each individual is either male or female and produces either male or female gametes. In most animals the male gamete (sperm) is brought into contact with the female gemete (ovum) throught the act of mating. Plants cannot mate, however, and most of them rely on wind or animals to carry their male gametes (in the pollen grains) to the female organs (Pollination). The fertilized ovum, whether plant or animals, is called a zygote and, by repeated cell division, produces an embryo which gradually develops into the new plant or animal.

Asexual reproduction involves no fusion of cells and in its simplest form, found among the unicellular plants and animals, it involves nothing more than the splitting of the body into two parts. Many higher plants produce special detachable buds which grow into new individuals, while the production of new plants from Runners, as in the strawberry, is another form of asexual production.

Hydra and many other coelenterates can reproduce in a similar way by budding or branching : new animals grow as branches on the parent and often break away to lead their own lives. Parthenogenesis is a special form of asexual reproduction in which the females lay fertile eggs or give birth to young without mating. It is particularly common in insects, including aphids and stick insects. Unlike sexual reproduction, in which the characteristics of two parents are combined in the offspring, asexual reproduction produces offspring which are genetically indentical to the parent. It does not produce variation, which is so important for Evolution.

Reproductive. Fertile male or female member of a colony of social insects. In ants, bees, and wasps the male (drone) dies soon after insemination, leaving the queen as the colony reproductive. In termites the male (king) lives with the queen, periodically inseminating her. Supplementary reproductives, present in termite colonies, take over colony reproduction if the founding king and queen (the primary reproductives) die.

Reproductive Isolating Mechanism (RIM). The means by which different species are kept reproductively isolated. These may be (a) chromosomal—if cross-mating occurs the incompatibility of the karyotypes makes any hybrid inviable or sterile; (b) mechanical—the two species cannot mate because they are of different sizes, or because the genitalia are shaped differently; (c) ethological—the courtship rituals of the two species diverge at some point so that an incorrect response is given and the sequence is brought to a stop; (d) ecological—the two species occuy different microhabitats and normally do not meet; or (e) other mechanisms include the breeding seasons being out of phase, or members of one species being unattractive to members of the other. Many RIMs, especially ethological ones, amount merely to mate preference, so that in the absence of a preferred partner (of the same species) a member of a different species will be accepted. In this way hybrids between different species may be bred in captivity and may even be found to be fully fertile.

Reproductive Isolation. The prevention of gene flow between all the members of a population due to the development of reproductive barriers (isolating mechanisms), which result in the formation of distinct noninterbreeding groups that may in time develop into separate species. Isolating mechanisms can arise in many ways. Populations may be separated geographically (allopatric). Populations occupying the same area (sympatric) may not interbreed because they have different flowering times or different pollinators, or because they occupy different niches. Such populations may also be isolated by the inviability or sterility of any hybrids that do form.

Reproductive Organ

1. An organ which functions in the process of reproduction.
2. *zool.* The primary reproductive organs are the gonads (testes and ovaries); secondary or accessory reproductive organs include glands, ducts, storage servoirs, and copulatory structures which function in reproductive activities or development of the young.
3. *bot.* In sexual reproduction, the principal organs are gametangia (antheridia and archegonia); in asexual reproduction, sporangia.

Reproductive System. All the organs concerned with the production of gametes, the bringing of the gametes together (fertilization), and the development of the young.

Reptile Any member of the class Reptilia, comprising poikilothermous vertebrates with four pentadactyl limbs and body usually covered with scales or scutes. Living members include snakes, lizards, turtles, crocodiles, and the tuatara; fossil reptiles include the dinosaurs, ichthyosaurs, and pterodactyls abundant during the Mesozoic era.

Reptilia. The class that contains the first entirely terrestrial vertebrates, which can live in dry terrestrial habitats as their skin is covered by a layer of horny scales, preventing water loss. They breathe atmospheric oxygen by means of lungs assisted by respiratory movements principally involving the ribs (there is no diaphragm). Reptiles are cold-blooded (poikilothermy) but behavioural patterns make it possible for them to maintain a fairly even body temperature throughout the day. Fertilization is internal and the majority of reptiles lay eggs on land. These eggs have a porous shell to provide protection from desiccation and allow gas exchange. In some reptiles the eggs are retained within the body of the mother until the young are ready to hatch, thereby greatly reducing juvenile mortality (ovoviviparity).

The class includes the modern crocodiles, lizards and snakes (Squamata), and tortoises and turtles, as well as many extinct forms, such as the dinosaurs and Pterosauria.

Repugnatorial Gland. A gland in an animal which produces a substance which has repellent properties, as the stink gland of hemipterans.

Repulsion. In genetics, the tendency of linked genes to separate in the formation of gametes; the opposite of coupling.

Repulsion Theory (field theory). The theory that the pattern of origin of leaf primordia at the shoot apex is regulated physiologically by inhibitory substances synthesized by the apex and the older primordia. A new primordium arises in a position where the concentration of these substances has fallen below a certain threshold level. Although no such inhibitors have yet been isolated various surgical and modelling experiments support the theory. Compare available space theory.

Resect. To cut away.

Resection Surgical removal of a portion of an organ.

Reservoir. A cavity where something is stored or kept in reserve; a cisterna.

Reservoir Host. In parasitology, a species which serves as a host of an organism which is pathogenic in or normally inhabits individuals of other species, as wild animals in Africa serving as a reservoir host for human trypanosomes.

Resin. A naturally occurring acidic polymer secreted by many trees (especially conifers) into ducts or canals. Resins are found either as brittle glassy substances or dissolved in essential oils. Their functions are probably similar to those of gums and mucilages, *i.e.*, protective.

Resin Canal (resin duct). A longitudinal resin-containing channel in the secondary xylem and leaves of many gymnosperms. Resin canals usually form by separation of parenchyma cells, which later form a lining to the canal termed an epithelium.

Resin Duct. A duct in a stem or leaf of a conifer which is involved in the secretion and conduction of resins.

Resinous. Resembling or having the properties of a resin.

Resistance. The ability of a plant to restrict the activities of a pathogen so that its growth is not significantly affected. Complete resistance is termed immunity. Resistance may be specific, *i.e.*, effective against a particular strain of the pathogen, or nonspecific, *i.e.*, effective against all strains. Specific resistance is usually controlled by one or a few major genes, *e.g.*, resistance of barley to mildew and of flax to rust are inherited as single genes. Non-specific resistance is conferred by the combined action of a number of minor genes. Such multigenic or field resistance is usually more stable and less likely to be overcome by mutants or recombinants of the pathogen. Environmental factors may influence the expression and degree of resistance. Compare susceptibility.

Resorption

1. The act of resorbing.
2. The removal of tissues by absorption, as resorption of the tail of a tadpole during metamorphosis.

Respiration. The metabolic process in animals and plants in which organic substances are broken down to simpler products with the release of energy, which is incorporated into special energy-carrying molecules (ATP) and subsequently used for other metabolic processes. In most plants and animals respiration requires oxigen, and carbon dioxide is an end product. The exchange of oxygen and carbon dioxide between the body tissues and the environment is called external respiration. In many animals the exchange of gases takes place as respiratory organs (*e.g.*, lungs in air-breathing vertebrates) and is assisted by respiratory movements (*e.g.*, breathing). In plants oxygen enters through pores on the plant surface and diffuses through the tissues via intercellular spaces or dissolved in tissue fluids.

Respiration at the cellular level is known as internal (or tissue) respiration and can be divided into two stages. In the first, glycolysis, glucose is broken down to pyruvate. This does not require oxygen and is a form of anaerobic respiration. In the second stage, the Krebs cycle, pyruvate is broken down by a cyclic series of reactions to carbon dioxide and water. This is the main energy-yielding stage and requires oxygen. The processes of glycolysis and the Krebs cycle are common to all plants and animals that respire aerobically.

Respiration-biomass Ratio (R/B ratio). The relationship between total community biomass (*i.e.* standing crop) and respiration. With larger biomass, respiration will increase but the increase will be less if the individual biomass units or organisms are large (reflecting the inverse relationship between size and metabolic rate).

Natural communities tend towards larger organisms and complex structure with low respiration rates per unit biomass.

Respiratory. Of or pertaining to respiration.

Respiratory Chain. A series of membrane-linked oxidation-reduction reactions in which electrons are transferred from reduced cofactors, formed in TCA cycle and other dehydrogenase reactions, to oxygen, which then combines with hydrygen ions to form water.

At present seven different electron-transferring enzymes or cofactors are known intermediates between NAD, the starting point of the chain, and oxygen. The redox potential is most negative at the start of the chain, and rises as the electrons flow towards oxygen.

For every two electrons travelling down the respiratory chain, three molecules of ATP are generated by the process of oxidative phosphorylation, which is linked to respiratory electron transfer.

Respiratory Enzyme. Cytochrome.

Respiratory Movement. Movement of parts of an animal which keeps either the water or the air from which the animal receives oxygen constantly fresh. Human beings renew the air in their lungs by movements of the chest and diaphragm.

Respiratory Organ. Any animal organ across which exchange of carbon dioxide and oxygen takes place. The surface membranes of such organs are always moist, thin, and well-supplied with blood. Examples are the lungs of air-breathing vertebrates, the gills of fish, and the tracheae of insects.

Respiratory Pigment. A coloured compound that is capable of reversibly binding with oxygen at high oxygen concentrations and releasing it at low oxygen concentrations. Such pigments are present in the blood, transporting oxygen within the circulatory system from the respiratory organs to the tissues of the body. In vertebrates the respiratory pigment is haemoglobin, contained in the erythrocytes (red blood cells).

Respiratory Quotient (RQ). The ratio of the volume of carbon dioxide evolved during respiration to the volume of oxygen absorbed, *i.e.* RQ=volume CO_2/volume O_2. The complete respiratory breakdown of sugars by aerobes often gives an RQ value of one, but it rises very considerably under anaerobiosis. When fats or proteins are used in respiration, the RQ value is less than one as less carbon dioxide is produced.

Respiratory Root. Pneumatophore.

Respiratory Tree

1. In holothuroids, a treelike structure attached to the cloaca into which water can be pumped.
2. In mammals, the trachea, bronchi, and bronchioles taken as a whole.

Respiratory Tube

1. A tube leading to a respiratory organ, as in various arthropods.
2. In lampreys, the tube through which water passes from the pharynx to the gill sacs.

Response. An activity initiated by or resulting from a stimulus, as in animals, movement, secretion, conduction; in plants, various tropisms, movement, etc.

[1]**Rest.** *physiol.* To cease activity; repose, sleep, quiescence.

[2]**Rest.** *anat.* A mass of epithelial cells which persists after cessation of development; called fetal or embryonic rest.

Resting Cell

1. A cell not in active division; one that is in the interphase between two mitotic divisions.

2. *bacteriol. a.* A cell freed from the medium upon which it was grown. *b.* An inactive cell; one not multiplying.

Resting Egg. In rotifers and other invertebrates, a thick-walled, haploid egg which is resistant to unfavorable conditions and usually requires a long period for development.

Resting Potential. The difference in electrical potentil that exists across the membrane of a nerve cell that is not in the process of transmitting a nerve impulse. The resting potential is maintained by means of the sodium pump. Compare action potential.

Restriction Enzyme (restriction endonuclease). An enzyme that recognizes and binds to specific short sequences of double-stranded DNA and cuts the DNA at or near this point. Such enzymes are produced by certain bacteria in response to invasion by bacteriophage—they destroy the virus by cutting up its DNA. Restriction enzymes are a useful tool in genetic engineering work.

Resupinate. Inverted; turned in a direction opposite from normal; upside down.

Ret. Retting.

Rete pl. **Retia.** An interlacing network or plexus of vessels or nerve fibers.

Rete Mirabile pl. **Retia Mirabilia.** A small, dense network of blood vessels, as that present in the red bony of a teleost fish.

Reticular. In the form of a network

Reticular Connective Tissue. A type of connective tissue consisting of reticular fibers enclosing primitive reticular cells and macrophages, as that comprising lymphatic tissue and organs.

Reticular Formation. A structure in the brainstem consisting of a network of nerve cells and their fibers which monitors incoming sensory impulses and controls various muscular and glandular responses.

Reticulate

1. Resembling or having the form of a network.
2. *bot.* Net-veined, with reference to veins in a leaf.

Reticulate Chloroplast. A complex plastid that forms a cylindrical network in the peripheral region of the cells of some green algae, *e.g.* Oedogonium.

Reticulate Thickening. A type of secondary wall patterning in tracheary elements in which the secondary cell wall is laid down to form a network. Unlike annular thickening and spiral thickening, reticulate thickening permits little further elongation and therefore occurs in tissues such as mataxylem, which have already completed most or all of their elongation. Compare pitted thickening, scalariform thickening.

Reticulodromous. Describing net or reticulate leaf venation as, for example, seen in Rhododendron leaves.

Reticuloendothelial System. Collectively, the fixed phagocytic cells of the body identified by their ability to take up certain colloidal dyes, as trypan blue. It includes macrophages, histiocytes, Kupffer's cells, duct cells, and reticular cells of lymphatic tissue.

Reticulopodium. A branching and anastomosing rhizopodium, as in foraminiferans.

Reticulum

1. A netlike structure.
2. A delicate interlacing network of fibers.
3. The second division of the stomach of a ruminant; honeycomb.

Retina. A light-sensitive layer found inside the eye-ball. It is developed only at the back of the eye. There are two distinct layers making the retina. The innermost layer is transparent and contains the light-sensitive structures (rods and cones); the outer layer is heavily pigmented. Nerve impulses caused by light hitting the retina pass to the brain along the optic nerve. The place where the optic nerve joins the back of the eye-ball has no retina. This is the blind spot.

Retinoaculum

1. *zool.* A retaining band or structure, as the curved setae on the forewing of lepidopterans, the carpal ligament in man, or the hamula or tenaculum of a springtail.
2. *bot. a.* The structure in orchins or milkweeds to which pollinia are attached. *b.* A curved, hooklike funicle, as in certain fruits.

Retinene. A decomposition product of rhodopsin formed in the retina when rhodopsin in the rods is exposed to light.

Retinol. Diterpene compound, composed of four isoprene units structurally related to carotenes, which is involved in the synthesis of the visual pigments. A deficiency of this compound results in a number of symptoms, including cessation of growth, cornification of epithelial structures, and, most notably, night blindness.

Retinula. A group of elongated sensory cells in the ommatidia or ocelli of insects.

Retort Cells. Elongated, flask-shaped, hyaline cells, each with an apical pore, in cortex of sphagnum mosses.

Retract. To withdraw; to draw back in. Compare protraction.

Retreat. A hiding place, den, or other structure into which an animal can withdraw for protection.

Retreat Makers. Caddis flies.

Retrofection. Reinfection, with reference to the reentry of eggs and larvae of pinworms.

Retrogress. To go backward; to proceed from a higher to a lower state of development or from a specialized condition to a generalized.

Retrorse. Directed or turned backward or downward. Compare antrosse.

Retroversion State of being turned backward or downward.

Retrovirus. An RNA-containing virus, that causes cancer in animals. Retroviruses contain oncogenes (cancer-causing genes; oncogenic), which are activated when the virus enters its host cell and stars to replicate.

Retting. A process employed in the preparation of flax, involving soaking followed by rotting and decomposition during which fibers are freed.

Retuse. Having a rounded or obtuse apex with a shallow notch, with reference to leaves.

Reverse Mutation (reversion). The production by further mutation of a pre-mutation gene from a mutant gene. This reverse mutation restores the ability of the gene to produce a functional protein. Strictly, reversion is the correction of a mutation *i.e.* it occurs at the same site; more loosely, though, the term is applied also to a mutation at another site that masks or suppresses the effect of the first mutation—in fact such organisms are not nonmutant, but double mutants with the same phenotype. Compare suppressor mutation.

Reverse Transcriptase. An enzyme present in some micro-organisms that reverses the normal transcription sequence and synthesizes DNA from messenger RNA. It is widely used in research for producing intron-free DNA.

Reversion

1. The appearance of a hereditary train which resembles that of a grandparent or a more remote ancestor.

2. A backward change in which an organism assumes a condition or takes to an environment occupied by its ancestors, as a land mammal reverting to an aquatic life.

Revolute. Curved backwards or downwards as, for example, the leaf margins of the white rockrose (Helianthemum apenninum). The term is also used to describe this form of vernation (illustration at vernation).

Rhabditiform Larva. A type of nematode larva in which the esophagus has a thick anterior portion connected by a narrow isthmus to a posterior bulb, as in the hookworm.

Rhabdocoel. A turbellarian flatworm with a simple, unbranched digestive cavity.

[1]Rhabdoid. Rodlike.

[2]Rhabdoid. A rod-shaped structure present in the epidermis and sometimes the mesenchyme of a turbellarian flatworm.

Rhabdome. A rod-shaped refractive body in the midaxis of an ommatidium or in the retina of an ocellus, each surrounded by retinacular cells.

Rhabdomere. A component of a rhabdome.

Rhachis. rachis.

Rhagon. A type of sponge with a broad base and tapering to a tip which bears an osculum; each possesses a leuconoid type of canal system.

Rhammite. A long, slender, and sometimes sinuous rhabdoid.

Rhamnose. A methylated pentose sugar, rarely occurring free, but common as a constituent of many glycosides, *e.g.* the flavonol glycoside quercitrin, isolated from the bark of the oak Quercus tinctoria. Rhamnose is also found in certain gums (*e.g.* gum arabic and the gum of flax seeds), mucilages, and in bacterial polysaccharides. It has been identified in the free state in poison ivy (Rhus toxicodendron).

Rhamphotheca. The covering of the entire bill of a bird.

Rhea. This flightless ostrich-like bird is the largest bird in the New World. It stands about 1.5 metres high and, like the ostrich, it has an almost featherless head and neck. The long powerful legs have three toes, compared with only two in the ostrich. Rheas live on the grasslands of South America.

Rheobase. The minimal or liminal electric stimulus which will induce a response.

Rheoreceptor. A sense organ which in stimulated by currents or movement of water.

Rheotaxis. The reaction of an organism in response to a moving current of water.

Rhesus Factor (Rh factor). An antigen whose presence or absence on the surface of red blood cells forms the basis of the rhesus blood group system. (The factor was first recognized in rhesus monkeys). Most people possess the Rh factor, *i.e.* they are rhesus positive (Rh+). People who lack the factor are Rh−. If Rh+ blood is given to an Rh−patient, the latter develops anti-Rh antibodies. Subsequent transfusion of Rh+blood results in agglutination, with serious consequences. Similarly, an Rh−pregnant woman carrying an Rh+fetus may develop anti-Rh antibodies in her blood; these will react with the blood of a subsequent Rh+fetus, causing anaemia in the newborn baby.

Rhesus Monkey. One of the sacred monkeys of India, the rhesus is about 45 cm long with a 25-cm tail. It ranges in colour from grey-green to yellow-brown on the back with a white belly. When frightened a rhesus becomes red in the face. It belongs to the group known as macaque monkeys. There are several species living in India and South-East Asia.

Rh Factor. One of several antigens naturally present in or on erythrocytes, responsible for certain adverse reactions which occur following the injection of anti-Rh serum;

originally found in the rhesus monkey but present also in man.

Rhinoceros. A large, heavy-bodied, thick-skinned perissodactyl mammal of the genera Rhinoceros, inhabiting Asia, and Diceros, inhabiting Africa.

Rhinophore. One of the second pair of tentacles of a nudibranch mollusk.

Rhinotheca. The sheath or covering of the upper mandible (maxilla) of a bird.

Rhipidium. A scorpioid cyme (monochasium) that is usually flattened in one plane and hence fan shaped. Examples are seen in certain Iris species. Compare bostryx.

Rhizanthous. Flowering or apparently flowering from the root.

Rhizine. A bundle of hyphae by which a lichen is attached to its substrate.

Rhizobium (family Rhizobiaceae). Genus of bacteria which bring about the formation of root modules on leguminous plants. The bacteria live in the root nodules and benefit the plant by making available to it nitrogen which they fix from the atmosphere. There are several species.

Rhizocaline. A substance thought to be present in stems which, interacting with auxin, induces the development of roots.

Rhizocarpous. Having a perennial root but an annual stem.

Rhizocephalan. A degenerate, parasitic crustacean of the order Rhizocephala, as Sacculina which lives in and on crabs.

Rhizogenic. Root-producing, as certain cells.

Rhizoid. One of a group of delicate and often colourless hairlike outgrowths found in certain algae and the gametophyte generation of bryophytes and some pteridophytes. They anchor the plant to the substrate and absorb water and mineral salts.

Rhizom. The nutritive network which develops from the kentrogen larva of Sacculina within a crab.

Rhizome. A horizontal underground stem. It enables the plant to survive from one growing season to the next and in some species it also serves to propagate the plant vegetatively. It may be thin and wiry, as in couch grass, or fleshy and swollen, as in Iris. Compact upright underground stems, as in rhubarb, strawberry, and primrose, are often called rootstocks.

Rhizomorph. A tough cordlike mass of fused hyphae that acts to carry a fungus from one favourable location to another, across unsuitable substrates. Rhizomorphs are seen, for example, in the tree parasite Armillaria mellea (the bootlace or honey fungus) and the dryrot fungus Serpula lacrymans.

Rhizophore. Any of the leafless branches, seen in many species of Selaginella, that arise from the stem at points of forking. Usually two rhizophores form at each fork but only one continues to develop. The rhizophore grows towards the soil, often branching repeatedly before reaching the soil surface. On contact with the ground, roots are produced from the swollen tips of the rhizophore.

Rhizoplast. In flagellates, a threadlike structure which connects the basal granule to the nucleus.

Rhizopod

1. Any protozoan of the class Sarcodina (Rhizopoda).
2. A rhizopodium.

Rhizopodium. A thin outgrowth of cytoplasm formed by certain algae that lack rigid cell walls. Rhizopodial algal cells are seen in the Chrysophyta, Xanthophyta and Dinophyta.

Rhodophyta (red algae). A division of algae that are often pink or red in colour due to the presence of the pigments phycocyanin and phycoerythrin. Members of the Rhodophyta may be unicellular or multicellular, forming branched flattened thalli or filaments. They are commonly found along the coasts of tropical areas.

Rhodophyte. Any member of the division Rhodophyta which comprises the red algae.

Rhodopsin (visual purple). The light-sensitive pigment found in the rods of the vertebrate retina. Light falling on the rod causes a chemical change in rhodopsin, which initiates the transmission of a nerve impulse to the brain. The great sensitivity of rhodopsin allows vision in dim light (night vision).

Rhombencephalon. The hindbrain.

Rhubarb A common garden plant of the genus Rheum, grown for its succulent, acid leafstalks.

Rhynchocoel. A closed, fluid-filled cavity in nemerteans which contains the proboscis.

Rhynchus. The oral sucker of a digenetic trematode.

Rhynie Chert. A siliceous rock of the Devonian period in Scotland, in which well preserved psilopsid fossils are found. In some, anatomical details can be clearly seen. The plants are similar to Psilotum, a living psilopsid, in having aerial branches, tracheids, an epidermis with stomata, and sporangia at the ends of the branches. Examples are Rhynia and Horneophyton. These extinct psilopsids are placed in the order Psilophytales, named after the Devonian fossil Psilophyton, discovered in eastern Canada in 1859. Another important fossil in the Rhynie chert, Asteroxylon, resembles a lycopsid.

Rhythm. A sequence of events or activities repeated at regular intervals.

Rhytidome. The outer bark.

Rib. One of a series of slender curved bones that form a cage to enclose, support, and protect the heart and lungs (thorax). Ribs occur in pairs, articulating with the thoracic vertebrae of the spinal column at the back and (in reptiles, birds, and mammals) with the sternum (breastbone) in front. Movements of the rib cage, controlled by intercostal muscles between the ribs, are important in breathing.

Ribbed. Bearing ribs or riblike structures.

Ribbon Worm. A nemertean.

Riboflavin (vitamin B_2). A flavin pigment that has been implicated both in the perception of the phototropic stimulus and in photooxidation of endogenous auxins. It consists of an isoalloxazine ring substituted with the sugar alcohol ribitol. In its active phosphorylated form riboflavin phosphate, otherwise known as FMN, it acts as a coenzyme for various oxidizing enzymes. Riboflavin is not synthesized by animals.

Ribonuclease. An enzyme which hydrolyzes RNA, splitting the phosphate bonds linking the adjacent nucleotides.

Ribonucleic Acid. RNA, one of a number of nucleic acids which, upon hydrolysis, yield ribose; of importance in the synthesis of proteins. Three types are : messenger (mRNA), of nuclear origin; transfer (tRNA), which conveys amino acids; ribosomal (rRNA), located in the ribosomes of the cytoplasm).

Ribose. A monosaccharide $C_5H_{10}O_5$, rarely occurring free in nature but important as a component of RNA (ribonucleic acid). Its derivative deoxyribose, $C_5H_{10}O_4$, is equally important as a constituent of DNA (deoxyribonucleic acid), which carries the genetic code in chromosomes

Ribose Nucleic Acid. Ribonucleic acid (RNA), *q.v.*

Ribosomal RNA (rRNA). A form of RNA that is confined entirely to the ribosomes. Synthesis of rRNA takes place on distinctive parts of the chromosomes associated with the nucleolus, called nucleolar organizers. The base composition of rRNA is very similar in all species. After synthesis it combines with protein to form nucleoprotein.

The partly constructed ribosomes then leave the nucleus, via nuclear potes, and enter the cytoplasm where synthesis is completed. The absence of fully constructed ribosomes in the nucleus may account for the absence of protein synthesis there. Compare messenger RNA, transfer RNA.

Ribosome. Subcellular granule, 10—20nm in diameter, composed of RNA and protein, which is found in large numbers in all types of cells and in some subcellular organelles. Ribosomes are the site of protein synthesis : m-RNA attaches to them and there receives t-RNA molecules bearing amino acids. In eukaryotic cells they are synthesized in the nucleolus, but are found predominantly in the cytoplasm, singly or in chains (polysomes or polyribosomes, probably linked by the m-RNA), or attached to the endoplasmic reticulum, which is then termed 'rough ER'.

Ribulose. A five-carbon ketose sugar (illustration as ketose). In the phosphorylated form, ribulose 5-phosphate, it is an intermediate in the pentose phosphate pathway and the Calvin cycle. As ribulose bisphosphate it is important as the carbon dioxide acceptor in photosynthesis.

Ribulose Bisphosphate (RuBP). A phosphorylated form of ribulose that acts as the initial carbon dioxide acceptor in C_3 photosynthesis and as the eventual acceptor in C_4 photosynthesis and crassulacean acid metabolism. Addition of carbon dioxide occurs between the second and third carbon atoms and results in the formation of two molecules of phosphoglyceric acid. These feed into the Calvin cycle, which allows the fixed carbon dioxide to be converted into carbohydrate and regenerates the ribulose bisphosphate.

Ribulose Bisphosphate Carboxylase (RUBP carboxylase, carboxydismutase). An enzyme that catalyses the carboxylation of ribulose bisphosphate to two molecules of phosphoglyceric acid. This is the first step in the Calvin cycle. RUBP carboxylase is the fraction 1 protein of chloroplasts. It is very abundant in chloroplasts and may account for up to 15% of the total protein.

This enzyme can also act as an oxygenase, forming a molecule of phosphoglyceric acid and a molecule of phosphoglycollic acid from ribulose bisphosphate and oxygen. This reaction forms the basis of photorespiration.

Ribulose-1,5-diphosphate (RDP). Phosphorylated derivative of the ketopentose monosaccharide ribulose, which acts as an acceptor molecule for carbon dioxide in the Calvin cycle. The reaction between one molecule each of these two substrates results in the formation of two molecules of phosphoglyceric acid.

Rice. A cereal grass (Oryza sativa) extensively cultivated as a food crop; collectively, the grain or seeds of this plant.

Ricin. A toxic albumin present in the seeds of castor bean plant.

Rickettsia. A very small rod-shaped non-motile microorganism that resembles a bacterium in its cellular structure and method of asexual reproduction but, like a virus, is totally parasitic, being unable to reproduce outside the cells of its host. Rickettsiae can infect such arthropods as ticks, fleas, lice, and mites, through which they can be transmitted to vertebrates, including man. The group includes the causal agents of trench fever, Rocky Mountain spotted fever, and forms of typhus.

Rickets. A deficiency disease of children characterized by defective bone formation due to a deficiency of vitamin D which impairs absorption of calcium and phosphorus.

Rickettsiales. An order containing obligately parasitic bacteria that are much smaller (0.2-0.5 μm) than other bacteria. They cause a number of serious diseases in animals, *e.g.* typhus and O fever.

Rictus

1. *zool.* The gape of the mouth, with reference to birds.
2. *bot.* The mouth of a bilabiate corolla.

Rigor Mortis. The condition following death in which muscles become stiff and rigid.

Rimose. Rimous; having numerous clefts or fissures, as the bark of trees.

Rind. A thin, tough, external covering or layer, as that on the surface of various fruits and plant stems.

Rinderpest. An infectious viral disease of herbivores characterized by inflammation of the digestive tract.

Ring. A circular structure.

Ring Canal. A circular canal, as that *a.* in the water-vascular system of an echinoderm; *b.* in the tentacle of an ectoproct.

Ringed. Resembling, marked by, or possessing a ringlike structure or marking.

Ringent. Gaping, with reference either to *a. zool.* the valves of bivalve; *b. bot.* an open, bilabiate corolla.

Ringer's Solution. An isotonic solution of three chlorides. For human tissues, it is composed of 8.6 g. of sodium chloride, 0.30 g. of potassium chloride, and 0.33 g. of calcium chloride in each 1000 ml. of water.

Ring Gland. In dipterous insects, the ring of Weissman, composed of the corpus cardiacum, corpus allatum, and prothoracic gland fused to form a neurosecretory structure surrounding the aorta. Also called retrocerebral complex.

Ringing Experiments. A means of investigating the routes of water and carbohydrate translocation in plants by removing a ring of the outer tissues of the stem containing the phloem. This results in sufficient water still reaching the upper shoots to keep them turgid but photosynthetic products from the leaves are not translocated to regions below the ring and tend to accumulate above it. Such observations confirm that water is transported within xylem and photosynthates within phloem vessels, the former being undisturbed and the latter disrupted by the ringing process.

Ring-porous Wood. Secondary xylem in which there is marked seasonal variation in tracheary-element diameter with wider elements being formed in spring and early summer and narrower elements being formed later in the year. Growth rings are distinct in such wood, *e.g.* that of pedunculate oak, Quercus robur. Compare diffuse-porous wood.

Ringworm. An infectious disease of the skin and its appendages (hair, nails), caused by various fungi, as Microsporum, Trichophyton and Epidermophyton. Also called dermatomycosis, trichomycosis, tinea.

Ritualization An evolutionary process in which the form or context of an action is altered because it comes to play a role in social communication. For example, many courtship and greeting ceremonies in animals include ritual food presentation, derived from the action of feeding the young.

River Blindness. The name given to extreme infections by the nematode worm Onchocera, which is transmitted by black flies (genus Simulium, family Simuliidae). Blindness is caused by damage to capillaries resulting from the lodging of the small worms, and the blockage of the blood supply to the eye tissue.

RNA (ribonucleic acid). A complex organic compound (a nucleic acid) in living cells that is concerned with protein synthesis. In some viruses, RNA is also the hereditary material. Most RNA is synthesized in the nucleus and then distributed to various parts of the cytoplasm An

RNA molecule consists of a long chain of nucleotides in which the sugar is ribose and the bases are adenine, cytosine, guanine, and uracil (compare DNA). Messenger RNA (mRNA) is responsible for carrying the genetic code transcribed from DNA to specialized sites within the cell (known as ribosomes), where the information is translated into protein composition (transcription; translation). Ribosomal RNA (rRNA) is present in ribosomes; it is single-stranded but helical regions are formed by base pairing within the strand. Transfer RNA (tRNA, soluble RNA, sRNA) is involved in the assembly of amino acids in a protein chain being synthesized at a ribosome. Each tRNA is specific for an amino acid and bears a triplet of bases complementary with a triplet on mRNA.

Rockfish. One of a number of fishes that inhabit rocky habitats, especially marine fishes of the family Scorpaenidae.

Rockweed One of a number of brown algae which grow attached to rocks along the shore line, as Fucus, Ascophyllum.

Rod. A type of light-sensitive receptor cell present in the retinas of vertebrates. Rods contain the pigment rhodopsin and are essential for vision in dim light. They are not evenly distributed on the retina, being absent in the fovea and occupying all of the retinal margin. Compare cone.

Rod Cell. Macrosclereid.

Rodent. Any mammal of the order Rodentia (Glires), which includes rats, mice, squirrels, chipmunks, woodchucks, gophers, porcupines, and beavers, characterized by two chisel-shaped incisors in each jaw and absence of canine teeth. Comprise over 6500 species, the majority of living mammals.

Rodentia. An order of mammals characterized by a single pair of long curved incisors in each jaw. These teeth are specialized for gnawing : they continue growing throughout life and have enamel only on the front so that they wear to a chisel-shaped cutting edge. Rodents often breed throughout the year and produce large numbers of quickly maturing young. The order includes the squirrels, beavers, rat, mice, and porcupines.

Rod Organ. A structure in holozoic euglenoids which functions in the ingestion of food, as in Peranema.

Roe

1. The eggs of a fish, especially when still contained within the ovarian membrane.
2. The eggs or ovaries of certain invertebrates, as the coral of a lobster.
3. A roe deer.

Roebuck. The male of the roe deer.

Rogue

1. Any plant that varies from the rest of the crop and is consequently not wanted. Examples are wild oats (Avena fatua) growing in fields of cultivated oats (A. sativa), plants grawing from self-pollincted seed in a field of F_1 hybrids, and diseased plants, such as wheat plants affected with covered smut.
2. To remove and destroy such plants.

Kook. Though similar in size, shape and colour to the carrion crow, the rook can be distinguished by the grey patch of skin around the base of its beak. The plumage of a rook also has a bluish sheen compared with the greenish sheen of the crow and the feathers on its upper legs give the impression that the bird is wearing a pair of short baggy trousers. Rooks are gregarious birds and gather in huge flocks to build a colony or rookery of nests in tall trees, and to feed on a wide variety of plants and animals, ranging from grubs to grain.

Rookery. The breeding grounds or place for *a.* a colony of rooks; *b.* any gregarious bird, as the penguin; *c.* aquatic mammals, as the fur seal.

[1]Roost. To sit, rest, or sleep on a pole or a limb of a tree, said of birds at night.

[2]Roost

1. A place where birds rest at night.
2. A group of birds roosting together.

Rooster. The male or cock of domestic fowl.

Root. The usually underground part of the plant axis, specialized for anchorage, absorption, and, sometimes food storage. It may usually be distinguished from a stem by the absence of chlorophyll and buds. (Exceptions are the aerial roots of certain epiphytes, *e.g.*, Taeniophyllum, that can develop chlorophyll when illuminated. Adventitious buds may form on roots and give rise to suckers). The root system may include an obvious main root derived from the radicle (taproot) or may be fibrous due to repeated branching of the radicle. Alternatively it may include or consist solely of adventitious roots arising from the base of the stem.

The vascular tissues of the root normally form a solid central stele, which is better able to resist the tensions and pressures exterted on a root than would be a hollow stelar cylinder, typical of most stems. The absorptive properties of the root are enhanced by the formation of root hairs behind the tip. Beyond these the root branches to form lateral roots. Unlike stem branches, these do not arise superficially but develop from the outer tissues of the stele and grow through the root cortex. Lateral root formation is thus said to be endogenous. Roots are usually positively hydrotropic and geotropic A root cap (calyptra) at the root tip protects the root as it grows down through the soil. Numerous modifications of roots exist (aerial root, climbing root, contractile root, pneumatophore, prop root). Symbiotic associations between plant roots and various fungi, bacteria, and blue-green algae are common (mycorrhiza, root, nodule).

Root Cap (calyptra). A cone-shaped structure that covers the root tip and develops as a result of cell division by a meristem at the root apex (calyptrogen). It protects the root tip as it grows between the soil particles. The cells are constantly worn away by friction and are replaced by the meristem.

Root Climber. A plant which develops adventitious root from the stem for support and attachment, as English ivy.

Root Hair. A trichome originating from the piliferous layer of the root. Root hairs are projections from single epidermal cells in direct contact with the soil and serve to increase the surface area for absorption. They are responsible for the first stage in absorption of water and solutes from the soil. They are also thought to help retain contact between the root tip and the soil when dry conditions tend to cause the soil to contract away from the roots.

Rootlet. A small root.

Root Nodule. A tumorous growth that develops on the roots of leguminous and certain other plants in response to infection by symbiotic microorganisms In legumes the symbiont is always a bacterium of the genus Rhizobium. In nonleguminons plants with root nodules the symbiont appears to be either a member of the Plasmodiophorales, *e.g.*, in the roots of bog myrtle (Myrica gale) and alder (Alnus glutinosa), or a blue-green alga, *e g.*, in the roots of some Gunnera species. In legumes, following invasion of the root tissues, the bacteria induce a localized proliferation of the host tissues. Like the induction of crown gall (tumuor inducing principle), the ability of Rhizobium to induce nodules appears to be controlled by a plasmid. The plasmid also controls the host specificity of different Rhizobium strains. Nitrogen-fixation is carried out by the bacteria, which assume a characteristic shape and size within the host cells (bacteroid).

Root Pressure. The pressure that can build up in the root systems or plants so as to force water upwards through the xylem vessels. The force is a function of the osmotic potential of the root cell contents and is evidenced by the continuing flow of water from the cut surface of a recently severed stem. Positive root pressures tend to build up at night, when the rate of transpiration is very low, and lead to the process of guttation. Root pressure is not of great importance in water uptake and varies seasonally, being lowest in magnitude during the summer.

Root Rot. A plant disease in which there is disintegration of the root tissues. Above-ground symptoms are often initially similar to those of nutritional disorders or bad drainage. Annual plants appear sickly and eventually wilt and die as a result of shortage of water and nutrients. Affected tress usually snow symptoms of gradual decline and dieback of the crown. Numerous different species of fungus cause root rots. Armillaria mellea (the honey fungus) is a ubiquitous root pathogen affecting many forest and garden trees. Other common root-infecting fungi include Corticium, Phytophthora, and Fusarium.

Root-shoot Ratio. Ratio of the amount of plant tissues that have supportive functions to the amount of those that have growth functions. Plants with a higher proportion of roots can compete more effectively for soil nutrients, while those with a higher proportion of shoots can collect more light energy. Large proportions of shoot production are characteristic of vegetation in early successional phases, while high proportions of root production are characteristic of climax vegetational phases.

Rootstock

1. A short erect underground stem, as seen in various angiosperms, *e.g.*, plantains (Plantago), and certain pteridophytes, *e.g.*, Isoete, Osmunda. It is the equivalent of a vertical rhizome.

2. Any underground part of a plant.

Rostrum

1. The forward projection or extension of the snout of a fish. The typical profile of an oceanic shark reveals a massive rostrum projecting well forward and above the low-slung mouth.
2. The snout-like extension to the head that forms the specialized piercing and sucking mouthparts of the Hemiptera (true bugs). The stylets are sheathed by the labrum, which forms a jointed tube closed dorsally at the base by the labrum. In feeding, only the stylets enter the tissues of the host plant or prey.

Root System. All the roots of a plant taken collectively, comprising one of three types : fibrous, tap, and fascicled.

Root-tipping. The development of roots at the tips of stems, as in plants with arching of trailing stems which root upon contact with the ground.

Rosaceae. A large cosmopolitan dicotyledonous family containing about 3400 species in some 122 genera. It includes both woody and herbaceous plants. The leaves are usually alternate and, except in Spiraea and some other members of the subfamily Spiraeoideae, have two stipules at the base. The flowers are usually actinomorphic and often large and showy. There are numerous stamens arranged in whorls and the carpels are also usually numerous and free. An epicalyx is often present. Many different types of fruit are formed, the pome being characteristic of the subfamily Maloideae, *e.g.*, Malus (apples), Pyrus (pears), and Cydonia (quinces), and a drupe characteristic of the subfamily Prunoideae, *e.g.*, Prunus (plums, cherries, apricots).

The family contains most of the important orchard fruits, many bush fruits, *e.g.*, blackberries and raspberries (Rubus), and other soft fruits, *e.g.*, strawberries (Fragaria). It also includes many important ornamental genera, notably Rosa, of which there are estimated to be over 5000 cultivars. Other ornamentals include Cotoneaster, Kerria, Potentilla, and Spiraea.

Rose. A plant of the genus Rosa of the family Rosaceae, an erect or climbing shrub with prickly stem and showy flowers.

Rose Family. The Rosaceae, a family of angiosperms comprising over 2500 species, many of commercial importance, as the rose, peach, apple, cherry, strawberry, hawthorn, and blackberry.

R-selection. Selection for maximizing the intrinsic rate of increase (r) of an organism so that when favourable conditions occur, *e.g.*, in a newely-formed habitat, the species concerned can rapidly colonize the area. Such species are opportunists. An opportunist strategy is advantageous in rapidly changing environments as in the early stages of a succession.

Rosette

1. Any of a number of structures in which the parts have a circular, radiate arrangement, as *a. bot.* a cluster of leaves arising from a short stem; *b. zool.* the fringed, posterior holdfast organ of certain cestodarians, or in crinoids, an ossicle on the aboral surface.
2. One of several plant diseases resulting from virus infection or mineral deficiency.

Rosette Plant. Any plant with its leaves radiating outwards from a short stem at soil level. The rosette habit enables such plants to survive grazing and trampling and to be more successful in competing with other species for space. Examples are dandelions, daisies, and plantains.

Rosidae. A subclass of the dicotyledons containing both woody and herbaceous species. Its members usually have bisexual flowers that often contain numerous stamens, which develop centripetally. The Rosidae may contain some 14—21 orders depending on the classfication scheme referred to. The inclusion of the following 13 orders is generally agreed : Rosales including the Rosaceae; Fabales, including the Leguminosae; Myrtales, including the Rhizophoraceae (*e g*., mangroves) and Myrtaceae; Proteales; Podostemales; Santalales, including the Santalaceae (e.g. sandalwoods); Celastrales, including the Celastraceae (*e.g*., spindle tree) and Aquifoliaceae (*e g*., hollies); Rhamnales, including the Rhamnaceae (*e.g*. buckthorns) and Vitaceae (*e.g*., grape vines); Sapindales, including the Sapindaceae (*e g*., soapberries), Hippocastanaceae (*e.g*., horse chestnuts), and Aceraceae (maples); Geraniales, including the Geraniaceae, Oxalidaceae (*e g*., wood sorels) and Balsaminaceae; Polygalales; Umbellales (or Cornales), including the Araliaceae (*e.g*., ivies) and Umbelliferae; and **Haloragales** (or Hippuridales).

In addition, the following, four orders may be recognized but these are often included in other orders of the Rosidae : Saxifragales, including the Crassulaceae (*e.g*., stonecrops) and Saxifragaceae, oftenplaced in the Rosales; Connarales (*e.g* , zebra woods), and Rutales, including the Rutaceae (citrus family), Meliaceae (*e.g*., mahogonies), and Anacardiaceae (*e.g*., cashews), both often placed in the Sapindales; and Elaeagnales, containing the Elaeagnaceae (*e.g* , oleasters), often placed in the Proteales).

Some classifications include the Rafflesiales (often placed in the Magnoliidae) and the Juglandales (often placed in the Hamamelidae) in the Rosidae. The order Oleales, including the Oleaceae (*e.g*., olives, lilacs), is often seen in the order Gentianales of the subclass Asteridae. The Euphorbiales, including the Euphorbiaceae (spurge family), is sometimes classified in the Dilleniidae. Finally the two families Droseraceae (*e.g*., sundews) and Nepenthaceae (pitcher plants) making up the order Nepenthales are sometimes split and allocated to the Rosales and Aristolochiales (subclass Magnoliidae) respectively.

Rosorial. Of or pertaining to gnawing animals.

Ross. The roughened external surface of bark.

Rostellate. Having a small beak or rostrum.

Rostellum

1. *zool.* A small projection or rostrum, as *a.* the projecting anterior end of certain flagellates. The beak of certain sucking insects. *c.* A rounded process on the tip of the scolex of certain tapeworms; may be retractile and surrounded by recurved books.
2. *bot.* A sterile, beaklike lobe on the stigma of an orchid.

Rostral. Of or pertaining to a beak or rostrum.

Rostrate. Having a beak or rostrum.

Rostrum. A beak or beaklike projection, as *a.* a middorsal projection on the head of a roifer; *b.* the median process extending anteriorly from the cephalothorax of a malacostracan; *c.* the plates opposite the carina in a senssile cirriped; *d.* a prominence a the posterior end of the shell of a cuttlefish; *e.* the cone-shaped, basal portion of the proboscis in dipterans; *f.* in hemipterans, the beak projecting posteriorly from the head; *g.* in weevils, the elongated vertex bearing at its tip the mouth parts; *h.* in mites, the capitulum or gnathosoma; *i.* in vertebrates, an anterior extension of the cranium in the shark, paddlefish, sawfish, and sturgeon; *j.* an anterior extension of certain bones, as the basisphenoid.

Rosulate. In the form of or resembling a rosette.

Rot. A plant disease in which there is disintegration of the tissues. Rots are particularly important as postharvest diseases.

Rotate. Wheel-shaped; flat and circular in outline, with reference to the corolla of certain flowers.

Rotting. The process of decomposition or decay brought about by extracellular enzymes of various bacteria and fungi which dissolve pectin, reducing plant tissues to a soft, moist, pulpy mass.

Rotula

1. One of the five radial plates in Aristotle's lantern.
2. The patella or kneecap.

Rough. Having a surface marked by irregularities, ridges, or projections; not smooth.

Rough Colony *bacterial* A type of colony marked by a flat, uneven surface containing abnormal cells which cling together after fission and differ physiologically from cells of cantrasting smooth colonies.

Rough Endoplasmic Reticulum. Endoplasmic reticulum.

Rouleau pl. **Rouleaux.** A row of red blood cells which resembles a roll or stack of coins.

Roundworm. A nematode.

Rove Beetle. A slender, elongate beetle of the family Staphylinidae found principally around decaying matter, dung, and carrion.

Royal Jelly. A substance produced by the pharyngeal glands of worker bees which, when fed to the female larvae, results in their development into queens.

RQ. Respiratory quotient.

RNA. Ribosomal RNA,

Rubber. An elastic substance prepared from latex, the milky juice of various plants of the tropics, especially Hevea brasiliensis.

Rubber Tree. Any of several trees and bushes yielding latex, but especially the hevea tree, or para rubber tree of Brazil. It is a tall, slender evergreen, producing pale yellow flowers.

Rubiaceae. A large family of dicotyledonous plants containing about 7000 species in some 500 genera. It is mainly tropical in distribution, all the tropical species being woody. Temperate representatives are always herbaceous and include such species as Galium saxatile (heath bedstraw) and Asperula arvensis (blue woodruff). The temperate species characteristically have square stems and leaves borne in whorls. All members, both temperate and tropical, bear stipules and the flowers are usually actinomorphic and hermaphrodite. The ovary is normally inferior and in most members contains to carpels.

Commercially important praducts of the Rubiaceae include coffee, from Coffea arabica and C. canephora, and quinine, from species of Cinchona. Gardenia species are much planted as ornamentals.

Rubidium-strontium Dating. A method of dating geological specimens based on the decay of the radioisotope rubidium—87 into the stable isotope strontium—87. Natural rubidium contains 27.85% of rubidium—87, which has a half-life of 4.7×10^{11} years. The ratio $^{87}Rb/^{87}Sr$ in a specimen gives an estimate of its age (up to several thousand million years).

RuBP. Ribulose bisphospate.

RuDP. Ribulose diphosphhate.

Rudiment

1. An organ or structure which is just beginning to develop or one in which development has been arrested; an anlage or primordium.
2. A vestige or the remains of a structure which was functional in an earlier stage of evolutionary development.

Ruff

1. A ring or collar of elongated or modified feathers about the neck of certain birds.
2. A small European perch (Acerina cernua).
3. The male of the sandpiper (Philomachus pugnax).

Ruffed Grouse. An upland game bird (Bonasa umbellus), males of which are noted for their drumming.

Rugose. Wrinkled.

Rumen. The paunch, the first of four chambers of the stomach of a ruminant.

Ruminant. Member of the suborder Ruminantia, an herbivorous animal with complex digestion characterized by a stomach having three or four parts. In the rumen millions of symbiotic bacteria and other cellulase-producing micro-organisms partially digest the cellulose-rich food. The enzyme cellulase cannot be made by mammals themselves. After some time the partially digested food, the cud, is assembled into pellets in the reticulum ready for regurgitation. The regurgiated cud is chewed thoroughly before passing to the omasum and abomasum where normal digestion occurs. In some ruminants the rumen and recticulum form a single large chamber.

Ruminantia. A suborder of hooved mammals comprising the sheep, cattle, goats, deer, and antelopes. They are characterized by a four-chambered stomach, the first part of which is the rumen, which contains microorganisms that break down cellulose. Food is temporarily stored in the rumen, then regurgitated and chewed to a pulp before being swallowed and passed to the rest of the stomach where digestion is continued.

Ruminate. Describing endosperm that is irregularly grooved or ridged and so appears chewed as, for example; seen in many members of the Myristicaceae.

Rump

1. The region of the buttocks in a quadruped.
2. *ornith.* The region between the back and upper tail coverts; the region of the sacrum.

Run. The movement of a school of fishes up a river to spawn, as a salmon run.

Runcinate. Deeply incised with lobes or segments directed backwards, as the leaf of a dandelion.

Runner. A stem that grows horizontally along the soil surface and gives rise to new plants either from axillary or terminal buds. Runners are seen in the creeping buttercup and the strawberry. Offsets, *e.g.* those of the houseleek, are short runners.

Rupicolous. Living in or frequenting rocks or rocky areas.

Russet. A brown, roughened area on the skin of various fruits resulting from insect injury, disease, spray damage, or some other causative factor.

Russetting. The development of brown corky patches on certain fruits, especially apple varieties, in response to various chemicals. Russetting of leaves, tubers, and other plant organs may also occur in response to damage or infection.

Rusts. A group of parasitic fungi belonging to the Basidiomycetes. Many of these species attack the leaves and stems of cereal crops : characteristic rust-coloured streaks of epores appear on infected plants. The life cycles of some rusts may be complex; many form a number of different types of spore and some require two different host plants. Compare smuts.

Rutabaga. A turniplike vegetable (Bractica napobrassica) grown for its root and the lower portion of the stem; used extensively for stock feed.

Ruthenium Red. A temporary stain that turns mucilage and certain gums pink. It is used as a test for pectin in the middle lamella of plant cells.

Rye

1. A hardy annual grass (Secale cereale), a minor cereal, grown extensively in Europe for its seeds, used for good. Also grown for hay, winter pasturage, and for cover to prevent erosion.
2. The grain (seeds) of the rye plant.

Encyclopaedic Dictionary of

BIOLOGICAL SCIENCES

ENCYCLOPAEDIC DICTIONARY OF BIOLOGICAL SCIENCES

Vol. 6

K. NARANG
R. RANI
M. PRAKASH

ANMOL PUBLICATIONS PVT LTD
New Delhi-110002

ANMOL PUBLICATIONS PVT LTD
4374/4B, Ansari Road
Daryaganj, New Delhi-110 002

Encyclopaedic Dictionary of Biological Sciences

© Reserved

First Edition, 1991
ISBN 81-7041-462-8 (Set)
ISBN 81-7041-468-7 (Vol.6)
Reprint 1994
Reprint ... 1998

PRINTED IN INDIA
Published by J.L. Kumar for Anmol Publications Pvt. Ltd. New Delhi and Printed at Mehra Offset Press.

Preface

The *Encyclopaedic Dictionary of Biological Sciences* (set of six volumes) has been carefully compiled and edited to meet the long felt needs of increasingly large number of, those who have to deal with the different aspects of biological sciences in colleges, universities, and research institutes. These volumes provide a speedy means of reference to easily interpreted definitions of the terms selected from botany, zoology, environmental science, ecology, genetics, biochemistry, forestry, agriculture geomorphology, cell biology, plant pathology, anatomy, evolution and ecology.

This set of dictionary is more or less encyclopaedic in its contents and style of representation which is evident from the comprehensiveness of its coverage and contextual relevance of explanations with illustrations and chemical formulae wherever necessary.

The entries in this dictionary have been written in a clear and explanatory style to provide both straight forward definitions and invaluable background information. The presentation throughout has been aimed at sustaining the interest of readers while enriching their vocabulary and comprehension of technical terms and expressions.

Throughout the process of compilation and editing these volumes our sincere effort was to make the dictionary as a ready reference for undergraduate and post graduate biological, agricultural, environmental, medical, marine and biochemistry students and also for those appearing for competitive examinations, research scholars, teachers and authors.

The editors express their thanks to their friends and colleagues whose continuous inspiration have initiated them to bring out these volumes.

The Editors

S

Saber-toothed Tiger. An extinct, catlike mammal characterized by long, curved, thin, upper canine teeth, once common throughout Europe and North America.

Sable Antelope. A large, African antelope (Hippotragus niger) with glossy black body and recurved horns.

Sabulous. Sandy, gritty.

Sac. A pouch or baglike cavity.

Saccate. Shaped like a sac or pouch.

Saccharase. An enzyme which hydrolyzes disaccharides to monosaccharides.

Saccharide. A simple sugar or a compound composed of simple sugars; a carbohydrate.

Saccharomyces (family Saccharomycetaceae). Genus of yeasts which includes some economically important species and strains. In the absence of air, S. cerevisiae can ferment sugar to alcohol and carbon dioxide, and strains of this species are used in bread-making, brewing, wire-making, etc. The cells of S. cerevisiae are small and elliptical, and reproduce by budding. Saccharomyces is found naturally on ripe fruit.

Saccharomycetaceae (order Endomycetales). Family of fungi in which the vegetative stage is composed of single cells which reproduce by budding. Mycelium is formed occasionally in some genera. Most of the ascospore-forming yeasts belong to this family, including some of economic importance (*e.g.* Saccharomyces). Saccharomycetaceae are chiefly saprotrophic, and found in a range of habitats.

Saccharose. Cane sugar : Sucrose.

Sacculated. Consisting of or possessing sacs or saclike compartments.

Saccule

1. A little sac.
2. A cavity, as that of the green gland in crustaceans or the coxal gland in scorpions.
3. A cavity of the membranous labyrinth located in the vestibule of the internal ear. In its wall are the maculae acoustica, sensory receptors responding to changes in the position of the head. Also called sacculus.

Sacculus (saccule). A chamber of the inner ear from which the cochlea arises in reptiles, birds, and mammals. It bears patches of sensory epithelium concerned with balance (macula).

Saccus Vasculosus. A thin-walled vascular sac forming the distal end of the infundibulum in fishes and amphibians.

Sacellus. A seed consisting of a one-seeded pericarp surrounded by a hardened clayx.

Sac Fungi. Fungi of the order Ascomycetes.

Sacral. Of or pertaining to the sacrum or the region of the sacrum.

Sacral Vertebrae. The vertebrae that lie between the lumbar and the caudal vertebrae in the vertebral column. The function of the sacral vertebrae is to articulate securely with the pelvic girdle, and they are usually fused to form of a single bone (the sacrum) to provide a firm support. The number of sacral vertebrae varies from animal to animal. Amphibians have a single sacral vertebra, reptiles have two, and mammals have three or more.

Sacrum. A triangular bone of the vertebral column consisting of three to five ankylosed vertebrae located between the lumbar vertebrae and caudal vertebrae; in man, between the lumbar vertebrae and coccyx. It articulates with the hip bones.

Safranin. A stain used in optical microscopy that colours lignfied tissues, cutinized tissues, and nuclei red and chloroplasts pink. It is used mainly for plant tissues, in conjunction with a green or blue counterstain.

Sage. A mint (Salvia officinalis), a shrublike plant highly esteemed as a spice and a source of sage oil used in perfumery.

Sagebrush. One of a number of species of Artemisia, especially A. tridentata, a shrub which covers vast areas of western United States.

Sage Grouse. A grouse (Centrocercus urophasianus) formerly common in sagebrush areas of the United States. Females are called sage hens, males sage cocks.

Sagittal

1. Pertaining to or resembling an arrow in shape.
2. Of or pertaining to a sagittal plane or section.

Sagittal Plane. In a bilaterally symmetrcial animal, a vertical plane through the body dividing it into right and left portions

Sagittal Section. One cut through a sagittal plane.

Sagittate. Describing a structure shaped like an arrowhead. Sagittate leaves have two barbs extending back behind the point where the petiole is joined to the leaf. They are characteristic of the genus Sagittaria. The marsh arrow-grass (Triglochin palustris) is so named because of its sagittate dehisced fruits.

Sago. A starch obtained principally from stems of the sago palm, used extensively for food and as a demulcent.

Sago Palm. Any palm which yields sago, especially Metroxylon sagu, cultivated extensively in Malaya and Indonesia.

Saki. A large, New World monkey of the genera Pithecia and Chiropotes, with a bushy, nonprehensile tail and long, curly hair.

Salamander. A tailed amphibian of the subclass Caudata (Urodela), small lizardlike forms but lacking scales; larvae aquatic with gills, adults terrestrial, as the tiger salamander (Ambystoma tigrinum).

Salicylic Acid (1-hydroxybenzoic acid). A naturally occurring carboxylic acid, HOC_6H_4COOH, found in certain Plants. It is used in making aspirin and in the foodstuffs and dyestuffs industries.

[1]Salientian. Of or pertaining to the Salientia (Anura), a taxon (subclass or order) of the class Amphibia which includes the tailless forms, as frogs and toads.

[2]Salientian. Any amphibian of the Salientia.

Saline. Describing a chemical compound that is a salt, or a solution containing a salt.

Saline Solution. A solution of sodium chloride. A physiological saline solution is one that is isotonic, as a 0.7% solution for amphibians or a 0.9% solution for mammals.

Saliva. A watery fluid secreted by the salivary glands in the mouth. Production of saliva is stimulated by the presence of food in the mouth and also by the smell or thought of food. Saliva contains mucin, which lubricates food and eases its passage into the oesophagus, and in some animals the enzyme ptyalin, which beings the digestion of starch. The saliva of insects is rich in digestive enzymes, and that of bloodsucking animals contains an anticoagulant.

Salivary Glands. Glands in many terrestrial animals that secrete saliva into the mouth. In man there are three pairs;

the sublingual, submandibular, and the submaxillary glands. The salivary gland cells of some insect larvae produce giant (polytene) chromosomes, which are widely used in the study of genetics and protein synthesis.

S Alleles. A multiple allelic series governing incompatibility reactions in certain plant species. Plants possessing the same two S alleles are incompatible. Plants sharing one S allele are semicompatible in that about half the pollen grains will be able to germinate on the style and subsequently achieve pollination. Such plants are usually indistinguishable from fully compatible plants (plants possessing two different pairs of S alleles) since pollen is usually produced in sufficient quantity to mask the fact that 50% is inviable.

S alleles have been found in many fruit crops (*e.g.* Prunus avium), in several grasses, in clover, and in brassicas. There may be more than 40 such alleles in a species and complex dominance relationships are found.

Salmon

1. A large, soft-finned, anadromous fish (Salmo salar) of the East Coast.
2. One of a number of fishes of the genus Onchorhynchus of the North Pacific which ascend freshwater streams, especially the Columbia River, to spawn, as O. tschawytscha, the chinook, quinnat, or tyee salmon, and O. kisutch, the coho salmon, now established in the Great Lakes.

Slap. A free-swimming. marine tunicate of the class Thaliacea, especially those of the genus Salpa.

Salpinx pl. **Salpinges.** A trumpet-shaped tube, as the Eustachian or Fallopian tube.

Salt Absorption. The uptake of inorganic ions across the semipermeable membranes of plants. If the absorption is against a diffusion gradient, as is often the case across the tonoplast, then active transport is involved. In addition, the uptake is often selective. For example, in sea water the concentration of sodium ions is around forty times higher than that of potassium ions. However within the cells of marine algae the potassium concentration is often about six times greater than that of sodium.

Saltation

1. A jump or a leap.
2. An abrupt change.
3. A mutation.

Saltatory

1. Pertaining to leaping or dancing.
2. In evolution, occurring by sudden, abrupt changes.

Salt Gland. A gland located above the orbit in certain marine reptiles and birds which discharges its secretion containing large quantities of salt into the nasal cavity.

Salt Marsh. A type of vegetation found in sheltered river estuaries subject to frequent covering by the tides. Salt marshes are formed from stabilized pioneer communities (halosere).

Salverform. Having a slender tube which expands abruptly into a flat limb; as the flower of the primrose or phlox.

Samara. A dry single-seeded indehiscent fruit in which the fruit wall hardens and extends to form a long membranous winglike structure that aids dispersal. Examples are ash and elm fruits. The sycamore fruit is a double samara and technically a schizocarp.

Sambar. An Indian deer (Rusa unicolor).

Sand. Mineral particles, usually consisting mainly of quartz, with a diameter of 0.05—2.0 mm. A sandy soil is defined as one containing at least 85% sand and not more than 10% clay.

Sandalwood. Wood obtained from an Oriental tree (Santalum album) or the three that produces it, the source of sandalwood oil used in perfumery and medicine; also the source of a dye.

Sand Dune. An accumulation of blown sand found on the coast and in inland desert areas. Coastal dunes are formed by inshore winds that carry sand particles and deposit them on various obstacles in their path, such as pieces of seaweed. In regions that are relatively undisturbed by the tides, seeds of xerophytic plants germinate and establish a pioneer community termed a psammosere. The plants tolerate abrasion by blown sand, high winds, high temperatures in the day, and some salt from sea spray. Sand twitch (Agropyron junceiforme) helps to stabilize the dune with its extensive network of rhizomes. It is also tolerant to limited immersion in sea water. Marram grass (Ammophila arenaria) then becomes established, although in some cases it may itself be the pioneer plant. Like sand twitch, marram grass has a network of rhizomes that stablizes the dune but it is intolerant to immersion in sea water. The landward slopes of the dunes are more sheltered and less steep than the seaward slopes and other plants grow including lyme grass (Elymus arenarius), sea holly (Eryngium maritimum), etc. A dune system is established, the innermost series being stable and termed fixed dunes. Behind these, dune pasture occurs with typical dune plants together with species commonly found in pasture.

Sand Dab. A flatfish of the genera Limanda or Citharichthys.

Sand Dollar. A flat, disc-shaped echinoderm of the class Echinoidea, as Echinarachnius.

Sanderling. A small sandpiper (Crocethia alba) frequenting sandy flats and beaches.

Sand Flea

1. The chigoe or jigger (Tunga penetrans).
2. A beach flea.

Sand Fly. A small, bloodsucking fly of the genus Phlebotomus, a transmitter of leishmaniasis and other diseases to man.

Sandhill Crane. A large crane (Grus canadensis) of North America.

Sand Hopper. A beach flea.

Sandpiper. One of a number of shorebirds of the family Scolopacidae, as the spotted sandpiper (Acitis macularius).

Sandworm. Any of a number of polychaete annelids which burrow in the sand, as Neanthes, Nereis.

Sanguine. Red, blood-colored; resembling blood.

Sanguivore. An animal which feeds upod blood, as an insect, bat.

Sap. Plant juice or the fluid substance of a plant, especially the fluid which circulates through the vascular tissues.

Saponin. Any of a class of bitter-tasting glycosides in which the aglycone portion (the sapogenin) is a steroid alcohol. Saponins are soluble in water, characteristically producing a foam, hence their name. Many are toxic to animals and have been used as fish poisons. Some saponins are important in the commercial production of steroid hormones, notably diosgen, obtained from various yam (Dioscorea) species. The function of saponins in the plant is obscure though they may serve to deter predators.

Saprobe. The preferred term for a saprophyte when the organism concerned is a fungus.

Saprogenic. Causing decay or putresaction; saprogenous.

Saprolegniales (water moulds). An order of the Oomycetes containing some 32 genera and about 200 species of aquatic, mainly saprobic, fungi (*e.g.*, Saprolegnia), often with diplanetic zoospores. Some are parasitic on fish, *e g.*, S. parasitica, which often attacks salmon and goldfish.

Sapropelic. Pertaining to bottom deposits in lakes which are rich in decomposing orgagic matter.

Saprophagous. Feeding on decaying matter.

Saprophyte. Any plant or microorganism that feeds by absorbing dead organic matter. Most saprophytes are bacteria and fungi; the term saprobe is frequently used to indicate saprophytic fungi. Saprophytes are important in food chains as they bring about decay and release nutrients for plant growth. Compare parasitism.

Saprotroph. A saprotrophic organism.

Saprotrophic. Designating a type of nutrition in which an organism obtains its nourishment from dead or decaying matter.

Saprovore. A saprozoan.

Saprozoan. An animal which feeds upon dead or decaying matter.

Sapsucker. A woodpecker or the genus Sphyrapicus.

Sapwood. The outer and softer wood (xylem) in stems which functions in conduction, food storage, and in providing mechanical support. Compare heartwood.

Sarcina. The characteristic arrangement of bacterial cell in an eight-called, cube-shaped packet.

Sarcobiont. An organism which feeds upon flesh.

Sarcocarp. The mesocarp.

Sarcolemma. The thin membrane closely investing a striated muscle fiber, consisting of the piasma membrane and associated reticular fibers.

Sarcoma. A malignant tumor composed principally of non-epithelial cells.

Sarcomere. A contractile unit of a striated muscle fiber, comprising the region between two Z bands or discs

Sarcophagid. A flesh fly.

Sarcophagous. Feeding upon flesh.

Sarcoplasm. The fluid portion of a striated muscle fiber as distinguished from the myofibrils.

Sarcoptid. A mite of the family Sarcoptidae which includes the itch mites, the causative agents of scabies and mange in domestic animals and man.

Sarcosome. A mitochondrion of striated muscle fibers.

Sarcostyle. A nematophore.

Sarcous. Of or pertaining to flesh or muscle.

Sardine. One of a number of small fishes of the genus Sardinella, used extensively for food.

Sargasso. The gulfweed, a seaweed of the genus Sargassum, a brown alga, forming the major portion of the vegetation of the Sargasso Sea.

Sarment. A runner or stolon.

Sarmentose. Possessing runners or stolons.

Satellite (trabant). A spherial body seen sttached to one end of a chromosome arm by a narrow filament at mitotic metaphase. Often a pair of satellites are apparent. Usually satellites are only found on one or two chromosomes but occasionally more are found. The number and position of satellites are one of the features of the karyotype. The satellite stalk functions as a nucleolar organizer.

Satellite Cell. A neuroglial cell which lies close to the cell body of a neuron, as oligodendroglial cells of the brain and spinal cord or capsular cells of a spinal ganglion.

Satellite DNA. A protion of the DNA in plant and animal cells that consists of repeating sequences of nucleotides. Some 30% of human DNA consists of such satellite regions. They do not appear to form part of any genes but their function is unclear. The term is sometimes applied to DNA other than that found in the cell nucleus, in particular mitochondrial DNA, which differs in its density.

Satyr. A small to medium sized butterfly of the family Satyridae, as the wood nymph (Minois alope).

Sauger. A pike perch (Stizostedion) canadense) resembling the walleye but smaller.

Saurian. Of or pertaining to the Sauria (Lacertilia), a suborder of the Squamata comprising the lizards.

Saurischian. An extinct dinosaur of the order Saurischia which includes a number of carnivorous, bipedal forms some of which attained large size, as Tyrannosaurus.

Sauropsidan. A reptile or bird.

Savana. A tppe of grassland in dry tropical and subtropical regions containing scattered trees and shrubs, as in southeastern United States, especially Florida.

Sawbuck. A turtle of the genus Graptemys, as C. oculifera, the ringed sawbuck of the southern states.

Sawfish. A large, elasmorbranch fish (Pristis pectinatus) with an elongated rostrum bearing sharp, toothlike processes on each side.

Sawfly. One of a large number of hymenopterous insects with a well-developed ovipositor used in depositing eggs in the host plant, as those of the families Tenthredinidae (typical sawflies) and Cephidae (stem sawflies).

Sawyer. A wood-boring beetle of the family Cerambycidae, especially those of the genus Monochamus.

Saxicolous. Living in, on, or among rocks; saxicoline.

Scab. Any plant disease having conspicuous raised scablike lesions that develop as a result of the formation of cork layers. The host response to the disease is similar to that found in canker but occurs to a lesser degree. Scab diseases are very varied. Examples include common scab of potatoes caused by the bacterium Streptomyces scabies and apple scab caused by the fungus Venturia inaequalis.

Scabellum. The expanded distal portion of a halter.

Scabies. An infectious skin disease caused by the itch mite (Sarcoptes scabiet); also called the itch or seven year itch.

Scab Mite. One of a number of mites which cause scab or mange, especially those of the genera Psoroptes or Chorioptes which infect domestic animals.

Scabrous. Having a rough surface; rough to the touch; scaly.

Scalariform. Resembling a ladder as, for examle, certain secondary xylem statements possessing parallel bands of the meening or some performation plates that have several pores separated by parallel bars of tissue.

Scalariform Thickening (scalariform-reticulate thickening). A type of reticulate secondary wall patterning in tracheary elements in which the network is broken by elongate unthickened areas arranged in a more or less parallel fashion. Whereas annular thickening and spiral thickening permit further elongation, reticulate and scalariform thickenings allow little further extension, and are therefore to be found in tissues, such as metaxylem and secondary xylem, that do not elongate after maturation. Compare pitted thickening.

Scala Vestibuli. A canal of the cochlea extending from the vestibule to the tip of the cochlea where it is continuous with the scala tympani.

Scald

1. A disease of fruits in which superficial browning occus, thought to be due to immaturity at harvesting.
2. A fungus disease of forage grasses characterized by scaldlike blotches.

Scale Insect. One of a number of small, homopterous insect of the family Coccidae, comprising three groups; mealy bugs, soft scales, and armored scales. Females feed on plant juices and secrete a wax which hardens, forming a protective covering. Some are serious plant pests; others the source of commercial products, as cochineal, shellac, and China wax.

Scale Leaf. A modified leaf which is scalelike, as a bud scale.

Scale Moss. A leafy liverwort of the Jungermanniales which bears delicate, scalelike leaves.

Scales. The small bony or horny plates forming the body covering of fish and reptiles. The wings of some insects, *e.g.* the Lepidoptera (butterflies and moths), are covered with tiny scales that are modified cuticular hairs.

In fish there are three types of scales. Placoid scales (denticles), characteristic of cartilaginous fish, are small and toothlike, with a projecting spine and a flattened base embedded in the skin. They are made of dentine, have a pulp cavity, and the spine is covered with a layer of enamel. Teeth are probably modified placoid scales. Cosmoid scales, characteristic of lungfish and coelacanths, have an outer layer of hard cosmin (similar to dentine) covered by modified enamel (ganoine) and inner layers of bone. The scale grows by adding to the inner layer only. In modern lungfish the scales are reduced to large bony plates. Ganoid scales are characteristic of primitive ray-finned fishes, such as sturgeons. They are similar to cosmoid scales but have a much thicker layer of ganoine and grow by the addition of material all round. The scales of modern teleost fish are reduced to thin bony plates.

In reptiles there are tow types of scales; horny epidermal corneoscutes sometimes fused with underlying bony dermal osteoscutes.

Scale Worm. A polychaete of the family Aphroditidae with platelike scales (elytra) on the dorsal surface of the body.

Scandent. Climbing.

Scansorial

1. Having the habit of climbing,
2. Adapted for climbing, as the feet of reptiles and birds.

Scape. The leafless stem of a solitary flower or inflorescence, such as that of the dandelion inflorescence.

Scaphognathite A flattened process on the second maxilla of a decapod trustacean which functions in the creation of a respiratory current over the gills; a bailer.

[1]**Scaphoid.** Boat-shaped.

[2]**Scaphoid.** The navicular bone of the carpus and tarsus.

Scapula (shoulder blade). The largest of the bones that make up each half of the pectoral (shoulder) girdle. It is a flat triangular bone, providing anchorage for the muscles of the forelimb and an articulation for the humerus at the glenoid cavity. It is joined to the clavicle (collar bone) in front.

Scapus. The collar (parapet) of a sea anemone.

Scar

1. A mark, as that which remains on the skin after the healing of an injury; a cicatrix.

2. *bot. a.* A mark on a stem marking the former attachment of a leaf bud, flower, or fruit. *b.* The hilum of a sedd.
3. *zool.* A mark on the inner surface of a bivalve shell marking point of attachment of a muscle.

Scarab. A dung beetle, especially the Egyptian sacred scarab beetle (Scarabaeus sacer).

Scarification. The abrasion or chemical treatment of the surface of a hard seed to make it permeable to water and is hasten germination.

Scarify

1. To make small cuts or scratches in the skin.
2. To slit the outer seed coat in order to speed germination.

Scarious. Having a dry membranous appearance, but fairly stiff.

Scat. Excrement, dung, feces, ordure.

Scatology. The study of excrement, especially for determination of nature of food.

Scaup. A diving duck of the genus Aythya, commonly called bluebill.

Scavenger

1. An animal which devours dead animals or feeds on dead organic material.
2. A phagocytic cell, as a macrophage or leukocyte.

¹Scent. To perceive through stimulation of olfactory receptors; to smell.

²Scent

1. The order left by an animal by which it may be traced or tracked down.

2. A distinctive smell, odor, a fragrance.

Scent Gland. A modified sweat or sebaceous gland which produces an odorous secretion which serves as an attractant, a repellent, or for defensive purposes, as that in many mammals.

Schemochrome. A structural color, at that produced by uneven surfaces; an iridescent color.

Schiffs Reagent. A reagent used for testing for aldehydes and ketones; it consists of a solution of fuchsin dye that has been decolorized by sulphur dioxide. Aliphatic aldehydes restore the pink immediately, whereas aromatic ketones have no effect on the reagent. Aromatic aldehydes and aliphatic ketones restore the colour slowly. It is named after the German chemist Hugo Schiff (1834—1915).

Schistosome. A blood fluke of the genus Schistosoma which lives as a parasite in the blood vessels of man and domestic animals.

Schistosomiasis (bilharzia). Any one of a group of diseases of humans and some other Mammalia caused by infestation by blood flukes, Trematoda of the genus Schistosoma. The trematode requires two hosts, the first being an aquatic snail in which larvae emerging from eggs hatched in water develop through several stages, finally to fork-tailed forms (cercariae) which escape from the snail, swim freely in the water, and attach themselves to, and penetrate, the skin of their second host, a mammal. In the mammalian body they move through blood vessels, feeding upon glycogen in the blood plasma and growing, eventually migrating to a site that varies from species to species, where they mature, mate, and lay eggs. These eggs leave the body in urine or faeces. Symptoms vary according to the species causing the infestation, but may include swelling and tenderness of the liver, dropsy, enlargement of the spleen, watery skin eruptions, fever, cough, haemorrhage, diarrhoea, and reduced function of the affected organs. The diseases are common in low latitudes.

Schizaeaceae. Family of ferns in which the sporangia are borne naked and singly on the margins of the leaves, sometimes protected by the incurved leaf margin. The sporangia are relatively massive, somewhat intermediate in character between those of eusporangiate and leptosporangiate ferns, with very short, thick stalks, and a terminal ring of thickened cells; they may contain more than 200 spores. All sporangia mature at the same time (simple type of development) The gametophytes are either green and filamentous, like moss protonemata, or (in Actinostachys) may be fleshy, subterranean, cylindrical structures with mycorrhizal fungi. There are five genera, mostly tropical, but the family extends into temperate parts of America.

Schizocarp. A dry fruit that is derived from two or more one-seeded carpels that divide into one-seeded units at maturity. The one-seeded units may be achenes, berries, follicles, mericarps, nutlets, or samaras. This form of fruit is intermediate between the dehiscent and indehiscent types.

Schizocoel. A coelom which arises by a splitting of the lateral plates of the mesoderm, as in arthropods and mollusks.

Schizocoelomate. An animal which possesses a schizocoel.

Schizogenous. Arising by fission or splitting.

Schizogeny. The localized separation of plant cells to form a cavity (surrounded by the intact cells) in which secretions accumulate. Examples are the resin canals of some conifers and the oil ducts of caraway and aniseed fruits. Compare lysigeny.

Schizogony. A form of asexual reproduction in which multiple division occurs, resulting in numerous individuals (schizonts), as in the malarial parasite (Plasmodium) and various coccidians.

Schizomycetes (fission fungi). Formerly, a class of the fungi containing the bacteria. With the realization that bacteria have no affinities with fungi the name is going out of use.

Schizont

1. A cell which reproduces by schizogony.
2. In the malarial organism (Plasmodium), an amebalike trophozoite which divides into many (6-36) daughter merozoites.

Schizopetalous. With split or divided petals.

Schizophyllaceae (order Aphyllophorales). Family of fungi in which the fruit bodies bear characteristic longitudinally-divided gills. There are several genera. Schizophyllum commune forms fan-shaped fruit bodies that are attached on one side to the substrate. It is found on wood and is common in Europe, especially in the south.

Schizophyte. Any member of the division Schizophyta which contains the classes Schizomycetes (bacteria) and Schizophyceae (blue-green algae), the fission plants.

Schizopod Larva A mysis larva; one having exopods on the thoracic appendages.

Schizozoite. A cell resulting from schizogony, as occurs in certain gregarines.

School (shoal). An aggregation of fish which are observed swimming together, possibly in response to a threat from a predator. More strictly, a grouping of fish, drawn together by social attraction, whose members are usually of the same species, size, and age, the members of the school moving in unison along parallel paths in the same direction. Sudden changes at the leading edge of the school are followed almost instantaneously by the remainder of the group, with the fish on the flank becoming the new leaders. In general, the overall size and shape of the school, as well as the cruising depth and speed, vary from one species to another.

Schultze's Solution (chlor-zinc iodide, CZI). A temporary stain containing a mixture of zinc dissolved in hydrochloric acid added to iodine dissolved in potassium iodide. It is used to detect the presence of cellulose in plant tissue, which it turns blue. Lignified walls stain blue-green, lignin and suberin yellow, and starch blue-black.

Schwann Cell A cell that forms the myelin sheath of a nerve fibre. Each cell is responsible for a single length of the fibre (called an internode); adjacent internodes are separated by small gaps (nodes of Ranvier). During its development the cell wraps itself around the fibre, so the sheath consists of concentric layers of Schwann cell membrane. These cells are named after the German anatomist T. Schwann (1880-82).

Sciatic. Of, pertaining to, or near the ischium, as sciatic nerve.

Scientific Method. A method utilized in acquiring knowledge and establishing laws and principles pertaining to natural phenomena based on observation and experimentation.

Scientific Name. Binomial nomenclature.

Scion. A shoot or bud taken from one plant and joined by grafting or budding onto another plant, the stock.

Sclera. The dense, fibrous outer coat of the posterior portion of the eye, continuous anteriorly with the cornea; the "white" of the eye.

Sclereid. A relatively short sclerenchyma cell, usually formed when the wall of a parenchyma cell undergoes secondary thickening and, often, lignification. The simple pits of sclereids are often more conspicuous than those of fibres. Sclereids are often present as idioblasts in other tissues. They may however be present in large numbers, as, for example, in those plants where they form the testa of the seed.

Sclereid. An elongated sclerenchyma cell with heavily lignified walls found in the cortex of stems and the hard shells of fruits and seed coats; sometimes present in the pith of stems and the leaves of certain plants; a stone cell, rod cell, or bone cell of a plant.

Sclerenchyma. The fibrous or woody tissue in a plant that provides mechanical support for the plant. It is formed from cells whose walls are thickened with cellulose or lignin, and when mature the cells usually contain no living protoplasm. The cells may occur singly or in groups and may be long and fibrous or stony. Stone cells (sclereids) are found in seed coats and some fruits (*e.g.* pears).

Sclerite

1. A hardened, platelike portion of the exoskeleton of an arthropod bounded by sutures and/or membranous areas.
2. A spicule of a sponge.

Scleroblast. A mesenchymal cell which secretes or forms spicules, as in sponges.

Scleroid. Hard; indurated.

Sclerophyllous. Possessing leaves with an excessive amount of sclerenchyma, as in certain desert plants.

Scleroprotein. Any of a group of proteins found in the exoskeletons of some invertebrates, notably insects. Scleroproteins are formed by conversion of the relatively soft elastic larval protein by a natural tanning process (sclerotization) involving orthoquinones. These are secreted and form cross linkages between polypeptides of the proteins, producing a hard rigid covering.

Sclerosis

1. An abnormal hardening or thickening of body tissues.

2. *bot.* The hardening and thickening of a cell wall by lignification.

Sclerotic

1. *anat.* Of or pertaining to the sclera.
2. *bot.* With hardened cell walls, as sclerotic cells (sclereids).

Sclerotium

1. The normally pseudoparenchymatous resting body of certain fungi, which can survive long periods of adverse conditions to produce either a mycelium or fruiting bodies. Sclerotia are important sources of inoculum for various root-rot diseases. The hard dark club-shaped structures seen in the ears of cereals and grasses affected with ergot (Claviceps purpurea) are sclerotia.
2. Plasmodium.

Sclerotome. The portion of a mesodermal somite which gives rise to the vertebrae and ribs.

Sclerous. Hard, dense, indurated.

Scobina. The rasplike rachilla of the spikelet of certain grasses.

Scorpions. Arachnida.

Scolophore. A specialized sensillum (chordotonal organ) in an insect.

Scolops. A sensory rod of a chordotonal organ.

Scolus. A spiny process on the larva of certain moths.

Scopula

1. A dense tuft of hairs on the tip of the tarsus in a spider.
2. An adhesive disc in a peritrich.

3. The structure which secretes the stalk in certain ciliates.

Scorploid

1. *zool.* Of, pertaining to, or resembling a scorpion.
2. *bot.* With reference to a circinately coiled inflorescence in which flowers are two-ranked and borne alternately on the right and left.

Scorpion. An arachnid of the order Scorpionida with an elongated, segmented body terminating in a curved, poison sting; pedipalps are elongated and end in chelicera. Sting is dangerous but rarely fatal to man.

Scorpion Fish. A mail-cheeked fish (Scorpaena) of the order Scleroparei.

Scorpion Fly. A medium-sized, slender-bodied insect of the order Mecoptera, males possessing an abdomen resembling that of a scorpion, as Panorpa.

Scoter. A diving duck of the genera Melanitta and Oidemia of northern regions.

Scotopic Vision. The type of vision that occurs when the rods in the eye are the principal receptors, *i.e.*, when the level of illumination is low. With scotopic vision colours cannot be identified. Compare photopic vision.

Scotopsin. A visual purple, as rhodopsin, present in rod cells.

Scouring Rush. A horsetail.

SCP. Single-Cell Protein.

Scraple. An infectious, virus-caused disease of sheep.

Screwworm. The larva of certain flies which deposit their eggs in wounds with resulting myiasis, as those of the genus Callitroga, a serious pest to livestock.

Scrobe. A groove of the rostrum of beetles for reception of the scape of the antenna.

Scrobiculate. Having numerous small hollows or shallow depressions; pitted.

Scrophulariaceae. A large family of dicotyledonous plants, numbering about 3000 species in some 220 genera. The family, commonly called the foxglove or figwort family, is distributed worldwide though the greatest concentration of species is in northern temperate regions. Most of its members are herbaceous. The leaves occur in a variety of forms but always lack stipules. There is also a range of flower and inflorescence types. The flowers are usually irregular and often two-lipped, as in the snapdragons (Antirrhinum, Misopates) and toadflaxes (Linaria, Cymbalaria). However in the mulleins (Verbascum) and speedwells (Veronica) the flower is almost actinomorphic. In many flowers there is a reduction in the number (assumed originally to have been five) of floral parts. For example, figworts (Scrophularia) only have four stamens, and speedwells have four sepals and four petals and only two stamens. The fruit is usually a dehiscent capsule.

Few members of the family are of economic importance though many genera, *e.g.* Calceolaria, Hebe, Mimulus, Antirrhinum, include ornamental varieties. Some species are parasitic on the roots of other angiosperms, especially grasses, and may be serious weeds, *e.g.* Striga (witchweeds). The foxglove (Digitalis purpurea) is the source of the drug digitalin (cardiac glycoside).

Scrotiform. Pouch-shaped.

Scrotum. The sac of skin and tissue that contains and supports the testes in most mammals. It is situated outside the body cavity and allows the testes to develop at the optimum temperature, which is slightly lower than body temperature.

Scrub. Vegetation consisting chiefly of shrubs and stunted trees, or a tract covered with such.

Scrub Vegetation. General term for vegetation dominated by shrubs, *i.e.* low-stature woody plants, which typically forms an intermediate community between grass or heath and high forest. Successional change is not necessarily implied though the term is often used for the transitional stage in succession to climax woodland when shrubby plants predominate.

Scup. A porgy (Stenotomus), a marine food fish.

Scurvy. A deficiency disease resulting from lack of vitamin C, characterized by bleeding of the skin and mucous membranes, swollen, hemorrhagic gums, and defective teeth and bone formation.

Scut. A short, erect tail, as that of a rabbit.

Scute. A thin, flat, bony or horny plate or scale, as those of the exoskeleton of fishes, snakes, and turtles.

Scutellate

1. Shaped like a small dish or platter.
2. Covered with small plates or scales, with reference to the tarsus of a bird.
3. Having a scutellum, as in certain insects.

Scutellum. An intermediate absorbing organ between the embryo and the nutritive endosperm in the grass fruit (caryopsis). During germination its secretes enzymes involved in the digestion of the endosperm. It is thought to be a modified cotyledon.

Scutiform. Shield-shaped; peltate.

Scutum

1. *bot.* The broadened apex of the style in milkweeds.
2. *zool.* A scute or hard, platelike structure, as *a.* the second sclerite in the notum of an insect. *b.* one of the plates of the carapace of a barnacle; *c.* the dorsal shield of a hard tick.

Scyphistoma. A stage in the development of a jellyfish consisting of a sessile, polyplike form which, by strobilization, gives rise to several ephyrula.

Scyphozoan. A coelenterate of the class Scyphozoa which includes the true jellyfishes, free-swimming medusae lacking a velum, as Aurelia.

Scyphus

1. A cup-shaped corolla.
2. The expanded cup-shaped portion of a podetium in certain lichens.

Sea Anemone An anthozoan coelenterate, typically a sessile, solitary polyp often beautifully colored, as Metridium.

Sea Bass. One of a number of fishes of the family Serranidae, especially Centropristes striatus, a food and game fish of the Atlantic.

Sea Bear. A fur seal.

Sea Beef. Chitons prepared for human consumption.

Sea Bottle. A large, bladderlike, primary cell of a green alga (Valonia) with an enormous vacuole.

Sea Butterfly. A pteropod.

Sea Cucumber. An echinoderm of the class Holothuroidea with an elongated body covered by a leathery integument containing minute endoskeletal ossicles or spicules, as Thyone, Cucumaria.

Sea Elephant. An elephant seal (Mirounga) of the family Phocidae, males possessing an inuatable snout or proboscis.

Sea Fan. A fan-shaped gorgonian, especially one of the genus Gorgonia.

Sea Feather. An anthozoan of the order Pennatulacea with a form resembling a feather, as Pennatula; a sea pen.

Sea Fig. An herb (Mesembryanthemum) with conspicuous, water-storing leaves.

Sea Hare. An opisthobranch gastropod with large, earlike tentacles, as Aplysia, Tethys.

Seal. One of several marine carnivores of the suborder Pinnipedia comprising two families, the Otarriidae or eared seals (sea lion and northern fur seal), and Phocidae, the earless or hair seals (harbor seal and sea elephant).

Sea Lettuce. A seaweed of the genus Ulva, a green alga.

Sea Lily. A stalked crinoid.

Seam. A junction or line of fusion; a suture, a raphe.

Sea Mat. An encrusting layer of colonial ectoprocts.

Sea Mew. A sea gull (Larus canus).

Sea Moss. Any of a number of red algae noted for their color and graceful form, as Dasya, Ceramium, and others, mostly tropical forms.

Seam Squirrel. The cootie or human body louse.

Sea Parrot. A puffin.

Sea Peach. A tunicate (Halocynthia pyriformis).

Sea Pen. A sea feather.

Sea Pork. A tunicate (Amaroucium stellatum).

Sea Robin. A bottom-living, marine fish of the genus Prionotus.

Sea Snail

1. A snailfish.
2. A marine gastropod.

Sea Snake. One of a number of swimming, venomous reptiles of the family Hydrophiidae, as Hydrophis and Hydrus, common in tropical waters.

Sea Spider. A long-legged marine arthropod of the class Pycnogonida.

Sea Squirt. An ascidian or tunicate.

Sea Star. A starfish.

Sea Turtle

1. A large marine turtle, as Chelonia mydas, the green turtle.
2. The loggerhead or hawksbill turtle.

Sea Urchin. A globe-shaped echinoderm of the class Echinoidea with a test of calcareous plates bearing long, movable spines, as Arbacia.

Sea Walnut. A ctenophore.

Sea Wasp. A coelenterate of the order Cubomedusae, so called because of the virulence of its sting.

Seaweeds. Large multicellular algae living in the sea or in the intertidal zone. They are commonly species of the Chlorophyta, Phaeophyta, and Rhodophyta.

Sea Whip. Any of the horny corals of the order Gorgonacea, especially those with long, flexible, axial rods bearing many polyps.

Sebaceous Gland. A small gland occurring in mammalian skin. Its duct opens into a hair follicle, through which it discharges sebum onto the skin surface.

Sebum. The substance secreted by sebaceous glands onto the surface of the skin. It is a fatty mildly antiseptic material that protects, lubricates, and water proofsthe skin and hair and helps prevent desiccation.

Secchi Disc. Disc used in a simple method for measuring the transparency of water. The disc is 20 cm across, and divided into alternate black and white quadrants. It is lowered into water on a line until the difference between the black and white areas just ceases to be visible—this depth is recorded. The Secchi disc provides a convenient method for comparing the transparencies of water at different sites.

Secodont. Pertaining to or designating teeth with sharp cutting edges.

[1]Secondary

1. After the first (primary) in importance.
2. Occurring after the first, as secondary development.

[2]Secondary. A secondary feather; a flight feather attached to the ulna.

Secondary Growth (secondary thickening). The increase in thickness of plant shoots and roots through the activities of the vascular cambium and cork cambium. It is seen in most dicotyledons and gymnosperms but not in monocotyledons. The tissues produced by secondary growth are called secondary tissues and the resultant plant or plant part is the secondary plant body. Compare primary growth.

Secondary Phloem. Phloem derived from the vascular cambium in plants exhibiting secondary growth. As in the secondary xylem, the secondary phloem consists of two systems : the axial (vertical) system, derived from the fusiform initials of the vascular cambium and consisting mainly of sieve elements, their associated companion cells, and some phloem fibres; and the ray (horizontal) system, derived from the ray initials of the vascular cambium and consisting mostly of ray parenchyma.

Secondary Ray. Ray.

Secondary Sexual Character. Characteristic of animals that differs between the two sexes, but excluding the gonads and the ducts and associated glands that convey the gametes. Examples are mammary glands, external genitalia, antlers in ungulates, and certain plumage patterns (*e.g.*, peacock's tail) in birds.

Secondary Sexual Characteristics. External features of a sexually mature animal that, although not directly involved in copulation, are significant in reproductive behaviour. The development of such features is controlled by sex hormones (androgens or oestrogens); they may be seasonal (*e.g.*, the antlers of male deer or the body colour of male sticklebacks) or permanent (*e.g.* breasts in women or facial hair in men).

Secondary Succession. Succession initiated by the disruption of a previously existing seral or climax community by some major environmental disturbance and leading to a marked change in the stable vegetation community. Secondary successions occur, for example, following fire, after removal of grazing pressure, or when previously cultivated areas are abandoned (as in shifting cultivation). Interactions between plants and the physical environment tend to be less clear in secondary than in primary successions.

Secondary Thickening. The formation of new tissue by the repeated lateral division of cells in the cambium of a woody plant, adding successive layers of new growth. This increases the girth of the stem or root and the growth can be seen as annual rings. Much of the woody part of a woody plant is the result of secondary thickening.

Secondary Tissue. Secondary growth.

Secondary Xylem. Xylem derived from the vascular cambium in plants exhibiting secondary growth. Secondary xylem is regarded as consisting of two systems: the axial (vertical) system, derived from the fusiform initials of the vascular cambium and consisting mainly of tracheary elements and fibres; and the ray (horizontal) system, derived from the ray initials of the vascular cambium and consisting mostly of ray parenchyma, forming the rays. As well as differing from primary xylem in origin, secondary xylem usually also has shorter tracheary elements, often arranged in regular rows, although these differences are not always reliable. Commercial wood is secondary xylem. There are two main types of commercial wood, softwood from gymnosperms and hardwood from angiosperms. However, these terms are somewhat misleading as there are hard gymnosperm woods and soft angiosperm woods. Softwoods contain only tracheids as the water-conducting elements, whereas hardwoods usually contain vessels.

Secretary Bird. A long-legged, African bird of prey (Sagittarius serpentarius) which feeds principally upon reptiles.

Secretin. A hormone produced by the anterior part of the small intestine (the duodenum and jejunum) in response to the presence of hydrochloric acid from the stomach. It causes the pancreas to secrete alkaline pancreatic juice and stimulates bile production in the liver. Secretin, whose function was first demonstrated in 1902, was the first substance to be described as a hormone.

Secretion. The manufacture and discharge of specific substances into the external medium by cells in living organisms. (The substance secreted is also called the secretion). Secretory cells are often specialized and organized in groups to form glands. The substances produced may be released directly into the blood (endocrine secretion; endocrine gland) or through a duct (exocrine secretion; exocriae gland). Secretions can be classified according to the manner of their discharge. Merocrine (eccrine) secretion occurs without the secretory cells sustaining any permanent change; in apocrine secretion the cells release a secretory vesicle incorporating part of the secretory cell membrane; and holocrine secretion involves the disruption of the entire cell to release its accumulated secretory vesicles.

Secretory. Of or pertaining to secretion.

Section. A rank in the taxonomic hierarchy above series but subordinate to genus. Genera containing a large number of species are often subdivided into sections. The section name is printed in italic with a capital first letter and either has the same form as the generic name or, if a plural adjective, agrees in gender with the generic name. For example, the genus Chenopodium, which contains about 110 species, is subdivided into the four sections Agathophytum, Chenopodium, Pseudoblitum, and Morocarpus. The section name is preceded by the abbreviation sect, to show its rank, thus Chenopodium sect. Pseudoblitum.

Sectorial Chimaera. A chimaera that results from a cell mutation in a meristem that subsequently gives rise to a group or sector of mutant cells. Such chimaeras are usually unstable.

Sedentary

1. Permanently attached to the substratum; not free-moving.
2. Remaining in the same place; not migratory.

Sedge. One of a number of grass or rushlike herbs of the family Cyperaceae, as Cyperus, Carex.

Sediment. That which settles to the bottom, as in a flask or lake.

Sedimentation Coefficient Symbol : *s*. The rate of sedimentation in centimetres per second that occurs when a solution is subjected to a centrifugal force of one dyne (10^{-5} newton). These rates are extremely low and are usually multiplied by 10^{13} to give a reasonable figure. In this modified form the unit is termed the Svedberg unit, symbol S. Different molecules and cellular inclusions tend to have characteristic sedimentation rates depending on the weight and shape of the molecule. For example, the ribosomes of prokaryotes have a value of 70S and those of eukaryotes 80S.

Seed. In the sexual reproduction of spermatophytes (seed plants), the discrete body from which a new plant develops. Formed from a fertilized ovule, the seed comprises an outer coat (testa), containing a food store and an embryo plant. The food may be stored in the seed leaves (cotyledons) of the embryo itself, or around the embryo in the endosperm.

Seed Coat. The outer covering of a seed, consisting of an outer tegmen and an inner testa; the part which develops from the integuments.

Seed Dressing A chemical applied to seeds to protect them against fungal diseases or insect attack. The chemicals are applied in dusts, slurries, or concentrated solutions. Treated seed is toxic and must be distinguishable from untreated seed to prevent it being used for feed.

Seed Fern A pteridosperm, a fossil plant of the order Cycadofilicales, class Gymnospermae, the oldest and most primitive of seed plants.

Seed Leaf. A cotoledon.

Seedless. Lacking seeds.

Seedless Fruit. A fruit that develops without fertilization occurring so no seed is formed.

Seedling. A young plant. The seedling often differs significantly from the mature plant in morphology and habit.

Seedling Blight. A disease of germinating seedlings. The term is sometimes applied to post-emergence damping-off but generally it is used when well established seedlings are affected Growth slows and foliage may become yellow or wilt. Roots of affected plants are found to be rotten and there may be lesions at soil level. The causal fungi include Pythium, Phytophthora, Rhizoctonia (Corticium), Fusarium, and Helminthosporium. Correct planting conditions, seed dressings, and soil sterilization are the usual preventative measures.

Seed Oyster. A young oyster, especially one used for transplanting.

Seed Plant

1. Any plant which produces seeds, comprising the ginkgo, cycads, conifers, monocots, and dicots.
2. A spermatophyte; a gymnosperm or angiosperm.
3. Any flowering plant.

Seeds Shrimp. Any crustacean of the class Ostracoda.

Seed Stalk. The funiculus or stalk by which a seed is attached to the wall of a mature ovary.

Segment

1. A part of an organism or a structure which is marked off or separated from adjacent parts, as a segment of a leg, worm, or stem.
2. A metamere.
3. A somite.

Segmental Allopolyploid. Allopolyploidy.

Segmentation

1. Metameric segmentation.
2. Cleavage.

Segmentational

1. The state of being divided into segments; metamerism.
2. *embryol.* Cleavage.
3. Something divided into parts, as the division of a nucleus in schizogony.

Segmentation Cavity. The blastocoel.

Segregation. The separation of pairs of alleles during the formation of reproductive cells so that they contain one allele only of each pair. Segragation is the result of the separation of homologous chromosomes during meiosis.

Segregation Ratio. The proportion of one type of offspring to another that occurs as a result of separation of allels at meiosis.

Seismonasty. A nastic movement in response to shock. The result, as in the collapse of Mimosa pudica leaflets after subjection to shaking or singeing, is often the assumption of the night position as normally found after the completion of nyctinasty.

[1]Selachian Of or pertaining to the Selachii, an order of the class Chondrichthyes, which includes the sharks, skates, and rays.

[2]Selachian. Any member of the Selachii.

Selachii. The major subclass of the Elasmobranchii (cartilaginous fishes), containing the sharks, rays, skates, and similar but extinct forms. Their sharp teeth develop from the toothlike placoid scales (denticles) and are rapidly replaced as they wear out.

Selaginella. Any member of the genus Selaginella, a lycopod, which comprises the little club mosses.

Selection. In evolution, any process by which certain individuals or groups are favored and survive and propagate while others fail to do so and become extinct.

Selection Pressure. The extent to which organisms possessing a particular characteristic and either eliminated or favoured by environmental demands. It indicates the degree of intensity of natural selection.

Selective. Describing herbicides that kill some plants and not others. Usually broad-leaved plants are killed while narow-leaved plants are unaffected. Selective weedkillers are therefore useful for cereal crops and lawns. Some selective weedkillers, *e g.* Simazine, kill germinating plants but not well established shrubs.

Selective Absorption. Salt absorption.

Selenium. A nonmetallic element, symbol Se, present in soils in parts of western United States. It accumulates in certain plants, as Astragulus, a vetch, which, when eaten by domestic animals, causes alkali poisoning or blind staggers.

Self-differentiation. The capacity of a part of the embryo to develop independently of other parts.

Self-fertilization. The union of male and female gamets produced by the same individual.

Self Incompatibility (self sterility). The failure of gametes from the same plant to form a viable embryo. In angiosperms this is usually due to complex interactions between the pollen and stigamatic tissues. Self incompatibility caused by the stigmatic tissues is described as sporophytic while that due to the pollen tube is termed gametophytic. It may be achieved by the prevention of pollen germination, the retardation of growth or the disorientation of the pollen tube, or by failure of nuclear fusion. Although self incompatibility is known to be genetically controlled (S alleles) the exact method by which the genetic information manifests itself is not clearly understood. Enzymes either on the pollen or stigma, antibodies and antigens, growth substances, or variable cell morphology may account for differential treatment of pollen grains on the stigma. Incompatibility is rarely total and usually develops as the stigma matures. Artificial crosses of normally incompatible lines can therefore be made by in-bud pollination, chemical treatment, or by stigma excision.

Selfish DNA. One of a number of hypotheses advanced in an attempt to explain the presence of surplus DNA in the genome which is not translated into protein. Three hypotheses have been put forward to account for the adaptive advantage of this apparently redundant DNA :

(*a*) that extra DNA separates the genes so as to increase the cross-over frequency;

(*b*) that the possibility of varying the total amount of DNA per cell allows the control of cell volume and cell growth rate; and

(*c*) (the selfish DNA hypothesis) that selection acts within the genome favouring any mathod by which DNA may more rapidly replicate itself, and that this can be better achieved if phenotypic expression can be bypassed. This is achieved, it is proposed, by DNA spreading laterally so as to be duplicated at new loci elsewhere in the genome. In this way the DNA may be viewed as acting 'selfishly', since the apparently surplus DNA confers no advantage on the organism bearing it and therefore supplying the materials from which it is made.

Self-pollination Pollination effected by pollen produced by an anther of the same flower or by pollen produced by another flower of the same plant.

Self-sterility. The condition found in many hermaphrodite organisms in which male and female reproductive cells produced by the same individual will not fuse to form a zygote, or if they do, the zygote is unable to develop into an embryo. In plants this is usually termed self-incompatibility.

Seliwanoff's Test. A biochemical test to identify the presence of ketonic sugars, such as fructose, in solution. If was devised by the Russian chemist. F. F. Seliwanoff. A few drops of the reagent, consisting of resorcinol crystals dissolved in equal amounts of water and hydrochloric acid, are heated with the test solution and the formation of a red precipitate indicates a positive result.

SEM. Electron microscope.

Semantide. An information-carrying molecule. DNA, as the carrier of the genetic code, is termed a primary semantide and is regarded by taxonomists and evolutionists as a primary source of information in drawing up classifications and evolutionary trees. RNA, as the transcription of the genetic code, is termed a secondary semantide, and proteins as the end product of this information transfer, tertiary semantides. Much effort has recently been directed to unlocking the information carried by such molecules. The amino acid sequences of various proteins, *e g.* cytochromes and plastocyanins, have been determined and compared for a number of species. It is now also possible, using restriction enzymes, to determine the base sequences of nucleic acid.

Sematic. Functioning as a warning or danger signal, as certain colors, odors, or sound devices.

Semen. A fluid containing sperm and nutrients that is produced by a male animal during compulation and is introduced into the body of the female. Spermatozoa are produced by the tests and the nutrient liquids by the prostate gland and seminal vesicles.

Semicanal. A canal open on one side; a sulcus.

Semicell. One of two nalves of a desmid separated by a constriction, the sinus, and connected by a narrow isthmus which contains the nucleus.

Semicircular Canals. The sense organ in vertebrates that is concerned with the maintenauce of physical equilibrium (sense of balance). It occurs in the inner ear and consists of three looped canals set at right angles to each other and attached to the utriculus. The canals contain a fluid (endolymph) that flows in response to movements of the head and body. A swelling (ampulla) at one attachment point of each canal contains sensory cells that respond to movement of the endolymph in any of the three planes. These sensory cells initiate nervous impuless to the brain.

Semicircular Duct. One of the three, curved semicircular ducts lying within the corresponding semicircular canal and forming a part of the membranous labyrinth. Each is filled with endolymph and has an expanded end, the ampulla, within which are located the cristae ampullares containing hair cells sensitive to movement.

Semiconservative Replication. The process by which DNA makes exact copies of itself. During this process, double-stranded DNA uncoils and the separated polynucleotides act as templates for the formation of new complementary polynucleotide chains. Hence any given DNA molecule will consists of one old strand and one new one and the original molecule is semiconserved during the manufacture of an identical copy (replica).

Semilethal. Partly lethal, with reference to genes which *a.* produce death in at least 50% of a population; *b.* cause death but not until some of the affected individuals reach maturity and produce offspring.

[1]Semilunar. Resembling a half-moon in shape.

[2]Semilunar. Old term for lunate bone.

Semilunar Valve. A heart valve consisting of three pocket-shaped cusps (valvules) which prevent backflow into the heart from the pulmonary artery or aorta.

Semilunate. Crescent-shaped; Semilunar.

Seminal. Of or pertaining to seed or semen.

Seminal Duct. A sperm-conveying duct, especially the ductus deferens.

Seminal Fluid. The semen.

Semimal Leaf. A cotyledon.

Seminal Receptacle. A saclike structure in various invertebrates which stores sperm received from the male; a spermatheca.

Seminal Root. Any of the adventitious roots that grow from the base of the stem during early seedling growth and take over the functions of the radicle.

Seminal Vesicle

1. A dilated portion of or a saclike structure connected with the sperm duct which stores sperm preliminary to their discharge from the body, as in various invertebrates.
2. In mammals, a glandular diverticulum of the ductus deferens which produces a viscid secretion rich in glucose which forms a part of the semen.

Semination. The discharge of sperm from the testes. Compare inseminate.

Seminiferous

1. *bot.* Producing or bearing seed.
2. *zool.* Producing or conveying sperm or semen.

Seminiferous Ampulla. A spherical, sperm-producing structure in the testes of lower vertebrates, as fishes, amphibians.

Seminiferous Tubule. A sperm-producing tubule in the testis of various vertebrates.

Semipalmate. With toes partially webbed, as in certain shorebirds.

Semipermeable. Partially permeable, with reference to the cell or plasma membrane, through which certain molecules or ions pass readily but others do not.

Semipermeable Membrane. A membrane that acts as a barrier to certain substances but will allow others to pass through. In many cases a semipermeable membrane will allow the passage of solvents, almost invariably water in biological situations, but not certain solutes. Such a membrane usually lets through small molecules but not larger ones. In such cases the membrane is said to be selectively permeable.

Semisterile. With reduced reproductive capacity.

Senescence. The complex deteriorative processes that terminate naturally the functional life of an organ or organism. In plants this may be associated with flowering and fruiting and an important contributing factor is the decrease in chlorophyll content and in the ability of the plant to photosynthesize. Plant senescence is controlled by hormones.

Sense Organ. A part of the body of an animal that contains or consists of a concentration of receptors that are sensitive to specific stimuli (*e.g.* sound, light, pressure, heat). Stimulation of these receptors initiates the transmission of nervous impulses to the brain, where sensory information is analysed and interpreted. Examples of sense organs are the eye, ear, nose, and taste bud.

Senile. Of, pertaining to, or characteristic of old age.

Senna. A leguminous plant (Cassia) or a cathartic drug obtained from it.

Sensation. A feeling; a state of consciousness or an awareness resulting from stimulation of a sensory receptor or arising subjectively from an unknown cause.

Sense. The faculty by which an organism is aware of an environmental change registered through a sensory receptor, as the sense of sight or muscle sense.

Sense Organ

1. A receptor.
2. An organ which contains sensory cells which, when stimulated, give rise to a sensation, as the eye, ear.

Sensibility. The ability to experience sensations; sense perception.

Sensillum pl. **Sensilla.** A sense organ or sensory receptor in insects and other arthropods.

Sensitive Plant. A tropical legume (Mimosa pudica) whose leaflets fold when touched.

Sensitivity Analysis. The consideration of a number of factors involved in the mathematical modelling of an ecosystem and its components. These include feedback and control, and the stability and sensitivity of the system as a whole to changes in some parts of the system. From the analysis, predictions can be made.

Sensitization

1. (of a cell). The alteration of the integrity of a cell membrane resulting from the reaction of specific antibodies, with antigens on the surface of the cell. In the presence of complement, the cell ruptures.
2. (of an individual). Initial exposure to a specific antigen such that re-exporure to the same antigen causes a severe immune response.

Sensorium. The region of the brain concerned with the development of sensations, comprising principally the cerebral cortex and thalamus.

Sensory. Of, pertaining to, or concerning sensations or the senses.

Sensory Area. A region in the cerebral cortex in which impulses arising in sensory receptors come into consciousness, as the somesthetic, visual, and auditory receptive areas.

Sensory Ganglion. A ganglion on the dorsal root of a spinal nerve or on a cranial nerve which contains the cell bodies of sensory neurons.

Sensory Neuron. An afferent neuron which conveys impulses from a receptor to the brain or spinal cord.

Sepal. One of the parts of a flower making up the calyx. Sepals are considered to be modified leaves with a simpler structure. They are usually green and often hairy but in some plants, *e.g.* monk's hood, they may be brightly coloured.

Sepaloid. Resembling a sepal.

Sepia

1. A cuttlefish of the genus Sepia.
2. A rich brown, melanin pigment obtained from the ink of various cuttlefishes.

Sepicolous. Inhabiting or living in hedges.

Sepsis. A condition resulting from the presence and spread of pathogenic bacteria, or their products, or both in the blood and tissues.

Septa. Plural of Septum.

Septal. Of or pertaining to a septum.

Septate. Divided into parts or divisions by one or more septa.

Septenate. Divided into seven parts.

Septicemia. The presence of and spread of pathogenic organisms throughout the body by way of the blood stream; blood poisoning; bacteremia.

Septicidal. Describing fruit dehiscence in which the slits in the pericarp arise along the junctions of the carpels.

Septifragal. Designating a type of dehiscence in which the valves break away from the partitions, which remain attached to the axis.

Septum. Any dividing wall in a plant or animal. Examples are the septa that separate the chambers of the heart.

Sequela

1. That which follows or is a consequence of.
2. *med.* An abnormal condition resulting from a disease.

Sequestrol. A preparation of trace elements used to treat deficiency diseases, particularly those caused by lack of iron or magnesium. The elements are chelated to promote their uptake by plant roots and prevent them becoming bound to the soil particles. A preparation containing a particular element is named accordingly, *e.g.* sequestering iron.

Sequoia. A coniferous tree of the genus Sequoia, as the giant sequoia (S. gigantea) and the redwood (S. sempervirens) of California, the oldest and largest of living things; estimated age, 3500 years; height, 275 feet.

Seral. Of or pertaining to a sere.

Sere (seral community, seral stage). Any plant community in a succession leading to a climax. The nature of a sere is influenced by that of the preceding sere and itself influences the development of the succeeding sere. The initial community (pioneer community) in a succession is known as a prisere. Subseres are the stages in the development of a secondary succession, white microseres are the stages in microhabitats, such as small puddles or animal droppings.

Serial. Arranged in a row or sequence; following one another in succession.

Serial Endosymbiotic Theory (progressive endosymbiotic theory). The proposal that plastids, mitochondria, and possibly also cilia and flagella arose from symbiotic prokaryotic organisms living within a eukaryotic host cell. It is thought that plastids probably originated from organisms similar to present-day blue-green algae while mitochondria arose from aerobic bacteria. Such conclusions are based on various similarities between plastids and mitochondria and free-living prokaryotes. For example, such organelles are self replicating and contain DNA, which in addition to having a different base composition from the nuclear DNA, is circular rather than linear. The ribosomes of mitochondria and chloroplasts are smaller (70S) than those in other parts of the cytoplasm (80S) but similar in size to those of prokaryotes. There is evidence moreover, that the origin of plastids could be polyphyletic, *i.e.* in different groups of plants different types of symbionts have been incorporated. Thus in the Chlorophyta, Rhodophyta, and higher plants, which all have chloroplasts with a double membrane, it is thought that the plastids are derived from a prokaryotic symbiont. However in other groups of algae the chloroplasts may be surrounded by three or four membranes, implying that these are derived from eukaryotic symbionts. Such evidence has been used in revising classifications at the kingdom and division level.

Serial Homology. That exhibited by a series of homologous structures arranged serially, as seen in the paired appendages of a crayfish and related crustaceans, in which all have the same basic structure but are modified according to the functions they perform.

Sericeous. Silky; covered with fine silky hairs closely appressed to the surface.

Sericulture. The raising of silkworms for the production of silk.

Series. A rank in the taxonomic hierarchy above species but subordinate to section.

Serine. A polar amino acid with the formula $HOCH_2CH(NH_2)COOH$ (illustration at amino acid). Serine is synthesized from phosphoglyceric acid. It is also formed during photorespiration and probably during the catabolism of cytokinins Breakdown of serine occurs by oxidative deamination to pyruvic acid. It is a component of several phosphoglycerides.

Serology. The laboratory study of blood serum and its constituents, particularly antibodies and complement, which play a part in the immune response.

Serosa

1. A serous membrane.
2. A membrane which envelops the embryo of an insect.
3. The chorion of reptiles and birds.

Serotinal. Developing later in the season than is customary; late in the day or season; serotinous.

Serotonin (5 hydroxytryptamine). A compound, derived from the amino acid tryptophan, that affects the diameter of blood vessels and also functions as a neurotransmitter. In the brain it is thought to influence mood : drugs, such as LSD, that alter serotonin levels have hallucinogenic effects.

Serous

1. Thin and watery, like serum.
2. Pertaining to, producing, or containing serum.

Serous Cavity. A cavity lined with a serous membrane.

Serous Cells. Gland cells which produce a thin, watery secretion, as those of the salivary glands.

Serous Fluid. A thin, watery fluid, as that present in a serous cavity.

Serous Membrane. A tissue consisting of a layer of mesothelium attached to surface by a thin layer of connective tissue. Serous membrane lines body cavities that do not open to the exterior; the peritoneum and the pleura are examples.

Serow. A heavy, ungainly, goatlike, bovine mammal (Capricornis) of eastern and southern Asia.

Serpent. A snake, especially a large one.

Serpentine. Sinuous, like a snake; winding, twisting.

Serpent Star. An echinoderm of the class Ophiuroidea.

Serrate. Describing a leaf margin that is toothed, with forward-pointing notches. Leaf margins finely foothed in this manner are termed serrulate.

Serrula. A comblike structure, as that on the chelicera of a pseudoscorpion or on the pedipalp of a spider.

Serrulate. Finely serrate; bearing minute teeth.

Sertoli Cell. A sustentacular cell in the epithelial lining of a seminiferous tubule of a mammalian testis.

Serum

1. The clear fluid which exudes from a clot in the coagulation of blood, consisting of plasma minus fibrogen.
2. A biological product obtained from the blood of animals or humans that is used for prophylactic, diagnostic, or therapeutic purposes.
3. A clear fluid which moistens the surfaces of serous membranes and fills spaces within serous cavities.

Sesame. An herb (Sesamum indicum), the source of sesame oil and sesame seeds used for flavoring.

Sesamoid Bone. One which develops in a tendon, as the patella.

Sessile

1. Describing animals that live permanently attached to a surface, *i.e.* sedentary animals. Many marine animals, *e.g.* sea anemones and limpets, are sessile.
2. Describing any organ that does not possess a stalk where one might be expected. For example, the leaves of the oak (Quercus robur) are attached directly to the twigs.

Sessoblast. An internal bud (statoblast) in an ectoproct which remains attached to the parent.

Seta

1. A bristle or hair in many invertebrates. Setae are produced by the epidermis and consist either of a hollow projection of cuticle containing all or part of an epidermal cell (as in insects) or are composed of chitin (as in the chaetae of annelid worms).
2. Sporogonium.

Setaceous

1. Bristlelike.
2. Bearing bristles.
3. Composed of bristles.

Setiform. Shaped like a bristle.

Setose. Bearing many bristles. Setaceous.

Setulose. Having many small bristles or setulae.

Sex

1. One of two types of organisms, male and female, as distinguished by the nature of the reproductive cells produced, males producing sperm or spermatozoa and females producing eggs or ova.
2. The total of the characteristics, both anatomical and physiological, which distinguish a male from a female.

Sex Cell. A male or female gamete;a spermatozoan or sperm cell; an ovum or egg; a macro-, micro-, or isogamete.

Sex Chromatin. A small chromatin body present at the periphery of the nucleus in certain somatic cells, as neurons and neutrophils; present in the cells of females, absent in males.

Sex Chromosome. Chromosome whose presence or absence is linked with the sex of the bearer, and plays a role in sex determination. It is present in all sexually reproducing diploid animals and plants. The sex that has a homologous pair of sex chromosomes in the nucleus is said to be homogametic (referred to as 'XX'), whereas the sex with a dissimilar pair or with an unpaired chromosome, is said to be heterogametic (referred to as 'X' or 'XY'). The homogametic sex produces gametes that are identical in their chromosome sets, all containing one X-chromosome. The heterogametic sex produces equal numbers of two different types of gametes, one with one X-chromosome, and one without (possessing either a Y-chromosome or none at all). Union of gametes of the two sexes thus results in equal numbers of offspring of the two sexes. In mammals and many other animals the presence or absence of a Y-chromosome determines sex; in birds and reptiles, ann in some fish, amphibians, and insects, sex is determined by the number of X-chromosomes in relation to the number of autosomes. Occasionally a mutation will produce an extra dosage of X-chromosomes in the gamete, and so in the progeny—in Klinefelter's syndrome in humans, for example, the individual genotype (a male) possesses an extra X-chromosome (XXY).

Sex Determination. The mechanism by which sex is determined. In many species, sex is determined at fertilization by the nature of the sperm that fertilizes the egg, Y-bearing sperm producing the male zygotes, and Y-bearing sperm, female zygotes.

Sex Differentiation. The process by which a sexually indifferent embryo develops into either a male or female.

Sex Gland. A gonad.

Sex Hormones. Steroid hormones that control sexual development. The most important are the androgens and oestrogens.

Sexine. The outer layer of the exine in a pollen grain.

Sex-limited Character. One which is expressed in only one sex, although its genes are present in the autosomes of both sexes, as milk production in cattle.

Sex-limited Inheritance. The restriction of a trait to one sex as a result of incomplete penetrance rather than allelic differences.

Sex Linkage. The location of a gene on a sex chromosome. Such a gene is usually unrelated to primary or secondary sexual characters, and is located on the X-chromosome. The heterogametic sex (*e.g.* a male mammal or female bird) receives the X-chromosome and therefore all its sex-linked genes from the homogametic parent, and passes them on to offspring of the homogametic sex. Since there is no partner to the X-chromosome in the heterogametic sex, recessive genes cannot be masked by their dominant alleles and so are expressed in the phenotype. It is for this reason that male humans manifest a larger number of recessive genes (*e.g.* red-green colour blindness, and haemophilia) than females.

Sex-linked Inheritance. The transmission of traits whose genes lie in or on the sex chromosomes, resulting in the character appearing more frequently in one sex than the other, as hemophilia in man.

Sex Organ. A reproductive organ.

Sex Ratio. The relative number of males to females in a population. The measure is usually applied to a given age class. The primary sex ratio is that immediately after fertilization (normally 1 : 1); the secondary sex ratio is that at birth or hatching; and the tertiary sex ratio is that at maturity.

Sex Reversal. Change in functioning as one sex to that of the other. Some organisms, *e.g.* certain molluscs, make this change as part of their normal life cycle, with most individuals functioning as males when young and then passing through a transitional stage to a period when they function as females. Sex reversal may otherwise be experimentally induced (*e.g.* by hormone transplants in humans) or environmentally induced (*e g.* by temperature effects on the production of male or female zygotes in some turtles).

Sexual. Of, pertaining to, or associated with sex.

Sexual Dimorphism. Phenomenon of morphological differences (besides primary sexual characters) that distinguish males from females of a species of organism—for example, male deer often have larger antlers than females, and the males of many birds have differing plumage (often more brightly coloured).

Sexual Generation. In cynipid, heterogynous wasps, the males and females that emerge from galls to mate and lay eggs that will become the agamic generation of parthenogenetically reproducing females. In general, sexual-stage galls follow a period of rich resources and precede a period of poor resources. Sexual individuals are generally smaller and less fecused than members of the agamic (asexual) generation.

Sexual Reproduction. A form of reproduction that involves the fusion of two reproductive cells (gametes) in the process of fertilization. Normally, especialy in animals, it requires two parents, one male and the other female. However, most plants bear both male and female reproductive organs and self-fertilization may occur, as it does in hermaphrodite animals. Gametes are formed by meiosis, a special kind of cell division in the parent reproductive organs that both reassorts the genetic material and halves the chromosome number. Meiosis thus ensures genetic variability in the gametes and therefore in the offspring resulting from their subsequent fusion. Sexual reproduction, unlike asexual reproduction, therefore generates variability within a species. However, it depends on there being reliable means of bringing together male and female gametes, and many elaborate mechanisms have evolved to ensure this.

Sexual Selection. Theory proposed by Darwin that in some species males compete for mates and that characteristics enhancing their success in mating would have value and be perpetuated irrespective of their overall value in the struggle for existence. Such characters would be used either in male display to attract females (inter-sexual selection) or in combat between rival males (intra-sexual selection), and both could act at the same time.

Shad. A herring (Alosa sapidissima) which spawns in fresh water; an important food fish.

Shade Plant. A plant that is able to flourish in conditions of low light intensity. Some shade species are sensitive to intense light and cannot live in the open. Shade plants usually have thinner epidermal and palisade layers and fewer stomata than normal. They also tend to have a short compensation period, *i e.* the food reserved used in respiration at night are quickly replaced by photosynthesis in the day. Shade plants grow in woodlands where the treess, when in leaf, form a canopy, cutting out much of the light. Green light, the part of the spectrum least absorbed by plants, is predominant beneath a closed canopy. Examples of shade plants are mosses, enchanter's nightshade (Circaea lutetiana), certain violes (Viola), and dog's mercury (Mercurialis perennis). Some trees are also tolerant of shade. For example, yew trees can tolerate the deep shade in beech woods but ash trees cannot. However ash trees can survive in oak woods where the shade is not as dense. Compare sun plant.

Shadowing (heavy-metal shadowing). A technique used in electron microscopy to determine the scale of surface features on a specimen. The specimen is partially coated with a thin layer of a heavy metal, *e.g.* platinum, palladium, or gold, which is evaporated in a vaccum chamber. The source of the metal ions is situated at a known angle to the specimen. Only the 'windward' side will be coated since metal atoms travel in straight lines. On placing the specimen in a beam of electrons, the uncoated 'leeward' side will allow freer passage of electrons and hence appear darker (a 'shadow') on the photographic plate. By measuring the length of the shadow cast it is possible, knowing the angle of the metal source, to calculate the height of the object casting the shadow. The technique has been used to gain more accurate measurements of very small specimens such as viruses.

Shadow Yeasts. Blastomycetes.

Shaft. The main axis or trunk of an elongated structure, as *a.* the diaphysis of a long bone; *b.* the rachis of a feather; *c.* the exposed portion of a hair.

Shag. A cormorant.

Shagreen

1. Sharkskin, bearing sharp-pointed placoid scales.
2. In Russia, untanned leather.

Shank

1. In man, the portion of the lower limb between knee and ankle.
2. In some vertebrates the part between the fetlock and the joint above.

Shark. Any of a number of voracious, predatory, elasmobranch fishes, as the dogfish shark (Squalus or Mustelus), great white shark (Carcharodon), hammerhead shark (Sphyrna), sand shark (Carcharius) and whale shark (Rhineodon).

Sheath

1. An investing covering or protective envelope.
2. *zool. a.* A tubular fold or sac into which a protrusible organ, as a penis proboscis, or cirrus, is retracted. *b.* The protective covering of a blood vessel, nerve, muscle, or tendon. *c.* The delicate covering of a

nerve fiber or a microscopic structure, as a mitochondrion.

3. *bot. a.* The gelatinous covering of certain algal cells or filaments. *b.* The base of a leaf which envelops a stem, as in grasses.

Sheep. A horned ruminant of the genus Ovis, family Bovidae, which includes many domesticated varieties raised for their flesh (mutton), wool, and hides. There are also a number of varieties of wild sheep.

Shell

1. *zool. a.* The hard, rigid exoskeleton or covering of various animals, as that of mollusks, crustaceans, and reptiles. *b.* The hard, calcareous covering of an egg.

2. *bot.* The hard, outer covering of a fruit or seed, especially a nut; a husk or pod.

Shifting Cultivation (slash-and-burn agriculture). The traditional agricultural system of semi-nomadic people, in which a small area of forest is cleared by burning, cultivated for 1—5 years, and then abandoned as soil fertility and crop yields fall and weeds encroach. Ideally vegetation succession subsequently returns the plot to climax woodland, and soil fertility is gradually restored. Shifting cultivation of this type was once practicsed worldwide but in modern times has been primarily associated with tropical rainforest areas. The system is best-suited to low population densities. With increasing population pressure abandoned plots are often cleared again before a full climax community has been restored, leading eventually to nutrient depletion of the system and degradation of forest to open savannah-type woodland, or scrub.

Shikimic Acid. An aromatic acid, abundant in certain higher plants, that is an intermediate in the synthesis of the aromatic amino acids phenylalanine, tyrosine, and tryptophan. It is also an intermediate in the synthesis of lignin and of the electron carriers ubiquinone and plastoquinone. The shikimic acid pathway is the normal route for the synthesis of phenolics and is one of the few pathways in which aromatic compounds are formed from aliphatic precursors.

Shellac. A lac resin, a substance prepared from stick-lac, a resinous substance secreted by the lac insect.

Shellfish. Any aquatic invertebrate possessing a shell, especially any edible mollusk or crustacean, as oysters, clams, lobsters, shrimps.

Shell Gland

1. The region of the oviduct in sharks or of the uterus in domestic fowl which secretes the shell of the egg.
2. Term formerly applied to Mehlis' gland of trematodes and cestodes.
3. The nidamental gland of a cephalopod.

Shell Membrane. A parchmentlike membrane underlying the calcareous shell in the eggs of various birds.

Shield. A protective structure, as a plate, scute, or carapace.

Shin

1. The sharp, anterior margin of the tibia.
2. In cattle, the lower portion of the forelimb.

Shinbone. The tibia.

Shipworm. One of a number of wood-borning bivalves, especially Teredo navalis, which causes extensive damage to wooden vessels and piles of wharves. Also called pileworm.

Shock. A state of collapse often following hemorrhage or severe physical or emotional trauma characterized by a marked fall in blood pressure; weak, rapid pulse; pale, cold skin; cyanosis; and thirst, these symptoms resulting from an inadequate volume of circulating blood.

Shoot. The aeial part of a vascular plant. It develops from the plumule and consists of a stem supporting leaves, buds, and flowers.

Shoot System. In a seed plant, the stem with its branches and leaves.

Short-day Plant. Plant in which flowering is favoured by short days and correspondingly long nights. There are two groups of such plants : some species in which there is an absolute requirement for these conditions for the onest of flowering, and other species in which flowering is merely hastened by them.

Shoulder Blade. The scapula.

Shoulder Gridle. The pectoral gridle.

Short-sightedness. Myopia.

Shoveller. A surface-feeding duck (Spatula (Anas) clypeata) with a long, broad bill.

Shrimp

1. One of a number of marine, decapod crustaceans of the suborder Natantia, especially those of the genus Crago, used extensively for food.
2. Any of a number of crustaceans which resemble true shrimps, as the brine shrimp, fairy shrimp, and many others.

Shrub. A bush; a low-growing, perennial plant, usually with several main stems arising near the ground.

Siamese Twins. Twins which are united; conjoined or parabiotic twins.

Siblings. Individuals that have both parents in common.

Sibs. Plants derived either by selfing, or by crossing between genetically similar parents. In the production of F_1 hybrid varieties occasional crossing may occur within rather than between the parent lines giving a proportion of nonhybrid seed. The plants that grow from such seed are called sibs.

The term sibling species is sometimes used to describe closely related populations having a common ancestry.

Sieve Area. A specialized part of the primary wall of a sieve element, perforated by a number of pores, derived from a primary pit field. These pores are lined with callose and penetrated by cytoplasmic strands. The sieve areas of gymnosperm sieve cells are relatively unspecialized, where as those of angiosperm sieve tubes are usually differentiated as sieve plates.

Seive Cell. A relatively primitive vascular cell in the phloem of the lower vascular plants and gymnosperms, whose main function is the translocation of sugars and other nutrients. Sieve cells have relatively unspecialized sieve areas compared to those of sieve tube elements and are longer and narrower in shape.

Sieve Element. A type of plant cell occurring within the phloem. Sieve elements combine to form a series of tubes (sieve tubes) connecting the leaves, sphots, and roots in a fine network. Food materials are transported from one element to another via perforations termed sieve areas or sieve plates. This is an active (energy-requiring) process but the mechanism is uncertain. Sieve elements contain little cytoplasm and no nucleus. It is believed that their metabolic activities may be controlled by companion cells in angiosperms and by albuminous cells in gymnosperms.

Sievert. The SI unit of dose equivalent.

Sieve Plate. A highly specialized sieve area, or collection of sieve areas, perforated by relatively large pores and usually located on the end walls of sieve tube elements. A sieve plate composed of a single sieve area is called a simple sieve plate. A number of sieve areas may be arranged collectively to form a compound sieve plate, as in Nicotiana. The pores of a sieve plate, so named for its resemblance to a sieve, are lined with callose and penetrated by cytoplasmic strands. Compare perforation plate.

Sieve Tube. A tube within the phloem tissue of a plant, composed of joined sieve elements.

Sieve Tube Element (Sieve tube member). A relatively advanced vascular cell in the phloem of angiosperms, characterized by the presence of a sieve plate, a nonlignified secondary cell wall, and a living enucleate protoplast. Sieve tube elements are joined together at their ends to form sieve tubes, their end walls having become modified to form the sieve plates. Sieve tube elements usually have specialized parenchyms cells associated with them. These are known as companion cells, the protoplast of the companion cell being connected to that of the sieve tube member by plasmodesmata. Compare sieve element, sieve cell.

Sight. Vision; the sense of seeing.

Sigmoid. Shaped like the letter S; curved in two directions.

Sign Stimulus (releaser). The essential feature of a stimulus, which is necessary to elicit a response. For example, a red belly (characteristic of courting male sticklebacks) is the sign stimulus necessary to provoke an attack from a rival male; even a very crude model fish is attacked if it has a red undersurface.

Silicle. Silicula.

Silica Silicon Dioxide. SiO_2, the principal constituent of sand. It occurs naturally as quartz, flint, opal, and in other forms comprising over 27% of the earth's crust. It is an important component of the skeletons of diatoms radiolarians, and sponges.

Silicon Symbol : Si. A grey metalloid element, atomic number 14, atomic weight 28. It is not considered essential to plant growth but nevertheless accumulates as silica (SiO_2) in high proportios in the cell walls of some plants. The cell walls of diatoms (Bacillariophyta) are largely composed of silica and certain members of the Xanthophyta and Chrysophyta also accumulate silica. Among higher plants, the stems of Equisetum are reinforced with silica and the leaves of many grasses also contain substantial amounts. The presence of silica bodies can be demonstrated by carbolics acid solution, which turns such bodies pink. Other crystals remain colourless.

Silicula. A type of capsule formed from a bicarpellary ovary. It is longitudinally flattened and divided lengthwise into two cavities (loculi). It is broader than a siliqua. Examples include the fruits of Alyssum and candytuft.

Siliqua. A type of capsule formed from a bicarpellary. ovary. It resembles a silicula but is longer than it is broad; an example is the fruit of the wallflower.

Silk

1. A fine, fustrous fiber produced by the silk glands of various insects, especially lepidopterans, and used in the construction of cocoons.
2. The fiber produced by silkworms and used for weaving into fabrics.
3. A fine fiber produced by spiders and used in making webs, egg sacs, insect traps, retreats, shelters, and aerial floats.
4. *Bot.* The elongated style of a single pistillate flower on the ear of maize.

Silkworm. The larva of certain moths, especially Bobmyx mori, raised for the production of silk.

Silt. Mineral particles having a diameter of 0 002 – 0.05 mm. A silt soil is defined as containing more than 80% silt and less than 12% clay and has a characteristic smooth soapy feel.

Silurian. A geological period of the Palaeozoic era following the Ordovician period and extending until the begining of the Devonian period. It began about 440 million years ago and lasted for about 45 million years. The Silurian was named by Roderick Murchison (1792-1871) after an ancient British tribe that inhabited South Wales, where he observed rocks of this period. The majority of Silurian life was marine but during the later part of the period primitive plants began to make their appearance on land. Trilobites and graptolites became less common, brachiopods were numerous and varied, crinoids became common for the first time, and corals also increased. The only known vertebrates during the Silurian were primitive fish; the first jawed fish appeared later in the period. The Caledonian orogeny (mountain-building period) reached its peak towards the end of the Silurian.

Silverfish

1. A primitive, wingless insect (Lepisma saccharina) of the order Thysanura, a common household pest; also called bristletail.
2. One of a number of fishes, as the tarpon, silverside.

Similarity Coefficient. Any measure of the similarity of two samples. In ecological work, the similarity index devised in 1920 by H. A. Gleason has been widely used. This measures similarity as $C=2W/(a+b)$, where a and b are the quantities of all the plants (or other commodity) found in the two stands, or other units to be compared, and W is the sum of the lesser values for those species common to both units. Complete similarity thus scores 1, complete dissimilarity 0.

Simple Pit. A pit lacking a border. Simple pits are found, for example in certain parenchyma cells, extraxylary fibres, and sclereids. Compare bordered pit.

Single-cell Protein (SCP). Protein produced by unicellular organisms for animal and human consumption. Microorganisms are considerably more efficient in producing protein than crops and farm animals. Thus yeast and bacteria can double their mass in a minimum of 20 minutes while cereals would take 7—14 days and young cattle 4—8 weeks to achieve this. Considerable research has consequently been directed towards developing suitable industrial plants for the large-scale cultivation of certain bacteria, fungi, and algae, Many products are already available, *e.g.* Pruteen from ICI.

The substrates used to grow the micro-organisms can be low-cost agricultural wastes, *e.g.*, straw, molasses, and animal sewage. The technology thus has potential applications in pollution control as well as food production.

Single-factor Inheritance. The determination of a character by one major gene, although the gene may exist in various allelic forms. Mendel' genes are examples of single-factor inheritance. Compare multiple factor inheritance.

Sink. A site within a plant or cell where a demand exists for particular substrates or catalysts. Thus the mitochondria are sinks for oxygen and respiratory substrates while the chloroplasts require carbon dioxide. At a higher level of organization fruits, roots, and shoot apices are sinks for photosynthates.

Sinoatrial. Pertaining to the sinus venosus and the atrium.

Sinoatrial Node. The S-A node, a mass of specialized cardiac muscle in the wall of the right atrium which is the source of impulses which initiate each heartbeat; the pacemaker of the heart.

Sinuate. Describing a leaf margin divided by irregularly spaced narrow notches into wide lobes.

Sinuous

1. Serpentine; bending in and out; winding.
2. *bot.* Sinuate.

Sinus

1. *zool.* A cavity, hollow, recess, channel, or space.
2. *bot.* A deep cleft or recess, as that separating *a.* two lobes or divisions of a leaf; *b.* two semicells of a desmid.

Sinus Gland. A neuroendocrine gland in certain crustaceans.

Sinusoid. A tiny blood vessel or blood-filled space in an organ. Sinusoids replace capillaries in certain organs, notably the liver; they allow more direct contact between the blood and the tissue it is supplying.

Sinus Venosus. A chamber in the heart of lower vertebrates which receives venous blood and passes it to the atrium; present as a temporary structure in the embryos of higher vertebrates.

Siphonaceous. Describing the tubular growth habit seen in certain algae, *e.g.*, Vaucheria.

Siphonales. Caulerpales.

Siphonaptera. An order of wingless insects comprising the fleas. The body of a flea is laterally compressed and bears numberous backward-directed spines. Fleas live as blood-sucking ectoparasites of mammals and birds, having mouthparts adapted to piercing their host, injecting saliva to prevent clotting, and sucking up the blood. The long bristly legs can transmit energy stored in the elastic body wall to leap relatively long distances (over 300 mm horizontally). Apart from causing irritation, fleas can transmit disease organisms, most natably bubonic plague bacteria, which can be carried from rats to humans by the rat flea (Xenopsylla cheopsis)'. The whitish wormlike legless larvae feed on organic matter. After two moults the larva spins a cocoon and undergoes metamorphosis into the adult.

Siphonostele. A stele containing a central core of pith internal to the xylem. The pith may be extrastelar in origin, *i.e.*, originating from invagination of cortical parenchyma, or it may originate in the xylem itself. In a simple siphonostele the leaf traces do not leave any gaps in the vascular cylinder. A siphonostele may be ectophloic, *i e.*, possessing phloem external to the xylem, or amphiphloic, *i e.*, possessing phloem external both external and internal to the xylem as in a solenostele. Siphonosteles are found in the stems of many ferns. Compare protostele.

Siphonozooid. A modified polyp which functions in the creation of water currents, as in polymorphic siphonophores.

Siphonous. Designating a type of algae in which the thallus consists of a filamentous structure composed of elongated, multinucleate cells.

Siphuncle. A long tube present in those cephalopods that posses external shells. It runs internally, through all the chambers, and contains the siphuncular cord of body tissue, extending from the visceral mass through a perforation in each septurn of the shell. The siphuncle releases gas into the empty chambers of the shell, making it buoyant.

Siphunculata (Anoplura). An order of wingless insects comprising the sucking lice : blood-sucking ectoparasites of mammals, with piercing and sucking mouthparts forming a snoutlike proboscis. They constitute an irritating pest to humans and domestic animals and can transmit diseases, including typhoid. The human louse (Pediculus humanus) exist in two forms : the head louse (P. humanus) capitis and the body louse (P. humanus corporis).

Siskin. A small songbird of the finch family, as Spinus pinus, the pine siskin.

Sisal. A fiber obtained from various species of Agave, especially henequen or Yucatan sisal, used principally for binder twine.

Skeletal. Of or pertaining to the skeleton.

Skeletal Muscle. A muscle or muscle tissue which is attached to or moves a part of the skeleton; in vertebrates, striated or striped muscle.

Skeletal System. In vertebrates, the structures composed of bone or cartilage which form a framework giving general form to the body and serving for support, protection, and attachment of muscles. It also is a source of blood cells.

Skeleton. The structure in an animal that provided mechanical support for the body, protection for internal organs, and a framework for anchoring the muscles. The skeleton may be external (exoskeleton) or internal (endoskeleton). Both types require joints to allow locomotion. The endoskeleton of higher vertebrates consists of a system of bones.

Skimmer

1. A dragonfly of the family Libellulidae.
2. A marine bird (Rynchops), as the black skimmer of the east coast.

Skin. The outer layer of the body of a vertebrate. It is composed of two layers, the epidermis and dermis, with a complex nervous and blood supply. The skin may bear a variety of specialized structures, including hair, scales, and feathers. This skin has an important role in protecting the body from mechanical injury, water loss, and the entry of harmful agents (*e g*. disease-causing bacteria). It is also a sense organ, containing receptors sensitive to pain, temperature, and pressure. In warm-blooded animals it helps regulate body temperature by means of hair, fur, or feathers and sweat glands.

Sknik. Any of a number of small lizards of the .family Scincidae, as Eumeces, Lygosoma, and Neoseps of the United States.

Skipjack

1. One of a number of fishes which swim at the surface of the water leaping in and out, as the bonito and related forms.
2. A click beetle.

Skipper

1. A small, stout-bodied butterfly of the family Hesperiidae characterized by short, rapid, and erratic flight.
2. A marine fish of the family Scombresocidae, with long, toothless jaws.

Skipping Blades. Narrow, elongated appendages (paddles) forming two clusters located at the posterior end of certain rotifers.

Skotophile. Photophile.

Skua. A large, predatory marine bird of the genera Catharacta and Stercorarius, related to the jaegers.

Skull. The skeleton of the head. In mammals it consists of a cranium enclosing the brain and the bones of the face and jaw. All the joints between the individual bones of the skull are immovable (suture) except for the joint between the mandible (lower jaw) and the rest of the skull. There is a large opening (foramen magnum) at the base of the skull through which the spinal cord passes from the brain.

Skunk. A fur-bearing mammal of the family Mustelidae, noted for the possession of perianal glands which secrete an offensive, nauseating, odorous fluid used for defense, as

Mephitis mephitis, the striped skunk of the United States.

Skunk Bear. The wolverine.

Slavery. The subjugation of individuals of one species by those of another, as that practiced by ants of the genus Polyergus which raid the nests of other ants.

Sleep. A readily reversible state of reduced awareness and metabolic activity that occurs periodically in many animals. Usually accompanied by physical relaxation, the onset of sleep in humans and other mammals is marked by a change in the electrical activity of the brain, which is recorded by an electroencephalogram as waves of low frequency and high amplitude (slow-wave sleep). This is interspersed by short bouts of high-frequency low-amplitude waves (similar to wave patterns produced when awake) associated with restlessness, dreaming, and rapid eye movement (REM); this is called REM (or paradoxical) sleep. Several regions of the brain are involved in sleep, especially the reticular formation of the brainstem.

Sleep Movement. A nyctinasty as occurs in certain plants in which the leaflets fold together at night or on cloudy days, as in clovers.

Sleeper. A marine, percomorph fish (Eleotris) of the family Eleotridae.

Sleeping Sickness

1. Trypanosomiasis, a chronic disease resulting from infection by protozoans of the genus Trypanosoma, as African sleeping sickness, caused by T. gambiense and T. rhodesiense and transmitted by the tsetse fly, and South American trypanosomiasis (Chagas' disease), caused by T. cruzi and transmitted by reduviid bugs.
2. Encephalitis lethargica, an epidemic disease of viral origin thought to be transmitted by arthropods.

Slider. A freshwater turtle of the genus Pseudemys, especially P. scripta, the pond slider.

Sliding-filament Theory. Hypothesis proposed by Huxley and Hanson to explain the mechanism of contraction of striated muscle. It proposes that the parallel, interdigitated thick myosin and thin actin filaments slide past one another to varying degrees to shorten the muscle. This is brought about throught the sequential formation of cross-bridges between the action and myosin molecules such that the filaments move past one another in a ratchetlike manner. The energy for these processes is provided by the hydrolysis of ATP.

Sliding Growth. A type of cell grown in which an area of the cell wall expands and slides over that part of the wall of the adjacent cell with which it was originally in contact. This results in the severance of plasmodesmata between adjacent cells but does not lead to cell disruption. Compare intrusive growth, symplastic growth.

Slime. A viscid, mucous secretion, especially that of the cutaneous glands of various animals, as snails, slugs, various annelids, hagfishes, catfishes, and amphibians.

Slime Bacteria. Myxobacters, bacteria of the order Myxobacterials, which produce a slimy growth, common in the soils, rotting material, and organic wastes.

Slime Bodies. Discrete bodies of a viscous, proteinaceous substance commonly present in the sieve tube cells and companion cells of dicots.

Slime Fungi (slime moulds). A group of small simple organisms widely distributed in damp habitats on land. They exist either as free cells or as multinucleate aggregates of cells (plasmodia). Cell walls are generally absent. Slime fungi show amoeboid movement and feed by ingesting small particles of food. They reproduce by means of spores. Since this group of organisms exhibits characteristics of both simple plants and simple animals its taxonomic position is uncertain. They are usually placed in a separate division, the Myxomycota.

Slime Gland

1. Any gland which produces slime.
2. In Peripatus, one of a pair of glands opening on the oral papillae from which slime can be forcibly ejected.

Slime Mold. Any fungus of the division Myxomycota comprising two groups, the true slime molds of the class Myxomycetes characterized by a naked, motile, multinuclear assimilative stage called a plasmodium, as Physarium, and the cellular slime molds of the classes Acrasiomycetes and Labyrinthulomycetes.

Slime Tube. A tube formed around the anterior segments and clitellum of an earthworm which, on being discharged, forms a cocoon within which fertilized eggs develop.

Slipper Animalcule. A ciliate protozoan of the genus Paramecium.

Slipper Shell. Any gastropod of the genus Crepidula.

Slite Sense Organ. A lyriform organ of an arachnid.

Sloth. A slow-moving, arboreal edentate of Central and South America with long claws by which it hangs downward from branches, as the at or three-toed sloth of the genus Bradypus, or the unau or two-toed sloth of the genus Choloepus.

Slough

1. The cast-off skin of an animal, as that shed by a snake.
2. *med.* A mass of necrotic tissue separated from living tissue.

Slowworm. A limbless lizard (Anguis fragilis) of the family Anguidae, the blindworm of the Old World.

Slug

1. One of a number of terrestrial, pulmonate gastropods resembling a land snail in structure but with shell much reduced or absent, as Arion, Limax, Testacella.
2. The larva of a sawfly which resembles a tiny slug.
3. A pseudoplasmodium.

Slug Caterpillar. The larva of lepidopteran insects of the family Limacodidae which are sluglike in appearance and movement.

Slump. Variety of landslide characterized by rotational slip along a concave-up failure surface. The upper unit of the slump is typically tilted back, and surface water may be retained in the depressed zone. The slump may be caused by basal undercutting, or by the over-steepening of artificial embankments. It is normally found in a uniform, relatively weak material, *e.g.* clay.

Small Intestine. The portion of the alimentary canal between the stomach and the large intestine. It is subdivided into the duodenum, jejunum, and ileum. It plays an essential role in the final digestion and absorption of food.

Smear. A preparation made for microscopic examination by taking a small amount of the substance, as blood, seminal fluid, or bacterial culture, and spreading it thinly on a slide.

Smegma. The cheeselike material which collects between the glans penis or glans clitoridis and the prepuce, secreted by sebaceous glands.

Smell

1. To perceive through the olfactory sense or organs of smell.

2. To detect a scent, as to smell a flower.

Smooth Colony. *bacteriol.* A type of colony characterized by a smooth surface, the individuals of which exhibit a sensitivity to bacteriophage, resistance to phagocytosis, and are good immunizing forms.

Smooth

1. Having an even surface or margin; devoid of irregularities.
2. *bot.* Lacking projections or hairs; glabrous.

Smooth Endoplasmic Reticulum. Endoplasmic reticulum.

Smooth Muscle. A type of involuntary muscle composed of elongated, nonstriated, spindle-shaped cells found in the walls of tubes and hollow organs, as the alimentary canal, blood vessels, urinary and gall bladder.

Smut Fungus. One of a number of basidiomycete fungi which are parasitic on higher plants, especially grasses. Some produce black, sootlike masses of spores (loose smut); others form smut balls containing covered or kernel smut. Important genera are Ustilago and Tille tia.

Smuts. A group of parasitic fungi belonging to the Basidiomycetes. Many of these species attack the ears of cereal crops, replacing the grain by a mass of dark spores. Compare rusts.

Snail. A mollusk of the class Gastropoda, especially those with a well-developed spiral shell.

Snailfish. A sea snail, a fish of the family Liparididae, with a sucker formed from pelvic fins, as Liparis.

Snake

1. An elongated, creeping reptile of the order Sequamata, suborder Serpentes (Ophidia).
2. One of a number of snakelike animals, as the glass snake, congo snake, horsehair snake.

Snakeroot. One of a number of plants which reputedly possess curative properties for snakebites, as the Virginia snakeroot (Aristolochia serpentaria).

Snapper

1. An animal that snaps, as a snapping turtle or snapping beetle.
2. An important food and game fish of the family Lutjanidae, as Lutjanidae, riseus, the gray snapper. However some species are highly poisonous, as the Cuban snapper.

Snapping Turtle. A large, predaceous, freshwater turtle of the family Chelydridae, comprising two species, Chelydra serpentina, the common snapping turtle, and Macrochelys temmincki, the alligator snapping turtle.

Snout

1. A long, projecting nose, as that of swine.
2. An anterior extension of the head, as seen in various animals, as weevils; a rostrum.

Snout Beetle. A beetle of the Rhynchophora characterized by possession of an elongated beak or snout, as the curculios and weevils.

Snowbird. A finch of the genus Junco.

Snow Goose. A species of goose of the genus Chen, as the greater snow goose (Chen hyperborea).

Sobole. A shoot, especially one coming from the base of the stem near the ground.

Soboliferous. Producing shoots near the ground and forming a clump, said of certain shrubs and trees, as the lilac.

Social. Living together in organized communities.

Social Insects. Termites, ants, bees, and wasps which develop highly organized colonies consisting of groups of individuals differing in structure and function which live and work together as a unit. Castes (queens, drones, workers, and soldiers) may exist.

Social Parasitism. Nest parasitism, a mode of life of certain birds, as cuckoos, cowbirds, and some ducks in which nest-building is dispensed with and eggs are laid in the nest of other birds, called hosts or fosterers which care for the young when hatched.

Sociobiology. The integrated study of social behaviour, based on the premiss that all behaviour is adaptive. It gives special emphasis to social systems considered as ecological adaptations, and attempts a mechanistic explanation of social behaviour in terms of modern biology and, in particular, evolutionary theory.

Society. A minor community within a consociation, with a particular dominant species. It arises because of some variation in conditions within a habitat. For example, in a consociation such as an oak wood there may be a society of bluebells or primroses.

Sodium Symbol Na. A soft silvery element that is a major essential element required by animals. It is important in maintaining the acid-base balance and in controlling the volume of extracellular fluid and functions in the transmission of nerve impulses (sodium pump).

Sodium Bicarbonate Indicator. A mixture of sodium bicarbonate solution and the dyes cresol red and thymol blue. It is used as an indicator to detect small changes in pH. It changes from red to orange and yellow with a slight increase in acidity.

Sodium Chloride. Common salt, NaCl, one of the principle electrolytes in body fluids.

Sodium coupled Transport. The entry of a metabolite into a cell against a concentration gradient, where this entry is coupled to the movement of sodium across the membrane. Sodium readily enters cells because of the concentration of its ions outside the cell membrane which is high compared with that inside. It is thought that carriers exist that can bind to sodium, so exploiting this feature, and also to a metabolite (such as glucose), which is thereby carried across the membrane.

Sodium Fluoride. A crystalline compound, NaF. It is highly toxic but in very dilute solution (less than 1 part per million) it is used in the fluoridation of water for the prevention of tooth decay on account of its ability to replace OH groups with F groups in the material of dental enamel.

Sodium Pump. A mechanism by which sodium ions are transported out of a neurone across the cell membrane. The process requires energy in the form of ATP, being a form of active transport. It maintains the different concentration of sodium ions on either side of the neurone membrane necessary for establishing the resting potential of the neurone.

Soft Palate. The velum palati, a thin, musculomembranous partition which forms the posterior portion of the roof of the mouth. It closes the posterior openings to the nasal cavity during swallowing movements.

Soft Rot. A disease, caused by fungi or bacteria, in which the tissues of the affected parts become soft. Soft rots are most notable as postharvest diseases. Bacteria of the genus Erwinia and fungi of the genus Rhizopus cause soft rots of stored vegetables and fruits—particularly in humid badly ventilated conditions. The tissues become soft as the enzymes from the pathogen break down the cell walls.

Soft-shell or **Soft-shelled.** Having a soft shell or lacking a hard one, a state often following molting.

Soft-shelled Clam. Mya arenaria, a burrowing clam with thin, whitish shell.

Soft-shelled Crab. A crab which has just molted, especially the blue crab.

Soft-shelled Turtle. A freshwater turtle (Trionyx muticus) with a flat, oval, leathery carapace, commonly called flapjack.

Softwood

1. Any wood that is soft in consistency and easily worked.
2. *forestry.* The wood of a coniferous tree. Compare hardwood.

Soil. The superficial layer that covers large areas of the earth's crust. It consists of mineral particles, decaying and decayed organic material, living organisms, air, and water. It is the medim in which plants grow, supporting them and supplying them with nutrients, and is also a habitat for numerous animals and microorganisms.

The mineral content of the soil is derived from the mechanical or chemical weathering of exposed rocks. A soil may be formed from the underlying bedrock (sedentary soil) or it may result from the deposition of mineral, particles transported by such agents as water or wind, resulting in a mixture of particles of different origins (sedimentary soil). The proportions of the various sizes of mineral particles (silt, clay, sand, gravel, etc) have a profound effect on the soil texture and structure. This it further influenced by the amount of organic matter present most of which is concentrated in the top 230—300 mm of soil.

Living organisms affect the soil in a number of ways. The larger animals, notably earthworms, mix and aerate the soil and billions of microorganisms feed on and decompose the dead organic matter, thus making nutrients available to the plants. The water in the soil contains dissolved mineral substances and gases that can be taken up by plant roots. The level at which the soil becomes saturated with water (the water table) rises and falls depending on the amount of precipitation. Its level affects soil aeration. The air present in the spaces between the soil particles is generally richer in carbon dioxide and poorer in oxygen that atmospheric air.

There are a number of different methods used to classify soil. Generally soil can be divided into three main groups : zonal soils, where the soil type reflects the prevailing climatic conditions; intrazonal soils, where some other factor, such as the nature of the parent rock, has more influence on soil development; and azonal soils, which are immature newly formed soils, *e.g.* alluvial soils. Zonal soils may be further subdivided into pedalfers and pedocals. Intrazonal soils can be subdivided into hydromorphic soils (with excessive moisture), halomorphic soils (with a high salt content), and calcimorphic soils (rich in lime from the parent rock).

Soil colour may be used as an indication of soil composition, amount of aeration, drainage, etc. For example, badly aerated soils are often bluish grey whereas well aerated soils are reddish because of the high concentration of iron oxides.

Soil-borne Diseases. Any plant disease that originates from inoculum in the soil. Damping-off and club root are typical soil-borne diseases. Control can be difficult and methods include crop rotation, fumigation, chemical treatment, soil sterilization, the use of seed dressings, and improved cultural methods (*e.g.* better drainage).

Soil Factors. Edaphic factors.

Soil Horizon. Soil Profile.

Soil Profile. The arrangement of the layers that can be seen in a section of soil extending from the surface to the bedrock. The layers are soil horizons and there are differences in colour, texture, and composition between them. The upper layers, horizon A or the zone of eluviation, contains the most humus, is most expose to weathering, and is the zone in which most decomposition by micro-organisms takes place. The underlying horizon B or zone of illuviation accumulates salts and colloids washed down from horizon A. Horizon C (the subsoil) consists of the mental rock produced mainly by the mechanical weathering of the parent rock. In horticulture, the term subsoil is taken to mean the soil beneath the humns-rich horizon A (topsoil). Some soils do not have such horizons and may be more or less uniform throughout. They are generally found in mature soil in moist cool temperate climates. In arid and semiarid climates where the rate of evaporation exceeds the amount of precipitation there is a tendency for the upward movement of water by capillarity, and mineral salts, particularly calcium salts, are deposited in the upper layers resulting in calcification.

Soil Structure. The arrangement of the mineral particles in soil. Particles may exist individually, *e.g.* sand particles, or they may be grouped together in larger units (peds). The products of decomposition of organic matter are often sticky and glutinous thus binding the particles together. The aggregates can be grouped in various ways and may be described as crumby, blocky, platy, etc. The structure provided by these aggregates makes the soil more fertile as the channels between the peds aid aeration and drainage. Soil structure can be broken down by overcultivation and removal of too much organic matter. Often a clay soil forms large sticky clods making it difficult to work. Clays soils can be improved by adding lime, which causes the individual clay particles to stick together (flocculate) in smaller aggregates.

Soil Texture. The relative sizes of the different mineral particles in a soil that affects its aeration, capillarity, porosity water absorption, and aese of cultivation. Gravel and stones are defined as being larger than 2 mm in diameter. On the same scale sand particles are 0 05—2 0 mm, silt 0.002—0.05 mm, and anything smaller than 0.002 mm is termed clay. Thus a sandy soil with larger particles has larger spaces and is well aerated and drained but dry. A clay soil is badly drained and becomes waterlogged.

Solanaceae. A large family of dicotyledonous plants commonly called the potato or nightshade family. It contains about 90 genera and some 3000 species have been described. However the actual number of species may be closer to 2000 since the great infraspecific variation seen in many species has led to taxonomic confusion and some species being given a variety of different names. The Solanaceae are cosmopolitan in distribution though there are concentrations of genera in Central and South America and Australia. The majority of solanaceous plants are herbaceous. The leaves are exstipulate and the flowers are usually regular and borne in a cyme. Most commonly there are five sepals and petals, more or less fused, and five anthers. In the largest genus, Solanum (about 1500 species), the flowers characteristically possess a column of touching, but not fused, stamens, which are particularly prominent because of the downward-turned petals. The fruit is usually a berry, though sometimes a capsule, as in henbane (Hyoscyamus niger) and thorn apple (Datura stramonium).

Solanaceous. Of or pertaining to the nightshade family, Solanaceae, a large family of herbs, shrubs and trees, including many of economic importance, as the genus Solanum which includes the white potato. It includes a number of plants which are the source of drugs, a belladonna, hyoscyamus, and stramonium.

Solarization. Inhibition of photosynthesis resulting from exposure to light of high intensity.

Solar Plexus. The coeliac plaxus, composed of sympathet ganglia and nerve fibers which innervate visceral organs of the abdominal cavity; located behind the stomach near the base of coeliac artery.

Solation. Conversion into a fluid or sol state, with reference a colloidal solutions.

Soldier. A member of a caste of termites having a greatly larged head and mandibles; a sterile male which functions in defense of the colony.

[1]Sole

1. The plantar or under surface of the foot.
2. The trivium of a holothuroid.
3. *bot.* The basal end of a carpel; that farthest from the apex.

[2]Sole. One of a number of flatfishes, especially Solea, solea, of European waters, a valuable food fish. Most American species belong to the genera Symphurus and Achirus.

Solehorn. The subunguis.

Solenocyte. An excretory cell in polychaetes which possesses a flagellum as the current-producing structure; also present in lancelets.

Solenostele. The type of vascular cylinder found in stems of many ferns, in which there is a central stem and an outer cortex, and the vascular tissue is limited both internally and externally by a continuous sheath of special cells, called the endodermis. Woody xylem tracheids form the bulk of the cylinder. On its outer and inner faces, within the endodermis, there is a zone of phloem tissue. When leaves arise from the stem, breaks occur in the cylinder, and if the leaves are close-set this may result in the cylinder of vascular tissue becoming so broken that it forms a cylindrical network, rather than a solid cylinder. It is then called a 'dictyostele' (from the Greek dictyon, a net). Flowering plants have separate vascular bundles in the young stem, and though secondary growth of woody tissue may join these into a cylinder around the pith, there is never an internal endodermis as in a true solenostele.

Solonchak (white alkalisoil). A type of intrazonal infertile soil with a high salt content (halomorphic). It is found in arid and semiarid inland regions and in areas where sea spray has blown inland resulting in the deposition of salt. The evaporation of the surface water results in salts from the underlying layers being drawn upwards and deposited on the surface. Solonchaks are usually associated with lime-rich soils (pedocals) and are commonly found in dry continental interiors. If leaching occurs either through heavier rainfall or by irrigation, the salts are washed down into the B horizon thus giving rise to a solonetz soil. If there is continued leaching and improved drainage a soloth or solod is formed, which is weakly acid.

Solute Potential. Osmotic potential.

Somatic

1. Relating to all the cells of an animal or plant other than the reproductive cells. Thus a somatic mutation is one that is not heritable.
2. Relating to organs and tissues of the body other than the gut and its associated structures. The term is applied especially to voluntary muscles, the s nse organs, and the nervous system.

Somatic Cell. Any cell of the body, *i.e.* any cell other than the spores, gametes, or their precursors.

Somatic Crossing-over. In genetics, crossing-over during mitosis of somatic cells such that parent cells heterozygous for a given allele, instead of giving rise to two identical heterozygous daughter cells, give rise to daughter cells one of which is homozygous for one of these alleles, the other being homozygous for the other allele. Phenotypically differing cell-lines may result. Studies of somatic crossing-over, somatic assortment, and cell fusion make up somatic-cell genetics, a modern asexual genetic technique that allows a wide range of in vitro manipulation of higher cells, including human cells as well as those of other organisms.

Somatic Hybridization. The production of cells, tissues, or organisms by fusion of nongametic nuclei. The phenomenon may be induced under laboratory conditions in cells that never normally fuse together and used as a plant breeding or genetic tool. It may also occur naturally, especially in fungi.

Somatic Mutation. Mutation.

Somatotrophin. Growth hormone.

Songbird. Any of a large number of birds of the order Passeriformes, suborder Oscines, which possess a syrinx enabling them to produce beautiful sounds.

Sora. A small, plump rail (Porzana carolina) of North America.

Soralia. Soredium.

Sorbitol. A common sugar alcohol round especially in certain algae and in the fruits of many higher plants, *e.g.* mountain ash (Sorbus aucuparia). It is formed by the reduction of D-glucose or L-sorbose. In some plants, *e.g.* crab apple (Malus sylvestris), sorbitol, rather than sucrose, is the main form in which sugar is translocated in the phloem.

Soredium. A small segment of a lichen thallus consisting of a number of algae cells loosely surrounded by a few fungal filaments. Soredia serve as agents of vegetative propagation and are seen as a powdery dust on the lichen surface. They are often formed in specialized structures termed soralia.

Sori. Plural of Sorus.

Soricine

1. Shrewlike.
2. Of or pertaining to the family Soricidae, which includes the true shrews.

Sorocarp. Pseudoplasmodium.

Sorghum

1. A cultivated grass (Sorghum vulgare) grown for stock feed and forage and used in the manufacture of syrup, brushes, and paper.

2. A syrup obtained from sorgo or sweet sorghum.

Sorophore. A stalk supporting a sorus in certain slime molds.

Sorosis. A type of composite fruit formed from an entire inflorescence spike. Mulberry and pineapple fruits are examples.

Sorrel. One of a number of plants with a sour juice, as the sheep sorrel (Rumex acetosella) or the wood sorrel (Oxalis).

Sorus

1. Any of the spore-producing structures on the undersurface of a fern frond, visible as rows of small brown dots.
2. A reproductive area on the thallus of some algae, *e.g.* Laminaria.
3. Any of various spore-producing structures in certain fungi.

Sound Production

1. In insects, sound produced by stridulation, vibration of wings or tymbals, tapping of the head, or friction of body parts.

2. In fishes, *a* by rubbing teeth, bones, or spines against each other; *b.* by expulsion of air from the air bladder or through the anus.

3. In land vertebrates, *a.* by vibrating structures within a larynx or syrinx; *b.* by drumming with the wings.

Soybean. A legume (Glycine max) indigenous to Asia but now extensively grown in the United States, its seed the source of soybean oil, milk, flour, and meal. Also grown for soil improvement.

Space Biology. The study of living things above the atmosphere or above an altitude of 50,000 ft., at which height environmental hazards of consequence to humans are encountered; exobiology, extraterrestrial biology.

Spadefish

1. A deep bodied, spiny-finned food fish (Chaetodipterus faber) of the Atlantic coast.
2. Common name for the paddlefish.

Spadiceous

1. Light brown or chestnut colored.

2. Resembling or bearing flowers on a spadix.

Spadix. A racemose infloresence in which the flowers are sessile and borne on an enlarged fleshy axis. The spadix is typical of the Araceae (arum family) in which the fleshy axis secretes sticky insect-attracting compounds and is usually surrounded by a large bract or spathe. The female maize inflorescence is also a spadix.

Spanish Moss. An epiphyte (Tilandsia usneoides) of the family Bromeliaceae, which hangs in long tufts from trees, especially in swamps. Also called black moss, long moss, or old-man's beard.

Spanish Needles. Elongated achenes with barbed awns produced by Bidens bipinnata or closely related plants (beggar-ticks); the plants which produce them.

Sparganosis. Infestation in man by the plerocercoid larva of tapeworms of the genus Spirometra, a tapeworm of dogs, cats, and other carnivores.

Sparganum. The plerocercoid larva of tapeworms of the genus Spirometra normally found in frogs, snakes, and amphibious mammals.

Sparrow

1. A weaver finch of the family Ploceidae, especially Passer domesticus, the house or English sparrow.
2. One of a large number of seed-eating birds of the family Fringillidae belonging to many different genera.

Sparrow Hawk

1. A small hawk (Falco sparverius) of the family Falconidae.
2. A European hawk (Accipiter nisus) and related species.

Spasm. A sudden, involuntary muscle contraction.

Spat. The young of oysters and other bivalves.

Spathe. A large bract enclosing a spadix, which may be highly coloured and petaloid, as in Anthurium. In such cases it functions in attracting insects to pollinate the plant.

Spatulate (spathulate). Describing structures that have a broad apex and a long narrow base, such as the leaves of the daisy (Bells perennis).

Spawn

1. The eggs of various aquatic animals, as fishes, oysters, especially when produced in large numbers.

2. *bot.* Dried manure and other organic matter containing the mycelium of mushrooms, used in starting new beds.

Spay. To remove the ovaries of a female animal; to castrate a female.

Spear. A young, pointed shoot or sprout, as in asparagus.

Spearmint. An herb (Mentha spicata) of the family Labiatae which produces an aromatic oil used extensively for flavoring.

Special

1. Of or pertaining to a species.
2. Unique, distinctive, unusual.

Special Creation. The belief, in accordance with the Book of Genesis, that every species was individually created by God in the form in which it exists today and is not capable of undergoing any change. It was the generally accepted explanation of the origin of life until the advent of Darwinism. The idea has recently enjoyed a revival, especially among members of the fundamentalist movement in the USA, partly because there still remain problems that cannot be explained entirely by Darwinian theory. However, special creation is contradicted by fossil evidence and genetic studies, and the pseudoscientific arguments of creation science cannot stand up to logical examination.

Specialization

1. Increasing adaptation of an organism to a particular environment.
2. Physiological specialization.

Specialized

1. Adapted for the performance of a specific function.

2. Adapted or adjusted to a specific type of habitat or environment.

Speciation. The separation of populations of plants and animals, originally able to interbreed, into independent evolutionary units which can interbreed no longer owing to accumulated genetic differences. In cladistics, the origin of one or more new species occurs inferentially by cladogenesis.

Species (sing. and pl). Literally, a group of organisms that resemble one another closely : the term derives from the Latin speculare, 'to look'. In taxonomy, it is applied to one or more groups (populations) of individuals that can interbreed within the group but that cannot exchange genes with other groups (populations)—an interbreeding group of biological organisms that is isolated reproductively from all other organisms (biospecies). A species can be made up of groups in which members do not actually exchange genes with members of other groups (though in principle they could do so), as for example at the two extremes of a continuous geographical range. However, if some gene flow occurs along a continuum, the formation of another species is unlikely to occur. Where barriers to gene flow arise (*e.g.* physical barriers, such as sea, or areas of unfavourable habitat) this reproductive isolation may lead either by local selection or by random genetic drift to the formation of morphologically distinct forms termed 'races' or 'subspecies'. These could interbreed with other races of the same species if they were introduced to one another. Once this potential is lost, through some further evolutionary divergence, the races may be recognized as species, although this concept is not a rigid one. Most species cannot interbreed with others; a few can, but produce infertile offspring; a smaller number may actually produce fertile offspring. The term cannot be applied precisely to organisms whose breeding behaviour is unknown.

Species. A category used in the classification of organisms that consists of a group of similar individuals that can usually breed among themselves and produce fertile offspring. Similar or related species are grouped into a genus. Within a species groups of individuals may become reproductively isolated because of geographical or behavioural factors. Such populations may, because of different selection pressures, develop different characteristics from the main population and so form a distinct subspecies.

Spectrophotometer. An instrument for investigating quantitatively the way in which electromagnetic radiation of different wavelengths is absorbed by a specimen. Typically, it consists of a source of the radiation (infrared, visible, or ultraviolet) from which a particular wavelength can be selected by means of a monochromater. A beam of this radiation is passed through the specimen (or reflected from it) and the intensity measured by a detector (*e.g.* a photocell). As the wavelength of incident radiation is changed, an absorption spectrum is produced showing how the intensity of transmitted (or reflected) radiation varies with wavelength. Typically, substances absorb the radiation over particular bands of wavelength, corresponding to energy-level changes in their molecules. Spectrophotometry is used extensively as a means of analysis and in the study of how radiation interacts with matter (*e.g.* the absorption of light in photosynthesis). The speed of a chemical reaction can also be followed in cases where the products of the reaction absorb radiation of a particular wavelength that the reactants do not.

Spectrum

1. A series of images formed when light rays are dispersed and their consitituents arranged in order of their wavelength. The visible spectrum, seen when white light is passed through a prism, consists of

colours from red to violet with wave lengths of 8000 A° (red) to 4000 A° (violet).

2. In a general sense, a series of units or entities possessing a common property arranged in a garded fashion, as an antibiotic spectrum, which is the range of effectiveness of an antibiotic against various types of bacteria.

Speculum

1. A brightly colored area on the wings of certain birds; formerly called mirror.
2. A clear area on the wings of certain lepidopterous insects.

Sperm

1. A mature male gamete; a spermatozoan.
2. The seminal fluid or semen.

Spermagonium. A pycnium.

Spermaceti. A waxy substance obtained from the head of a sperm whale used in the preparation of cerates and ointments.

Spermary. An organ which produces male gametes; a testis or antheridium.

Spermatangium. A male gamete-producing structure in certain algae.

Spermatheca (seminal receptacle). A sac or receptacle in some female or hermaphrodite animals (*e.g.* earthworms) in which sperm from the mate is stored until the eggs are ready to be fertilized.

Spermatia. Nonmotile male gametes produced in a spermagonium, as in rusts.

Spermatic. Of or pertaining to sperm or a sperm-producing structure.

Spermatic Cord. A cord in mammals which extends from the deep inguinal ring to the testis, containing blood and lymph vessels, nerves, and the ductus deferens.

Spermatid. A haploid cell formed from the division of a secondary spermatocyte which transforms into a functioral spermatozoan.

Spermatium

1. A small nonmotile male cell shed from the mycelia of certain ascomycete fungi and capable of fertilizing an ascogonium.
2. Pycnidium.

Spermatocyte. Diploid cell that undergoes meiosis and forms four spermatids. A primary spermatocyte undergoes the first meiotic division to form two secondary spermatocytes. These then divide (the second meitotic division) to produce two spermatids each (*i.e.* a total of four haploid cells).

Spermatogenesis. The series of cell divisions in the testis that results in the production of spermatozoa. Within the seminiferous tubules of the testis germ cells grow and divide by mitosis to produce spermatogonia. These divide by mitosis to produce spermatocytes, which divide by meiosis to produce spermatids. The spermatids, which thus have half the number of chromosomes of the original germ cells, then develop into spermatozoa.

Spermatogonium. A primordial germ cell which gives rise to a primary spermatocyte.

Spermatoid. Resembling a spermatozoon or sperm cell.

Spermatophore

1. Gelatinous cone of jelly secreted by the cloacal glands of male urodeles (class Amphibia) with a sperm cap on top. It is deposited by the male during the

courtship ritual and picked up by the cloacal lips of the female, thus enabling internal fertilization.

2. Packet of sperm, produced in a wide range of insect groups, which may be deposited on the ground or transferred directly to the female. The spreamatopbore has a gelatinous protein capsule produced by the male accessory glands.

Spermatophyta. A division of the plant kingdom containing plants that reproduce by means of seeds. These species make up the bulk of the present-day flora—trees, shrubs, grasses, and herbaceous plants. The division is subdivided into the Angiospermae and the Gymnospermae. In some classifications seed plants are included within the Pteropsida.

Spermatophyte. A seed-producing plant; a gymnosperm or angiosperm.

Spermatozeugma. A mass of sperim attached to a central cell, as in certain aphallate gastropods. Also spermiozengma.

Spermatozoid. A motile, male gamete or sperm produced by an antheridium; an antherozoid.

Spermatozoon (sperm). The mature mobile reproductive cell (gamete) of male animals, which is produced by the testis (spermatogenesis). It consists of a head section containing a haploid nucleus and an acrosome, which allows the sperm to penetrate the egg at fertilization; a middle section containing mitochondira to provide the energy for movement; and a tail section, which lashes to drive the sperm forward.

Sperm Cell. One of the two male gametes formed in the pollen tube of gymnosperms after mitotic diviosion of the body cell. In some species, *e.g.* Cycas and Ginkgo, they are flagellate and swim from the pollen tube to the archegonia. Such antherozoids, in contrast to the nonmotile generative nculei of angio-sperms, are associated with a large amount of cytoplasm and in Cycas reach a diameter of 300 μu. In other gymnosperms, *e.g.* the Gnetales and Coniferales, the sperm cells are not motile. The term sperm cell is sometimes applied to generative nuclei.

Spermiation. The release of mature sperm from the Sertoli cells of the testis.

Spermicidal. Destroying sperm.

Spermiogenesis. The transformation of a spermatid into a motile spermatozoon.

Spermiducal Glands. Prostate glands, especially those of oligochaete annelids.

Sperm Nucleus

1. *zool.* The nucleus of a spermatozoon which, in the zygote, becomes the male pronucleus.
2. *bot.* One of two male nuclei within a growing pollen tube.

Spermophile. The thirteen-striped ground squirrel (Citellus tridecemlineatus).

Spermogonium. Pycnidium.

Sperm Plug. A mass of coagulated semen in the vagina of a rat; also called copulation plug.

Sperm Sac. A receptacle in fishes which receives sperm from the seminal vesicle and in turn discharges them into the urinogential sinus.

Sperm Whale. A cachalot, a large whale (Physeter catodon), the source of spermaceti and ambergris; also Kogia breviceps, the pygmy sperm whale, a related form.

Sphacelated. Decayed, withered.

Sphacelial. Of or pertaining to decay or withering.

Sphaeridium. A rounded or oval, pedunculated sense organ in echinoids.

Sphaeriales. An order of the Pyrenomycetes mainly containing saprobic fungi though some are parasitic on plants. It contains over 5000 species in some 500 genera. They typically have hard dark perithecia, as seen, for example, in Daldinia concentrica.

Sphaeropsidales. An order of the Coelomycetes containing many fungi that are plant parasites, *e*.g. Septoria apiicola, which causes leaf spot of celery. It includes about 6000 species in some 750 genera. The conidiophores are formed within pycnidia.

Sphaeroraphide. Druse.

Sphagnicolous. Inhabiting sphagnum moss, as rotifers.

Sphagnum Moss. A peat or bog moss of the genus Sphagnum, noted for its ability **when dry** to absorb large quantities of water.

Sphase. The period of the cell cycle when DNA replication and histone synthesis occurs as chromosomes divide into chromatids.

[1]**Sphenoid**. Wedge-shaped.

Sphenopsid. Any plant of the Sphenopsida (Sphenophyta) which includes the horsetails or scouring rushes, abundant during the Paleozoic era but with only one by genus (Equisetum) now extant.

Sphenopsida. A class of the Pteridophta or a subdivision of the Tracheophyta, the only living members of which are the horsetails (Equisetum). Horsetails have a perennial creeping rhizome supporting erect jointed stems bearing whorls of thin leaves. Spores are produced by terminal conelike structures. The group has a fossil record extending back to the Palaeozoic with its greatest development in the Carboniferous period, when giant tree forms were the dominant vegetation with the Lycopsida.

Spherosome. An organelle 0.5—1.0 μm in diameter with a single membrane and a fairly granular matrix containing triglycerides. Spherosomes are abundant in cells in which lipids are stored and they contain the hydrolytic enzyme, lipase. They probably have a role in the mobilization of stored lipids when they are required for cell metabolism.

Sphincter. A specialized muscle encircling an opening or orifice. Contraction of the sphincter tends to close the orifice. Examples are the anal sphincter (round the opening of the anus) and the pyloric sphincter (at the lower opening of the stomach.

Sphingolipid. A type of complex lipid containing a long-chain amino alcohol, such as sphingosine, joined by an amide linkage to a long chain fatty acid. Sphingolipids are important as membrane components in both animal and plant cells. In yeasts and in higher plants the amino alcohol is commonly phytosphingosine.

Sphinx Moth. A hawkmoth of the family Sphingidae.

Spicate. Having the form of a spur or spike.

Spicule

1. A sharp, pointed, siliceous or calcareous body, as *a.* those forming the endoskeleton of sponges, corals, and certain protozoans; *b.* those formed in the development of bone.
2. One of a pair of curved copulatory structures in a male nematode; a spiculum.

Spider. An arachnid of the class Araneae.

Spider Crab. A decapod crustacean of the family Majidae with long slender legs, as Macrocheira, the gaint crab of Japan, with a leg span of eight feet.

Spider Mite. A red mite of the family Tetranychidae.

Spider Wasp. A wasp of the family Pompilidae which kills or paralyzes spiders which it uses as food for its young.

Spiderwort. A dicot plant of the genus Tradescuntia.

Spindle. The set of microtubular fibres that uppear to move the chromosomes of eukaryotes during cell division. The spindle is formed only at mitosis or meiosis, appearing at metaphase and first arranging the chromosomes at its equator. Movement apart of chromatids then occurs during anaphase, probably as a result af contraction of the fibres that run from the centromere (spindle attachment) to the spindle pole, and from pole to pole.

Spike. A racemose inflorescence in which the flowers are sessile and borne on an elongated axis, as in wheat. The catkin and spadix are types of spike.

Spikelet. The basic unit of a grass inflorescence. It consists of a short axis or rachilla, two bracts or glumes, and one or more florets and their bracts (the lemma and palea).

Spikelet characteristics such as size, number of florets, or how it fractures at macurity may be used as diagnostic traits for the genus. The whole spikelet is the unit of dispersal for such grasses as Holcus and Setaria.

Spike Potential. The action potential of a nerve, as seen in an oscillograph.

Spin. To form a thread or threads, as by a spider in spinning a web or a caterpillar in the formation of a cocoon.

Spinach. A pot herb (Spinacea oleracea) cultivated extensively.

Spinal Accessory Nerve. The accessory nerve, the eleventh cranial nerve (XI).

Spinal Animal. An experimental animal in which the spinal cord has been transected above the lumbosacral enlargement.

Spinal Canal. The canal within the vertebral column which contains the spinal cord; the vertebral canal.

Spinal Column. The vertebral column or backbone.

Spinal Cord. The part of the vertebrate central nervous system that is posterior to the brain and enclosed within the vertebral column. It consists of a hollow core of grey matter (H-shaped in cross section) surrounded by an outer layer of white matter; the central cavity contains cerebrospinal fluid. Paired spinal nerves arise from the spinal cord.

Spinal Cord. An elongated structure composed of nervous tissue extending posteriorly from the brain and contained within the spinal canal. It functions as a reflex center and a conducting pathway.

Spinal Nerves. Pairs of nerves that arise from the spinal cord (compare cranial nerves). In man there are 31 pairs (one from each of the vertebrae). Each nerve contains both motor and sensory fibres (*i.e.* they are mixed nerves), and the spinal nerves form an important part of the peripheral nervous system.

Spindle. A fibrillar structure formed in the cytoplasm from microtubules at the commencement of metaphase. When present, centrioles move so they are diametrically opposite each other on the disintegrating nuclear membrane. In the majority of plant cells, where there are no centrioles, poles still become established at opposite points. The fibrils radiate from each pole towards the centre or equator. The attached microtubules direct the chromatids (or chromosomes in the first meiotic division) towards opposite poles. Evidence tends to support the view that this is achieved by the microtubules becoming progressively shortened as a result of depolymerization in the regions nearest to the poles.

Spindle Attachment. Centromere.

Spindle Cell. A thrombocyte in the blood of vertebrates other than mammals.

Spindle Fibers. Spindle.

Spindle-sshaped. Fusiform; elongated and tapered at each end.

Spine

1. Vertebral column.
2. A hard pointed protective structure on a plant that is formed through modification of a leaf, part of a leaf, or a stipule. The edge of the holly leaf is drawn out into spines, but in the gorse the whole leaf is modified. Compare prickle; thorn.

Spinescent. Terminating in a spine; bearing a spine.

Spiniferous. Bearing spines; spiny.

Spinneret. One of the specialized silk-handling devices found in spiders. In general there are four pairs, two pairs on the tenth abdominal segment and two pairs on the eleventh, although few spiders retain the maximum complement in the adult stage. The anterior median pair is usually lost, but sometimes a remnant may remain in the form of a median cone (colulus) whose function is unclear. In some cases the anterior median pair fuse during embryonic development to form an oval plate covered with thousands of tiny spigots (the cribellum). Some spiders retain only two pairs of spinnerets, losing both the anterior media and posterior lateral pairs. Spinnerets are movable, sclerotized tubes composed of several segments; they vary in size, and are mostly conical in web-spinning species. The silk glands produce a protein (fibroin) as a liquid which is emitted through tiny spigots on the ends and ventral sides of the spinnerets. Polymerization of the liquid silk is not an oxidative or evaporative process, but relies on tension.

Spinose. Spinelike; bearing or possessing spines.

Spinous. Spiny; possessing spines.

Spinule. A small or minute spine.

Spiny. Covered with or bearing many spines.

Spiracle

1. Essentially a vestigial gill slit located between the mandibular and hyoid arches in adult sharks, rays, and some primitive bony fish, and visible as an opening behind the eye.
2. One of the ports on the body of an insect at which the tracheae open to the outside Spiracles are found on the thoracic and abdominal segments, and usually have some mechanism to close them.

Spiral

1. Winding; encircling; coiling about a center or central axis.
2. Helical, resembling the thread of a screw.

Spiral Cleavage. Cleavage in which the cells of the upper quartet in the eight-celled stage lie above and between the cells of the lower quartet, as in annelids, mollusks, polyclads, and nemerteans.

Spiral Intestine. An intestine which possesses a spiral valve.

Spiral Thickening (helical thickening). A type of secondary wall patterning in tracheary elements in which the secondary cell wall is laid down in a helical pattern. Spiral thickening, like annular thickening, permits further extension of the cell. It is therefore found in tissues such as protoxylem, which develop in young organs that are still elongating. Compare pitted thickening, reticulate thickening, scalariform thickening.

Spiral Valve

1. A spiral, longitudinal fold or valve in the conus arteriosus or truncus arteriosus of lung fishes and amphibians which directs deoxygenated blood into the pulmonary arteries.

2. A spiral, longitudinal fold in the intestine of elasmobranch fishes.

Spire

1. The pointed tip of a structure, as the horn of a ruminant.
2. The pointed portion of a spiral gastropod shell; the upper whorls from the apex to the last body whorl.
3. *bot.* A slender, tapering leaf or stem, as in grasses.

Spirea. A flowering shrub (Spiraea) of the rose family.

Spiricle. A minute, coiled, threadlike, hygroscopic structure in the coat of certain seeds, as Ruellia.

Spirillum. Any rigid spiral-shaped bacterium. Generally, spirilla are Gram-negative (Gram's stain), aerobic, and highly motile, bearing one or more tufts of flagella. They occur in soil and water, feeding on organic matter.

Spirochaetales. An order containing bacteria with slender flexible spiral-shaped cells. They lack flagella but are nevertheless motile. Many are animal parasites causing such diseases as syphilis and yaws.

Spirochaete. Any nonrigid corkscrew-shaped bacterium that moves by means of muscular flexions of the cell. Most spirochaetes are Gram-negative (Gram's stain), anaerobic, and feed on dead organic matter. They are particularly common in sewage-polluted waters. Some, however, cause disease in man; Treponema, the agent of syphilis, is an example.

Spirometer. An apparatus for measuring the volume of air inhaled and exhaled.

Spirotrich. Any protozoan of the subclass Spirotricha characterized by well-developed buccal ciliature, as Stentor, Spirostomum.

[1]Spit. To discharge from the mouth, saliva or other material.

[a]Spit. The material ejected from the mouth; spittle.

Spitting Snake. A snake, as the cobra, which is capable of ejecting venom usually toward the victim's eyes for a considerable distance (up to six feet).

Spittle

1. Saliva.
2. The frothy mass produced by and enclosing the nymphs of spittlebugs.

Spittlebug. A froghopper, a small, leaping, homopterous insect of the family Cercopidae, the nymphs of which feed upon various herbs and grasses, forming frothy masses of spittle.

Splake. The hybrid off spring of a cross between the brook trout and lake trout.

Splanchnocoel. The coelomic space between the visceral and parietal layers of mesoderm which gives rise, in mammals, to the serous cavities.

Splanchnocranium. The portion of the skull derived from the visceral (branchial) skeleton.

Splanchnopleure. *embriol.* The combined layers of splanchnic mesoderm and endoderm.

Splay. To expand or spread out.

Splayfoot. An abnormally expanded and flat foot.

Spleen. A vertebrate organ, lying behind the stomach, that is basically a collection of lymphoid tissue. Its functions include producing lymphocytes and destroying foreign particles It acts as a reservoir for erythrocytes and can regulate the number in circulation. It is also the site for the breakdown of worn-out erythrocytes and it stores the iron they contain.

Spleenwort. One of a number of ferns of the genus Asplenium.

Spleaial Bone. A dermal bone present in the lower jaw of certain amphibians, sometimes bearing teeth, as in the salamander (Siren).

Splenic. Of or pertaining to the spleen.

Splenic Corpuscle. A nodule of lymphatic tissue in the white pulp of the spleen. Also called Malpighian corpuscle.

Spodogram. The image of a slice of tissue following micro-incineration.

Sponge

1. Any animal of the phylum Porifera.
2. The porous, horny skeleton of various poriferans, especially Spongia and Hippiospongia which provide the bath sponge of commerce.

Spongin. A proteinaceous, fiberlike material which forms the skeleton of horny sponges.

Spongocoel. The central cavity of a simple sponge opening to the outside through the osculum. Formerly called gastral cavity, cloacal cavity, paragaster.

Spongy. Of the nature of or resembling a sponge in appearance or texture.

Spongy Bone. Cancellous bone, containing irregular spaces filled with bone marrow.

Spongy Mesophyll The part of the leaf mesophyll that is composed of variously shaped, often conspicuously lobed, cells with large intercellular spaces. It is sometimes regarded as a type of aerenchyma. A humid atmosphere is maintained in the intercellular spaces, thus facilitating gaseous exchange between the atmosphere and the mesophyll for photosynthesis and respiration.

Spongy Parenchyma. In a leaf, a layer of cells lying below the palisade layer, loose-textured and containing many air spaces. It is a part of the mesophyll.

Spontaneous. Originating from within; not the result of outside forces or influences.

Spontaneous Generation. The discredited belief that living organisms can somehow be produced by nonliving matter. For example, it was once thought that microorganisms arose by the process of decay and even that vermin spontaneously developed from household rubbish. Controlled experiments using sterilized media by Pasteur and others finally disproved these notions. Compare biogenesis.

Spoonbill

1. A wading bird of the family Threskiornithidae with a long, spatulate bill, as Ajaia ajaja, the roseate spoonbill.
2. The paddlefish.

Sporadic. Occurring here and there or occasionally, without continuity with others of the same kind.

Sporadin. The trophozoite stage of a gregarine, consisting of a primite and satellite.

Sporangiole. A one or few-spored sporangium, as in certain phycomycetes.

Sporangiophore. A structure bearing one or more sporangia. It may be a simple stalk, such as that formed on germination of the zygospore of such fungi as Rhizopus and Mucor. Alternatively it may be multicellular or branched as in certain pteridophytes.

Sporangiospore. A spore produced by a sporangium.

Sporangium. A reproductive structure in plants that produces asexual spores.

Spore

1. (mycol.) Microscopic structure which functions in reproduction and dispersal. A spore does not contain

an embryo and thus is distinct from a seed. Many different types of spore are produced by fungi.

2. (bacteriol.) Differentiated cell which may function as a propagule or as a resistant structure that allows the organism to survive adverse environmental conditions.

Spore Mother Cell (sporocyte). A diploid cell that gives rise to four haploid spores by meiosis.

Sporidium. A basidiospore which develops from a promycelium, as in smuts.

Sporine State. A sessile state in çertain protists in which cell division occurs during vegetative existence.

Sporling. A young plant which develops from a spore.

Sporoblast. One of four cells which develop from an oocyst, as in coccidians.

Sporobolomycetales. Blastomycetes.

Sporocarp. A hard usually globose multicellular structure that contains the spores in water ferns, *e.g.* Pilularia. It is formed by the fusion of the margins of a fertile frond. The spores are not released until the structure decays.

Sporocys

1. In protozoans, *a.* a resistant spore containing sporozoites, as in most sporozoans; *b.* the protective wall within which sporozotes are formed.
2. A stage in the development of a digenetic fluke consisting of a saclike structure arising from a miracidium and giving rise to rediae (in some cases daughter sporocysts or cercariae); occurs in snails or bivalves.

Sporocyte

1. *bot.* A spore mother cell.
2. *zool.* A binucleate cell produced by certain myxosporidians.

Sporogenesis. The formation of spores.

Sporogenous. Producing spares, said of tissues or organs.

Sporogonium. The sporophyte generation in bryophytes. It is made up if an absorptive foot, a stalk (seta), and a spore-producing capsule. It may be completely or partially dependent on the gametophyte.

Sporogony. The formation of spores; sporogenesis.

Sporont. A stage in the development of certain protozoans, sometimes the zygote, which gives rise to spores, as in myxosporidians.

Sporophore. The fruiting body of ascomycete and basidiomycete fungi.

Sporophyll. A modified leaf that bears the sporangia. In the lower plants, *e.g.* Lycopodium, it may be a leaf that has retained its normal structure and function and shows no great specialization. In the seed plants the leaf has become highly modified and lost its photosynthetic function, as in the carpels and stamens of the angiosperms.

Sporophyte. The spore-producing diploid generation in the life cycle of plants. In higher plants such as angiosperms and gymnosperms, the sporophyte is the dominant generation, forming the conspicuous plant. In lower plants such as mosses, liverworts, ferns, and fungi, the gametophyte is the dominant and conspicuous generation.

Sporoplasm. The protoplasm of a spore.

Sporopollenin. The highly resistant material making up the exine of spores and pollen grains. It is a polymerized carotenoid, capable of withstanding temperatures approaching 300°C and strong acids.

Sporosac. A reduced type of gonophore in hydroids in which sex cells ripen directly on the sides of the blastostyle.

Sporozoa (phylum Protozoa). Subphylum of protozoa in which the life cycle includes a sporeforming or cyst-forming stage. Asexual reproduction occurs by multiple fission.

All members are parasitic, parasitizing hosts throughout the animal kingdom. Some species can cause important diseases.

Sporozoan. Any protozoan of the class Sporozoa, which comprises parasitic forms which produce or bear spores. Locomotor organs are lacking and reproduction is principally by schizogony. Many are pathogenic, causing diseases as coccidiosis, Texas fever, and malaria.

Sporozoite. The active invasive from of various sporozoans, usually developing from a sporoblast.

Sport. An atypical form of an individual or part of an individual, due to mutation or segregation. The term is normally restricted to new forms and is most commonly used in horticulture.

Sporulation. The act or process of producing spores; the discharge or liberation of spores.

Spot

1. A small area differing in color or texture from the surrounding area.
2. *bot.* A definite diseased area, or the disease of which it is a symptom, as leaf spot.

[1]**Spout.** To eject liquid forcibly in a jet.

[2]**Spout.** The material discharged through the fused nostrils or blowhole of a whale.

Spouting. The discharge by a whale of the contents of the lungs through the blowhole.

Sprain. The twisting of a joint resulting in the stretching, tearing, or rupture of the ligaments.

Sprat. A small European herring (Clupea sprattus).

Spray Zone. In marine ecology, the region above high tide line which is repeatedly moistened by the spray of ordinary surf.

Spreader

1. An agent added to an insect spray in order to secure uniform coverage of the foliage.
2. *bacteriol.* An organism which spreads very rapidly over the culture medium, as the Hauch or H form of Proteus.

[1]Sprout. The shoot of a plant, especially the first from a seed or the first growth of a root or tuber.

[2]Sprout. To bring forth a new shoot; to germinate.

Spruce

1. One of a number of coniferous trees of the genus, Picea, family Pinacea.
2. Term loosely applied to other conifers, as Douglas spruce (Douglas fir) and hemlock spruce (hemlock).

Spur

1. A short thin side shoot from a branch, especially one that bears furit or, in conifers, the shoots that bear the leaves.
2. A tubular projection from a flower, usually from the base of a perianth segment. Well developed spurs are seen in columbine (Aquilegia vulgaris) and larkspur (Consolida ambigua).

Spurious. False, with reference to a structure which resembles another but differs morphologically, as a spurious fruit, spurious claw in spiders, or spurious wing or alula in birds.

Squab. The nestling or young of a pigeon.

Squama. A flat plate or scalelike structure; a squame.

Squamata (lizards, snakes; class Reptilia). Highly successful order, which includes 95% of all living reptiles. The lizards and snakes are each given ordinal status in some classifications. The earliest lizards had appeared by the

Triassic and the snakes, which might be regarded as 'legless' lizards, diverged from the ancestral line in the Cretaceous. The skull has lost the lower temporal arch, allowing mobility of the quadrate and increased gape. The tongue is notched or forked. Body scales are generally small and overlapping. Limblessness is common. They are divided into two suborders (or rders), Sauria (Lacertilia) and Serpentes (Ophidia).

Squamation. The arrangement of scales, as in a fish.

Squame

1. A squama.
2. A flat, pointed process which forms the exopodite of the antenna in decapod crustaceans.

Squamosal. A membrane bone of the skull in lower vertebrates located behind the orbit, as in the frog.

Squamous

1. Covered with, composed of, or bearing scales,
2. Flat, scalelike.

Squamule. A small lobe of a squamulose lichen.

Squamulose

1. Having minute scales.
2. Designating a type of thallus in lichens composed of many small, flat lobes.

Squarrose

1. Rough, with diverging scales or processess.
2. *bot.* Having parts spreading and recurved at their ends, as bracts surrounding on inflorescence.

Squash. A microscopical preparation in which the material is flattened before examination. It is commonly used in the study of chromosomes. Some tissues, *e.g.*, anthers, may be squashed directly while others, *e.g.*, root tips, must firt be softened. This is commonly achieved by adding a cellulase enzyme.

Squill

1. The sea onion (Urginea maritima), a liliaceous, bulbous plant of the Mediterranean coasts, the source of red squill, a rodenticide.
2. *Scilla*, an Old World genus of bulbuous plants of the lily family.

Squirrel. Any of a large number of small to medium-sized rodents of the family Sciuridae, most arboreal, diurnal animals with a large, bushy tail. Common representatives are the red, fox, and gray squirrels of the genus Sciurus. The North American red squirrel or chickaree belongs to the genus Tamiasciurus, flying squirrels to the genera Glaucomys and Pteromys, ground squirrels or gophers to the genus Citellus.

S-shaped Growth Curve (sigmoid growth curve). Pattern of growth in which in a new environment, the population density of an organism increases slowly initially, in a positive acceleration phase; then increases rapidly approaching an exponential growth rate as in the J-shaped curve; but then declines in a negative acceleration phase until at zero growth rate the population stabilizes. This decline reflects increasing environmental resistance which becomes proportionately more important at higher population densities. This type of population growth is termed 'density-dependent' since growth rate depends on the numbers present in the population. The point of stabilization, or zero growth rate, is termed the 'saturation value' (symbolized by K) or 'carrying capacity' of the environment for that organism. K represents the upper asymptote of the sigmoidal or S-shaped curve produced when changing population numbers are plotted over time.

Stab Culture. *bacteriol.* A culture made by plunging an inoculation needle deep into a mass of solid medium, such as gelatin.

Stachyose. A nonreducing tetrasaccharide made up of two galactose units and one unit each of glucose and fructose. It is found in many of Labiatae, especially the tubers of Stachys tuberifera, and in some of the Leguminosae.

Stadium pl. **Stadia** The interval between two successive molts, used especially with reference to insects but also applied to other invertebrates.

Stag

1. The adult male of members of the deer family; a hart.
2. The male of various mammals castrated after maturity.

Staining. A technique in which cells or thin sections of biological tissue that are normally transparent are immersed in one or more coloured dyes (stains) to make them more clearly visible through a microscope. Staining heightens the contrast between the various cell or tissue components. Stains are usually organic salts with a positive and negative ion. If the colour comes from the negative ion (organic anion), the stain is described as acidic, *e.g.*, eosin. If the colour comes from the positive ion (organic cation), the stain is described as basic *e.g.*, haematoxylin. Neutral stains have a coloured cation and a coloured anion; an example is Leishman's stain. Cell constituents are described as being acidophilic if they are stained with acidic dyes, basophilic if receptive to basic dyes, and neutrophilic if receptive to neutral dyes. Vital stains are used to colour the constituents of living cells without harming them (vital staining); nonvital stains are used for dead tissue.

Counterstaining involves the use of two or more stains in succession, each of which colours different cell or tissue constituents. Temporary staining is used for immediate microsopical observation of material, but the colour soon fades and the tissue is subsequently damaged. Permanent staining does not distort the cells and is used for tissue that is to be preserved for a considerable period of time.

Electron stains, used in the preparation of material for electron microscopy, are described as electron-dense as they interfere with the transmission of electrons. Examples are lead citrate, phosphotungstic acic (PTA), and uranyl acetate (UA).

[1]Stalk

1. *a.* The main supporting axis or stem of a plant. *b.* An elongated supporting structure, as a peduncle, pedicel, stipe, filament, or seta.
2. *zool.* A similar structure in an animal, as *a.* the stalk of a hydroid, barnacle, brachiopod, or crinoid; *b.* a connecting structure, as the optic, hypophyseal, or bony stalk.

[2]Stalk. To approach stealthily under, to cover, as when a predator stalks its prey.

Stalk Cell. One of two cells which develop from the generative cell within the pollen tube of a gymnosperm.

Stallion. An uncastrated male horse, especially one kept for breeding purposes.

Stamen. One of the male reproductive parts of a flower. It consists of an upper fertile part (the anther) on a thin sterile stalk (the filament).

Staminate

1. Possessing only stamens and lacking pistils, with reference to flowers.
2. Possessing only microsporophylls, with reference to strobili or cones.

3. Bearing only staminate flowers or cones, with reference to plants.

Staminate Flower. A flower possessing male parts (stamens) but no female parts, as in the male flowers of holly (Ilex aquifolium). Compare pistillate flower.

Stamineal. Pertaining to or consisting of stamens.

Staminode. A sterile stamen. It may remain rudimentary or partially developed, as in figworts (Scrophularia), or become highly specialized and modified, as in Iris, where it forms a consipicuous part of the flower.

Standard

1. The broad often erect petal at the top or posterior side of the flower of plants belonging to the subfamily Papilionoideae of the Leguminosae (*i.e.*, 'pea' flowers).
2. Any of the three erect twisted inner petals of an Iris flower.

Standing Crop. The total amount of living material in a specified population, expressed as biomass or its equivalent in terms of energy. The standing crop may vary at different times of the year; for example, in a population of deciduous trees between summer and winter.

Stapes (strirrup). The third of the three earossicles of the mammalian middle ear.

Staphylococcus. Any bacterium of the genus Staphylococcus which form masses resembling a bunch of grapes. Many are pathogens, being the causative agents of boils, carbuncles, abscesses, and septicemia.

Starch. A polysaccharide consisting of various proportions of two glucose polymers, amylose and amylopectin. It occurs widely in plants, especially in roots, tubers, seeds, and fruits, as a carbohydrate energy store Starch is therefore a major energy source for animals. When digested it ultimately yields glucose. Starch granules are insoluble in cold water but disrupt if heated to form a gelatinous solution.

Starch Sheath. In young stems of angiosperms, the innermost layer of the cortex containing many large starch grains, considered as homologue of the endodermis.

Starch-statolith Hypothesis. A possible explanation for the way plants pereceive gravity. Most gravity-sensitive organs contain specialized cells called statoliths, in their cytoplasm The statoliths gradually fall to the lower side of the cells under the influence of gravity. The settling out of these grains in reoriented cells is said to provide an internal stimulus, which is transmitted to the growing region of the organ so that appropriate amendments to the growth pattern can be made. These growth movements restore the original position of the cells and hence of the whole plant part.

Starfish. A sea star, an echinoderm of the class Asteriodea, with a characteristic star-shaped body, as Asterias forbesi of the East Coast.

Stargazer. A bottom-dwelling, marine fish (Astroscopus guttatus) of the family Uranoscopidae, with eyes on the dorsal surface of the head and directed upward.

Starling. A Old World passerine bird of the family Sturnidae, especially Sturnus vulgaris, introduced into the United States in 1890 and now widely distributed.

Starter. A pure culture inoculum added to milk or cream to bring about desired fermentations, as in the production of butter, cheese, and fermented milks.

Starvation. The state or condition of being starved.

Starve

1. To become weak of die of hunger.

2. To become weak or disabled by want of any kind.

Station. *bot.* A particular locality for a given plant.

Stasis. The slowing down or cessation of flow of a substance through a tube, as blood, lymph, bile, or intestinal contents.

Statistical Method. In modern usage, a method for analysing data based on probability theory. A statistical method permits the calculation of a value based on observations about some problem that may be tested for significance by comparison with the values that might be expected to arise by chance. Two main categories of statistical methods have been developed : classical or parametric tests, and the more recent non-parametric or distribution free tests. Parametric statistical methods may be applied only to data on an interval scale, and typically they make assumptions about the background population from which the sample is taken, most often that it is normally distributed. Where data are in nominal or ordinal from, or where assumptions about the distribution of data on which a parametric test is based cannot be justified, the non-parametric (distribution-free) methods can be used. In general, parametric tests are more rigorous than non-parametric tests. Formerly, and more colloquially, 'statistical methods' embraced any form of data gathering and analysis. Compare numerical method.

Statoacoustic. Pertaining to the senses of equilibrium and hearing.

Statocyte. Any gravity-sensitive cell that contains statoliths.

Statolith. Any inclusion in the cytoplasm, such as a starch grain, that moves in response to gravity and is believed to be involved in the geotropic response.

Statoreceptor. A receptor for the sense of position or equilibrium, as a statocyst, macula, or crista.

Statospore. A type of resting spore produced by certain algae as in the Chrysophyta.

Status Quo Hormone. SQH, a hormone secreted by the corporallata in certain insect nymphs and larvae which prevents premature metamorphosis.

Streapsin. A lipase present in pancreatic juice.

Stearic Acid (octadecanoic acid). A solid saturated fatty acid, $CH_3(CH_2)_{16}COOH$ that occurs widely (as glycerides) in animal and vegetable fats.

Stearin. A glycerol ester of stearic acid present in many animal fats.

Steatopygia. Excessive enlargement of the buttocks due to accumulation of fat, as in Hottentot women of Africa.

Steer. A young, castrated, male ox, especially one castrated before maturity and raised for beef.

Stegocephalian. A heavity armored, fossil amphibian of the subclass Stegocephalia, considered to be the ancestor of modern amphibians and reptiles.

Stegosaur. A heavily armored, herbivorous dinosaur of the suborder Stegosauria.

Stele (vascular cylinder). The central core of the stems and roots of vascular plants, comprising the vascular tissue, ground tissue, such as pith and medullary rays, and the pericycle. The pericycle is considered to represent the outermost layer of the stele at the boundary with the cortex. The many different types of stele are thought to reflect the direction of the evolution of the vascular system in plats (illustration) Different types of stele may be found in different regions of the same plant. In dicotyledons the root characteristically has a solid central core of vascular tissue (protostele), making it better able to resist pulling stresses, while the stem has a ring of discrete vascular bundles (eustele) and is better able to resist bending stresses.

Stellate. Star-shaped; with parts radiating from a center.

Stem. The part of a plant that usually grows vertically upwards towards the light and supports the leaves, buds, and reproductive structures. The leaves develop at the nodes and side or branch stems develop from buds at the nodes. The stems of certain species are modified as bulbs, corms, rhiomes, and tubers. Some species have twining stems; others have horizontal stems, such as runners.

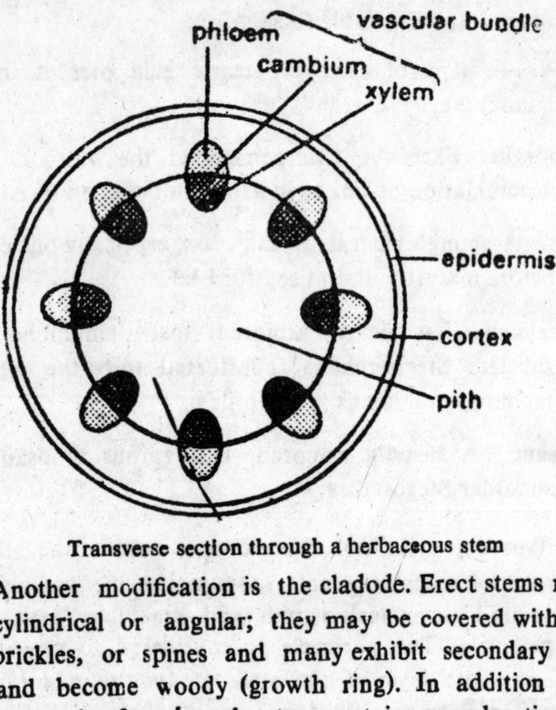

Transverse section through a herbaceous stem

Another modification is the cladode. Erect stems may be cylindrical or angular; they may be covered with hairs, prickles, or spines and many exhibit secondary growth and become woody (growth ring). In addition to its supportive funotion, the stem contains vascular tissue that conducts food, water, and mineral salts between the roots and leaves. It may also contain chloroplasts and carry out photosynthesis.

Stem Cell. An undifferentiated cell from which specialized cells arise.

Stemma

1. An ocellus, especially the lateral ocellus of an arthropod.

2. A facet of an ommatidium.

Stem Mother. In parthenogenetic animals, a female which develops from a zygote and then gives rise to a number of parthenogenetic generations, as in aphids.

Stem Reptiles. The cotylosaurs, thought to be the ancestors of reptiles, birds, and mammals.

Stenobathic. Having a restricted depth range, with reference to marine animals.

Stenobenthic. Restricted to a narrow depth range on the bottom of the ocean.

Stenophagous. Subsisting on a single kind or a limited variety of foods.

Stenopodium. A type of biramous aopendage in which the exopodite and endopodite are attached to a common stem, the protopodite; as a swimmeret of a crayfish.

Stenosis. A narrowing or constriction of a tube, duct, or orifice.

Stenotopic. Intolerant of environmental changes, hence restricted to a narrow geographic range. Compare eurytopic.

Steppe. Eurasian grassland.

Stercoraceous. Of, pertaining to or consisting of dung or feces.

Stercoral Pocket. A diverticulum on the dorsal surface of the rectum in spiders.

Stereoblastula. A blastula which lacks a blastocoel.

Stereid. Prosenchyma.

Sterigma. (pl. sterigmata). One of usually four projections at the apex of a basidium, each one of which bears a basidiospore. The cultivated mushroom is unusual in having only two sterigmata on each basidium, hence the name Agaricus bisporus.

Stereocilia. Nonmotile cilia, as those on epithelial cell lining the epididymis.

Stereogastrula. A gastrula with a solid interior, as in sponges.

Stereognosis. The ability to perceive objects through senses other than vision.

Stereome. The collenchyma and sclerenchyma combined.

Stereoscopic. Of or pertaining to three-dimensional vision, with perception of depth.

Stereotaxis. A taxis in which an animal responds to contact with a solid object; thigmotaxis.

Stereotropism. A tropism in which a plant responds to contact with a solid object; thigmotropism.

Sterigma pl. Sterigmata. One of four slender stalks at the tip of a basidium, each of which bears a basidiospore, as in mushrooms.

Sterile

1. Nontertile; incapable of producing functional gametes.

2. Aseptic; free from microscopic organisms, especially pathogens.

3. Lacking reproductive structures, as a sterile frond.

Sterility. The state or condition of being sterile.

Sterlize. To render or make sterile, as *a.* to deprive of the power of reproduction, as by removal testes or ovaries in animals or stamens and pistils in plants; *b.* to render free of microorganisms.

Sternite. The sternum of an arthropod or one of its sclerites.

Sternum (breastbone)

1. A shield-shaped or rod-shaped bone in terrestrial vertebrates, on the ventral side of the thorax, that articulates with the clavicle (collar bone) of the pectoral gindle and with most of the ribs. It is absent in fish, and in birds it bears a keel.
2. The ventral portion of each segment of the axoskeleton of arthropods.

Steroid. Any of a group of compounds characterized by possession of the perhydrocyclopenteneophenanthrene skeleton, which is made up of a series of four carbon rings (diagram). Steroids may be distinguished from certain terpenoids with a similar skeleton by their possession of methyl groups at carbons 10 and 13. All natural steroids also have an oxygen group at carbon 3. The majority of steroids are alcohols (sterol). Other types of steroid include certain of the pseudoalkaloids and the aglycone portions of the saponins and cardiac glycosides.

Sterol. A steroid alcohol. The sterols found in higher plants are known as phytosterols, while those found in yeasts and fungi are called mycosterols. Stigmasterol and sitosterol are common phytosterols, while ergosterol is an example of a mycosterol.

Stichosome. A long colvmn of stichocytes which encloses the slender esophagus of certain nematodes, as Trichurus.

Stigma. The receptive tip of the carpel, which receives pollen at pollination and on which the pollen grain germinates. The stigma is adapted to catch and trap pollen, either by combing pollen off visiting insects or by various hairs, flaps, or sculpturings. The sigmas of certain plants show haptotropic movements. For example, the monkey flower (Mimulus guttatus) has a two-lobed stigma, which closes together when touched, so removing pollen from a visiting insect. The stigmas of windpollinated plants tend to be feathery or branched to increase the chances of pollination. The stigma usually secretes sticky substances, which may act as a pollen trap but may also be involved in the complex pollen/stigma compatibility interactions. The stigma and style act as physiological filters in controlling cross fertilization, although the actual mechanisms appear to be variable and little understood.

In members of the primitive angiosperm family Winteraceae the stigma is found along the margins of the ventral suture. In the closely related Degeneria vitiensis the margins of the carpel are not fused but are held together by interwoven papillae, which form the stigmatic surface. Studies of such plants have thrown light on the evolution of angiospermy.

Stigmatic. Of or pertaining to stigma.

Stigmatoid Tissue. Tissue in a pistil which facilitates the growth of the pollen tube from stigma to ovule; also called transmitting tissue or pollen-transmitting tracts.

Stilt. A long-legged marsh bird with an upcurved bill, as Himantopus mexicanus, the black-necked stilt.

Stilt Bristles. Elongated bristles in nematodes for attachment or locomotion.

Stilt Root. Prop root.

Stimulus. Any influence that, however received and whether acting directly or indirectly on an organism, gives rise to some form of response within that organism. A stimulus may arise externally, as do light, gravity, and chemical stimuli, or it may be generated within the plant itself as in the case of autonomic movements.

Sting. The ovipositor of aculeate. Hymenoptera, which has lost its egg-laying function and serves as a means of injecting venom into the prey of hunting wasps, and is used as a means of defence by bees. The sting of honeybees (Apis species) and some social wasps is barbed and remains in the skin of the victim after the wasp or bee has become detached. In honeybees the muscular venom sac of detached stings continues to pump venom, and it also emits an alarm pheromone which alters other workers, which may be recruited to join the attack.

Stinger

1. An organism capable of stinging.
2. A stinging organ.

Stinging Cells. Nematocysts or nettle cells of coelenterates.

Stinging Hair. A stiff, glandular hair which secretes an irritating fluid, as those of *a.* plants of the nettle family, Uricaceae; *b.* various caterpillars of the order Lepidoptera.

Stingray. One of several large rays of the family Dasyatidae which posses a slender, whiplike tail armed with serrated spines with poison glands at their bases; a stingaree.

Stinkbug. One of a number of hemipterous insects of the family Pentatomidae which emit a distinctive, disagreeable odour.

Stinkhorn. Common name for the fungal fruit body in some members of the Phallales. The common stinkhorn, Phallus impudicus, has a white, spongy, hollow stem 10-20 cm tall. The cap is initially covered with an olive-brown slime containing the spores, but the slime is eventually removed by flies. This fungus has a strong, fetid odour detectable from a distance of several metres. It is common in woods, gardens, etc. in summer and autumn. The dog stinkhorn, Mutinus, is caninus similar but smells less strongly.

Stinkpot. A musk turtle (Sternotherus odoratus) of the southern states.

Stinking Smut. Bunt.

Stint. A small sandpiper of Britain of the genus Calidris.

Stipe

1. The stalk that forms the lower portion of the fruiting body of certain fungi, such as mushrooms, and supports the umbrella-shaped cap.
2. The stalk between the holdfast and blade (lamina) of certain brown algae, notably kelps.

Stipes pl. **Stipites.** *zool.* A stalk or supporting structure, as *a.* the second segment of an insect maxilla; *b.* the peduncle of a compound eye.

Stipitate. Having a stipe.

Stipula. A newly sprouted feather.

Stipulate. Bearing stipules.

Stipule. One of a pair of leaflike structures, spines, glands, or scales at the leaf base or along a petiole. Stipules are believed to protect the developing leaf in the embryonic state. They may occasionally be modified to enclose a bud, as in beeches (Fagus). Large green stipules are seen in the garden pea (Pisum sativum) and replace photosynthetic tissues lost by the modification of the leaflets into tendrils.

Stipulose. Possessing stipules.

Stirrup. The stapes, an ear ossicle.

Stotat. The common European weasel (Mustela erminea), especially with reddish-brown summer coat.

Stock

1. (rootstock). A plant onto which shoots or buds (scions) of another plant are grafted. The stock affects the size, vigour, and time of flowering and fruiting, of the scion, and specially bred root-stocks are selected accordingly. Where necessary root-stocks may be chosen that confer frost hardiness or resistance to certain soil-borne pathogens.
2. A maintained culture of a particular organism, the origins and characteristics of which are known.

Stolon. A long branch that is unable to support its own weight and consequently bends down to the ground. Where nodes on the stolon touch the soil a new plant may develop from the axillary bud. Examples of stolons are the long shoots of currents and gooseberries (Ribes). Often ordinary shoots will behave like stolons if pegged to the.ground, which is the basis of the layering method of vegetative propagation.

St oloniferous. Bearing or producing stolons.

Stolonization

1. The formation of stolons.
2. In annelids, the formation of new individuals at the posterionated, sometimes in chains, as in syllids.

Stoma (pl. stomata). A pore large numbers of which are present in the epidermis of leaves (especially on the under-surface) and young shoots. Stomata function in gas exchange between the plant and the atmosphere. Each stoma is bordered by two semicircular guard cells (specialized epidermal cells,) whose movements (due to changes in water content) control the size of the aperture. The term stoma is also used to mean both the pore and its associated guard cells.

Stomach. The portion of the vertebrate alimentary canal between the oesophagus and the small intestine. It is a muscular organ, capable of dramatic changes in size and shape, in which ingested food is stored and undergoes preliminary digestion. Cells lining the stomach produce gastric juice, which is throughly mixed with the food by muscular contractions of the stomach. The resultant acidic partly digested food mass (chyme) is discharged into the duodenum thorough the pyloric sphincter for final digestion and absorption. Some herbivorous animals (ruminants) have multichambered stomachs from which food is regurgitated, rechewed, and swallowed again.

Stomach Insecticide. Any insecticide that must be taken into the alimentary canal to be effective. Stomach poisons are often inorganic compounds containing such elements as arsenic, mercury, or fluorine.

Stomate. Stoma.

Stomatic. Of, pertaining to, or possessing a stoma; stomatal.

Stomatopod. A mantis shrimp of the order Stomatopoda, as Squilla.

Stomatous. Possessing a stoma or stomata.

Stomium. A region of thin-walled cells in certain spore-producing structures that ruptures to release the spores. For example, in the sporangium of the fern Dryopteris the stomium ruptures when the annulos dries out.

Stomodeum

1. *zool. a.* The gullet of an anthozoan. *b.* The foregut of an arthopod.
2. *embryol.* An external depression lined with ectoderm located ventral to the head. Upon rupture of the pharyngeal membrane, it becomes continuous with the foregut.

Stone

1. *anat* A calculus.
2. *bot.* The hard, inner portion of a stone fruit or drupe.

Stone Canal. In various echinoderms, the slightly S-shaped canal leading from the madreporite to the ring canal.

Stonecat. A small catfish of the genus Noturus.

Stone Cell. A brachysclereid, a cell present in stony or fibrous tissue, as that in fruits, seeds, and nuts.

Stonecrop. A flowering plant (Sedum) of the order Rosales.

Stone Fly. Any insect of the order Plecoptera.

Stone Fruit. A pyrene or drupe; any fruit with a a hard, stony endocarp, as a peach, plum, or cherry.

Stoneroller. A small, cyprinid minnow (Campostoma anomalum) with a long intestine wound many times about its air bladder.

Stonewort. A green alga of the genus Chara, with incrustations of calcium carbonate.

Stony Coral. A madrepore.

Stool

1. The basal portion of a plant, as a tree stump, from which shoots arise.
2. A pole to which a bird acting as a decoy is fastened.
3. The evacuation of the bowels or the material evacuated; the feces.

Storax

1. A tree or shrub of the genus Styrax.
2. An aromatic balsam (Levant storax) obtained from Liquidambar orientalis, a tree of southwestern Asia Minor used in medicine and perfurmery; American storax or styrax is obtained from the sweet gum (L. styraciflua).

Storied (storeyed). Describing the axial cells and rays of wood that are arranged in horizontal series as viewed in tangential section.

Strain. Any group of very similar or identical individuals, such as a pure line, clone, physiological race, or mating strain.

Strangle. To compress the windpipe until asphyxiation occurs; to suffocate, as by water enterning the windpipe.

Strangleweed. Dodder.

Strangulated

1. *bot.* Constricted at irregular intervals.
2. *med.* Having circulation or passage of substances through a tube stopped by compression.

Stratification

1. The arrangement of some factor in layers or strata. Thus vegetation in a woodland consists of an upper layer, the tree canopy, and a lower layer of herbs at ground level, often with one or more intermediate layers of shrubs and saplings. Other factors, such as temperature and light, show stratification, this being especially important in the study of aquatic ecosystem.
2. The practice of placing seeds between layers of moist sand or peat and exposing them to low temperatures, usually simply by leaving them outside during the winter. The treatment is necessary for those seeds that require a period of chilling before they will germinate. It is though that low temperatures may block the action of a germination inhibitor. Compare vernalization.

Stratified. Arranged in strata or layers.

Stratosphere. The atmospheric layer above the troposphere which extends on average from about 10 to 50 km above the Earth's surface. The stratosphere is a major stable layer whose base is marked by the tropopause, with temperatures on overall average around −60°C. Temperature in the lower stratosphere is isothermal but increases markedly in the upper part, to reach a maximum of about 0°C at the stratopause. High stratospheric temperatures result from absorption of ultraviolet radiation (0.20-0.32 μm wavelengths) by ozone concentrated at 15-30 km. Due to low air density, ozone concentrated in small amounts is particularly effective in absorbing radiation, giving high temperatures at 50 km. The isothermal condition at the base of the stratospheric inversion layer creates stability, which generally limits vertical extensions of cloud and leads to the lateral spreading of high cumulonimbus cloud with characteristic anvil heads.

Stratum pl. **Strata**. A layer.

Stratum Corneum. The layers of dead keratinized cells that form the outermost layers of mammalian epidermis. The stratum corneum provides a water-resistant barrier between the external environment and the living cells of the skin.

Strawberry. The juicy, red fruit of the genus Fragaria of the rose family, or the plant which produces it.

Streaking. *bacteriol.* The preparation of a streak plate.

Streak Plate. *bacteriol.* A culture of organisms prepared by passing a transfer loop back and forth on the surface of a solid medium, as agar, a technique for culturing isolated colonies of a mixed culture.

Strengthening Tissue. Mechanical tissue.

Strepsipteran. A styloid, an insect of the order Strepsiptera comprising insects which parasitize other insects, as Stylops, a parasite of bees.

Streptococcus pl. **treptococci**. Any bacterium of the genus Streptococcus, gram-positive bacteria of the coccus type arranged in beadlike chains.

Streptomyces (family Stretomycetaceae, order Actinomycetales). Genus of bacteria in which the spore-bearing mycelium is variously coloured, often green or blue. Many antibiotics are obtained from species of Streptomyces : *e.g.* streptomycin, erythromycin, kanamycin, and tetracyclines. There are hundreds of species. They are mostly saprotrophic, and found in soils, for example. A few can be pathogenic, *e.g.* S. scabies causes common scab of potato.

Streptomycin. An antibiotic produced by Streptomyces griseus, an actinomycete.

Stria pl. **Striae.** A narrow streak, line, band, or mark, especially when arranged in parallel fashion.

Striate

1. Striated.
2. Parallel, with reference to veins in a leaf.

Striated

1. Marked by cross bands or stripes.
2. Marked by fine parallel lines, grooves, or ridges.

Striated Border. A layer of microvilli of the free border of epithelial cells, especially absorptive cells of the intestine.

Striated Muscle. Muscle composed of fibers bearing transverse striations, as skeletal and cardiac muscle.

Striation. One of a series of parallel bands or lines; a stria.

Stricture. A constriction or narrowing of a tube, canal, or hollow organ.

Stridulate. To produce sound by rubbing a file across a membrane. Insects have a wide variety of mechanisms for sound production. In some of the most common examples a file on one wing rubs across a roughened surface on the other wing, or a file on the leg is drawn across the edge of the wing. The volume of sound production achieved by these mechanisms is often startling. The sound may be amplified by resonation in a wing or (*e.g.* in mole crickets) by causing a column of air to resonate in a chamber excavated in the ground and shaped for the purpose.

Stridulation. The production of sounds by insects rubbing one part of the body against another. The parts of the body involved vary from species to species. Stridulation is typical of the Orthoptera (grasshoppers, crickets, cicadas), in which the purpose of the sounds is usually to bring the sexes together, although they are also used in territorial behaviour, warning, etc.

Stridulatory Organ. A sound-producing structure in an insect consisting of two body parts which are rubbed against each other, as the inner surface of the femur against the forewing in locusts.

Striga pl. Strigae. A sharp, appressed hairlike scale or bistle.

Strigiform Of or belonging to the order Strigiformes which includes the owls, comprising two families, the Tytonidae (barn owls) and Strigidae (all other owls).

Strigose. Covered with bristles or strigae.

Strip

1. To express the contents of a canal or duct by milking movements.
2. To remove leaves from stalks, as from tobacco plants.

Strobila pl. t.obilae. A linear chain of similar structures, as *a* the stage in development of a scphozoan jellyfish consisting of disclike ephyrula; *b.* the body of a tapeworm consisting of a chain of proglottids.

Strobilaceous. Of, pertaining to, or resembling a cone.

Strobilation. Strobilization.

Strobile. A strobilus.

Strobilization. A sexual reproduction by transverse fission resulting in the formation of a strobila.

Strobilocereus. A cysticercus (bladderworm) with a chain of undeveloped segments.

Strobilus

1. A type of composite fruit that is formed from a complete inflorescence. It produces achenes enclosed

in bracts and when mature becomes cone-shaped. The hop fruit is an example.

2. Cone.

Stroma

1. The hydrophilic proteinaceous matrix of chloroplasts. It contains the enzymes and reagents necessary for the dark reactions of photosynthesis.
2. (pl. stromata). A solid mass of plectenchyma that may bear perithecia either on its surface, as in Nectria cinnabarina (coral-spot fungus), or embedded wlthin the tissue with only the ostioles appearing at the surface, as in Xylaria hypoxylon (candle-snuff fungus).

Stromatolite. A rocky cushion-like mass formed by the unchecked growth of millions of line-secreting blue-green algae. Stromatolites are found olny in areas where other organisms that would normally keep down the algal numbers cannot survive, such as extremely salty bays. It is thought that such formations were abundant 2000 million years ago, when blue-green algae were the most advanced form of life on earth, and that the white rings of fossilized microorganisms found in rocks of this age are the remains of stomatolites.

Strombus. A spirally coiled seedpod of a legume.

Strongyle

1. A straight sponge spicule rounded at both ends; a monaxon.
2. A nematode of the family Stongylidae.

Strongyliform Larva. A larva of a nematode which possesses a long cylindrical esophagus with a terminal bulb not sharply demarcated. Compare rhabditiform larva

Strophiole. A caruncle.

Structural Gene A length of DNA that codes for an enzyme or other protein. It is equivalent to a cistron.

Structure

1. The mode of construction, form, makeup, or arrangement of parts of an organ or organism.
2. Any part of a living thing, especially one which has a specific function; an organ or organelle.

Struggle for Existence. The conflict between an organism and its environment; the struggle to stay alive or survive.

Struma

1. *bot.* A swollen mass at the base of the capsule in certain mosses.
2. *med.* Goiter.

Strychnine. A colourless poisonous crystalline alkaloid found in certain plants.

Stud

1. A studhorse or stallion.
2. Any male animal kept for breeding.

Studfish. A killifish of the genus Fundulus.

Stunt. A plant disease characterized by retarded development.

Sturgeon. A primitive chondrostean fish of the family Acipenseridae, including several species of Acipensor, valued for its flesh and roe, the latter the source of caviar.

Stylar. Of or pertaining to a style.

Stylate. Possessing or resembling a style or stylet.

Style. The sterile portion of the carpel between the ovary and the stigma, which may be elongated or feathery, especially in wind-pollinated species, so that the stigma is presented in an effective place for pollination. In primitive forms the styles of individual carpels are separate. In more advanced forms they tend to be fused. In some plants, notably traveller's joy (Clematis vitalba) and the pasque flower (Pulsatilla vulgaris), the style elongates after pollination and remains attached to the fruit. This is an adaptation to promote wind dispersal of the seed.

Styles. In certain groups of insects, mainly Hemiptera true bugs, tubular, sucking mouthparts formed from mandibles and maxillae that are modified into slender, flexible structures. The two pairs of maxillary stylets are pressed closely together and the seprate salivary and food canals pass between them. The mandibular stylets slide freely and independently along the sides of the maxillary stylets.

Styloid. Long and pointed.

Stylopid. A strepsipteran, especially one of the genus Stylops.

Stylopodium. A dlsclike enlargement at the base of the style, as in flowers of the parsley family (Umbelliferae).

Stylostome. A minute, tubular cavity in the skin filled with semidigested tissue debris upon which redbugs (mites) feed.

Stylus. In symphylans, an eversible, pointed process in the body wall at the base of each leg.

Subarachnoid Space. The space between the arachnoid membrane and the pia mater, two of the membranes (meninges) that surround the brain and spinal cord. It is filled with cerebrospinal fluid.

Subchelate. Lacking an opposable jaw, with reference to chelicera.

Subclavian Artery. A paired artery that passes beneath the collar bone (clavicle) and branches to supply blood to the arm. The left subclavian artery arises from the aorta; the right from the innominate artery.

Subclimax. The stage preceding the climax stage for a particular climate.

Subclimax Vegetation. Climax.

Subcosta. A longitudinal vein in an insect wing lying between the radius and the costa.

Subcutaneous Tissue. The tissue that lies immediately beneath the dermis (skin). It is made up of loose fibrous connective tissue, muscle, and fat (adipose tissue), which in some animals (*e.g.* whales and hibernating mammals) forms an insulating layer or an important food store.

Suberin. A mixture of waxy substances, similar to cutin, present in the thickened cell walls of many trees and shrubs, particularly in corky tissues. The deposition of suberin (suberization) provides a protective water-impermerable layer.

Suberization. The deposition of suberin in the walls of plant cells resulting in the development of cork tissue.

Suberose. Corklike in texture.

Sub-erose. Appearing as if slightly gnawed.

Subgerminal Cavity. The blastocoel or segmentation cavity in a meroblastic ovum undergoing cleavage.

Subiculum. A dense mass of fungal mycelium on the surface of the host plant.

Subinferior. Somewhat inferior; half inferior, with reference to the ovary of a flower.

Subliminal. Below the threshold, as a subliminal stimulus.

Sublingual. Beneath the tongue.

Sublittoral

1. Designating or occurring in the shallow-water zone of a sea, over the continental shelf and below the low tide mark.
2. Designating or occurring in the zone of a lake below the littoral zone, to a depth of 6—10 metres.

Sublittoral Zone

1. In freshwater ecosystems, an alternative name for the limnetic zone.

2. The sea-shore zone lying immediately below the littoral (intertidal) zone and extending to about 200 m depth or to the edge of the continental shelf. Red and brown algae are characteristic of this area. Typical animals include sea anenomes and corals on rocky shores, and shrimps, carbs and flounders on sandy shores. The zone may alternatively be called the subtidal zone. It is approximately equivalent to the circalittoral zone.

Submicroscopic. Below the limit of resolution of an optical microscope; too small to be seen by such an instrument.

Submucosa. A layer of connective tissue which lies beneath a mucous membrane.

Subneural Gland. In tunicates, a glandular structure located ventral to the nerve ganglion, its duct opening into the pharynx; the neural or adneural gland.

Subpetiolar. Under a petiole and often enclosed or enveloped by it, with reference to buds.

Subsere. A secondary succession or a plant succession on a denuded area.

Subshrub. A perennial with a stem which is woody at its base.

Subsidiary. Secondary, auxiliary, tributary, accessory.

Subsidiary Cell (accessory cell). One of a group of morphologically differentiated epidermal cells immediately surrounding the guard cells. Stomatal complexes lacking subsidiary cells are termed anomocytic. The number, arrangement, and development of subsidiary cells are often useful taxonomic characters.

Subspecies. Technically, a race of a species that is allocated a Latin name. The number of races recognized within a species and the allocation of names to them is something of an arbitrary procedure. Systematic and phenotypic variations do occur within species, but there are no clear rules for identifying them as races or subspecies except that they must be (a) geographically distinct, (b) populations, not merely morphs, and (c) different to some degree from other geographic populations.

Substrate. The molecule or molecules on which an enzyme exerts its catalytic action. An enzyme may be specific for only one substrate, *e.g.* aspartase, which catalyses the interconversion of aspartic and fumaric acids, and is strictly specific for the L-isomer of aspartic acid. Other enzymes can act on a range of substrates; alkaline phosphatase can hydrolyse many esters of phosphoric acid. The substrate reflects the structure of the enzyme active site in that the substrate must have a binding group by which it can bind to the active site, and a susceptible bond at which the enzyme can attack the substrate. These groups must have complementary structures in the active site.

Substratum. A substrate.

Subtend. *bot.*

1. To stand below and close to.
2. To be adjacent to.
3. To enclose within its axil, as a bract which subtends a flower.

Subterminal. Located near the end but not at the extreme end, with reference to bacterial spores.

Subterranean. Underground, beneath the surface of the earth.

Subtilin. An antibiotic obtained from Bacillus subtilis, effective against gram-positive bacteria.

Subtropical. Nearly tropical, with reference to regions near the tropical zone or regions almost tropical in their climate.

Subulate. Shaped like an awl, *i.e.* narrow, pointed, and more or less flattened, *e.g.* the leaves of Subularia aquatica (awlwort).

Subumbrella. The concave, oral surface of the bell (umbrella) of a medusa or jellyfish.

Subungual. Below or beneath a claw, nail, or hoof.

Subunguis. The solehorn or ventral plate of a claw (unguis).

Succession. Sequential change in vegetation either in response to an environmental change are induced by the intrinsic properties of the plants themselves. Classically, the term refers to the colonization of a new physical environment by a series of vegetation communities until a final equilibrium state, the climax, is achieved. The presence of the colonizers, the pioneer plants, modifies the environment so that new species can join or replace the initial colonizers. Changes are rapid at first but slow to a more or less imperceptible rate at the climax stage. The characteristic sequence of developmental stages, *i.e.* nudation, migration, ecesis, competition, reaction, and stabilization, is termed a sere.

Succinic Acid. A four-carbon dicarboxylic acid with the formula $HOOC(CH_2)_2COOH$. Succinate is an intermediate in the TCA cycle, formed from succinyl CoA with concomitant formation of GTP. It is oxidized to fumarate by succinate dehydrogenase, a flavoprotein. In the reaction the FAD prosthetic group of succinate dehydrogenase is reduced to $FADH_2$. Succinate is also a product of the glyoxylate cycle, and succinly CoA is an important precursor in porphyrin synthesis.

Succulent. A plant that conserves water by storing it in fleshy leaves or stems. Succulents are found either in dry regions or in areas where there is sufficient water but it is not easily obtained, as in salt marshes. Such plants are often modified to reduce water loss by transpiration. For example the leaves of cacti are reduced to spines.

Succus Entericus. A mixture of enzymes produced by glands within the small intestine. These enzymes are responsible for most of the digestive processes that occur in the alimentary canal and include proteases, lipases, and amylases.

Suck. To take nourishment or draw milk from the breast; to draw into the mouth or digestive tract by producing a vacuum.

Sucker

1. Underground shoot arising adventitiously from the roots or lower stem of a tree or shrub and emerging from the soil to form a new plant, initially nourished by the parent plant. In cultivated species where grafting is practised (*e.g.* roses and fruit trees), production of suckers from the stock may seriously detract from the vigour of the grafted scion.
2. Organ with which an animal attaches itself to a surface.
3. Catostomidae.

Suckle. To nurse at the breast or the udder.

Suckling. A nursling: a child or animal before it is weaned.

Sucrase. Saccharase, an enzyme which hydrolyzes sucrose to glucose and fructose. Also called invertase.

Sucrose (cane sugar, beet sugar, saccharose). A nonreducing disaccharide of glucose and fructose linked through a highenergy bond between carbon two of fructose and carbon one of glucose. Sucrose is the major transport sugar in higher plants. It is formed in the chloroplasts and transported through the phloem to other organs and tissues, where it is either metabolized for energy or utilized in the synthesis of reserve and structural polysaccharides. Present evidence indicates that in vivo synthesis of sucrose is a two-step reaction involving fructose 6 phosphate and glucose. These react to form sucrose 6 phosphate, which is then dephosphorylated by the enzyme sucrose phosphatase. The enzyme sucrose synthase can catalyse the direct manufacture of sucrose from UDP-glucose and fructose, but in the cell sucrose synthase is thought to be the major route of sucrose breakdown, allowing direct formation of nucleoside diphosphate sugars from sucrose. The enzyme invertase also splits sucrose, to D-glucose and D-fructose, but its physiological significance is not clear. The mixture of D-glucose and D-fructose formed on hydrolysis by invertase is often termed invert sugar since the optical activity is inverted from dextrorotatory (sucrose solution) to laevorotatory (D-glucose and D-fructose mixture). Invert sugar is found in many fruits.

Table sugar is composed of sucrose crystals. Production is mostly from sugar cane (Saccharum officinarum), grown in the tropics, and sugar beet (Beta valgaris), grown in temperate zones. Small amounts are obtained from other sources, *e.g.* sugar maple (Acer saccharum) and sweet sorghum (Sorghum bicolor).

Suctorial. Adapted for sucking.

Suctorian. A protozoan of the class Suctoria, order Suctorida, ciliate protozoans but lacking cilia in the adult state; sessile protozoans with tentacles for attachment or piercing prey, as Podophyra, a stalked form.

Sudan Stains. Any of various temporary aniline stains used to colour fats and waxes. Examples are Sudan IV, Sudan blue, and Sudan black. They are used to stain cutinized and suberized tissues. Thus the Casparian band readily turns orange on staining with Sudan III or Sudan IV.

Sudd. A floating mass of dense vegetation, sometimes blocking navigable streams.

Suet. Fat in the abdominal cavity of domestic animals, especially that about the kidneys.

Suffrutescent. Of the nature of a shrub; low and woody.

Suffrutescent Habit. A growth form in which the plant is woody at the base but has herbaceous branches. It is seen in alpine willows.

Sugar (saccharide). Any of a group of water-soluble carbohydrates of relatively low molecular weight and typically having a sweet taste. The simple sugars are called monosaccharides. More complex sugars comprise between two and ten monosaccha rides linked together : disaccharides contain two, trisaccharides three, and so on. The name is often used to refer specifically to sucrose (table sugar).

Sugar Acid An oxidized derivative of a monosaccharide. There are two biologically important types of sugar acid, the aldonic acids and the uronic acids. In aldonic acids the aldehyde group of a monosaccharide is oxidized to a carboxylic acid. The aldonic acid of glucose, gluconic acid, is an intermediate in the pentose phosphate pathway. Ascorbic acid (vitamin C) is also an aldonic acid.

Sugar Alcohol. A monosaccharide in which the aldehyde group is reduced to an alcohol. Thus D-glucose yields the sugar alcohol sorbitol while the alcohol from mannose is mannitol. Other important sugar alcohols are glycerol, a central compound in lipid metabolism, and inositol, an important intermediate in cell wall polysaccharide synthesis. Sugar alcohols, other than glycerol, are limited in nature to the plant kingdom.

Sugar Beet. A variety of the common beet (Beta vulgaris) whose white roots are the source of beet sugar.

Sugarcane. A tall, grass plant (Saccharum officinarum), stems of which are the source of cane sugar.

Sugar Phosphate. A phosphate derivative of a monosaccharide. Sugar phosphates are important intermediates in carbohydrate metabolism. The pentose phosphate ribulose 1,5-bisphosphate reacts with carbon dioxide in the first reaction of the Calvin cycle. All the subsequent steps of the Calvin cycle also involve sugar phosphates as do the reactions of glycolysis.

Sulcate. With grooves or furrows.

Sulcus pl. **Sulci.** A groove or furrow.

Sulfa Drug. A drug of the sulfonamide types possessing marked bacteriostatic properties.

Sulphonamides. Organic compounds containing the group—$SO_2.NH_2$. The sulphonamides are amides of sulphonic acids. Many have antibacterial action and are also known as sulpha drugs, including :

sulphadiazine, $NH_2C_6H_4SO_2NHC_4H_3N_2$,

sulphathiazole, $NH_2C_6H_4SO_2NHC_3H_2NS$,

and several others. They act by preventing bacteria from reproducing and are used to treat a variety of bacterial infections, especially of the gut and urinary system.

Sulphur Symbol : S. A nonmetallic solid yellow element, atomic number 16, atomic weight 32.06. It is essential to growth, being found in the amino acids cystine and methionine, in the iron—sulphur proteins, *e.g.* ferredoxin, which are important in electron transport, and in coenzyme A. Sulphur is also found in various secondary metabolites, *e.g.* the mustard-oil glycosides. Sulphur is absorbed from soil as the sulphate (SO_4^{2-}) ion. Various nitrogen and potassium fertilizers are applied as sulphates and sulphur deficiency is not commonly a problem.

Sulphur is used to control various pathogens and pests (sulphur dust, dithiocarbamate fungicide). Sulphur dioxide, a by-product of many industrial processes, is an important atmospheric pollutant (also acid rain).

Sulfur Bacteria. One of several species of bacteria which store or metabolive elemental sulfur or its inorganic compounds, especially Beggiatoa, Thiobacillus.

Sulphur Dust. Powdered sulphur, used as an insecticide (especially against mites and scale insects) and as a fungicide, particularly in the control of mildew. It gives off sulphur dioxide when ignited and is thus often used as a fumigant. It is also mixed with soil to kill soil-borne pathogens. Elemental sulphur, in combination with calcium hydroxide and water, forms lime sulphur, an orange-coloured liquid used to kill various mites and to control peach leaf curl, scap, and powdery mildew.

Sulphur Fungus (sulphur polypore). Common name for the fruit bodies of Laetiporus sulphureus, which are bracket-like, typically growing in tiers. The upper surface is irregular, and is initially a bright sulphur-yellow or orange-yellow but later fades to a dull whitish colour. The tubes on the under-side are sulphur-yellow with small, more or less circular pores. The spore print is white. They are found on various broad-leaved (living or dead) trees, particularly oak.

Summer Kill. The partial or complete destruction of the fish population of a pond or lake during the summer season due to reduced oxygen content of the warm waters.

Summerwood. The outer layer of an annual ring consisting principally of small, thin-walled elements.

Sundew. An insectivorous plant (Drosera), a bog plant whose circular leaves bear long, glandular hairs ("tentacles") to which insects adhere.

Sunfish

1. A large, ocean sunfish (Mola mola) sometimes reaching a weight of 2000 lbs.

2. Any of a number of small, freshwater fishes of the family Centrarchidae, as Lepomis, and other genera.

Sunflower. A composite (Helianthus) with large, conspicuous, many-flowered heads.

Sun Plant. A plant that is able to flourish only in conditions of high light intensity. Sun plants usually have wide epidermal and palisade layers and numerous stomata on the lower surface of the leaf. Examples are the dominant trees of many woodland communities. Compare shade plant.

Sun Star. An asteroid echinoderm with numerous radiating arms, as Solaster, with 7 to 14 arms.

Superfecundation. The fertilization of two or more ova liberated at the same time following successive acts of coitus but not necessarily involving the same male.

Superfemale. *genetics.* In Drosophila, a weak, feeble female of low vitality with three X-chromosomes but the normal number of autosomes.

Superfetation. The development of a second fetus after one has already started development in the uterus.

Superficial. Of, pertaining to, or near the surface. Compare deep.

Superficial Cleavage. Cleavage in which the dividing cells form a surface layer about a central, uncleaved yolk, as in an insect egg.

Supergene. A segment of chromosome that is protected from crossing-over and so is transmitted intact from generation to generation, like a recon. The term is used to refer to several closely linked gene loci that affect a single trait or a series of interrelated traits, such as the genes coding for the expression of pin and thrum flower phenotypes in the primrose and other species of the genus Primula, and the set of gene loci controlling the colour and presence or absence of bands in the shell of the snail Cepaea nemoralis. Genes involved in the same biochemical function, *e.g.*, those controlling the synthesis of tryptophan, are often clustered together in close linkage within the geneome to form a supergene. The bacterial operon is one such example.

Superior. Describing a structure that is positioned above or higher than another structure in the body. For example, in flowering plants the ovary is described as superior when located above the other organs of the flower (hypogyny). Compare inferior.

Superior Ovary. Ovary.

Supermale *genetics*. In Drosophila, a weak, feeble male of low vitality possessing one X-chromosome and an extra set of autosomes.

Supernumerary. More than the usual or normal number, as supernumerary digits.

Supernumerary Chromosome. B-chromosome.

Superposition Image. One formed in compound eyes in dim light when pigment is retracted in which corresponding parts of images formed by different ommatidia are superimposed.

Super-regeneration. The development of extra organs or parts as a result of regeneration.

Supination. Rotation of the lower forearm so that the hand faces forwards or upwards sweat. The salty fluid secreted by the sweat glands onto the surface of the skin. Excess body heat is used to evaporate sweat, thereby resulting in cooling of the skin surface. Small amounts of urea are excreted in sweat.

Supine

1. Lying on the back with the face directed upward.
2. With reference to the hand, with the palm forward or upward. Compare pone.

Supplemental. Extra, additional.

Suppressor. That which restrains, inhibits, counteracts, or prevents an action, as a suppressor gene.

Suppressor Mutation (suppressor). In genetics, a second mutation that masks the phenotypic effects of an earlier mutation. This second mutation occurs at a different site in the genome (*i.e.*, it is not a strict reversion); 'intragenic suppression results from a second mutation that corrects the functioning of the mutant gene (*e.g.*, a mutation of a different nucleotide in the same triplet, such that the codon then encodes the original amino acid); 'intergenic suppression' results from mutation of a different gene, the product of which compensates for the dysfunction in the first (*e.g.*, a mutation that produces a mutant transfer-RNA molecule that inserts an amino acid in response to a nonsense codon, thus continuing a protein that would otherwise have been terminated). If a single suppressor mutation can suppress more than one existing mutation, it is said to be a supersuppressor. Compare reverse mutation.

Suppuration. The formation of pus.

Suprabranchial. Above the gills; epibranchial.

Suprabranchial Cavity. In bivalves, a channel lying to each gill which receives water from water tubes and conveys it to the excurrent siphon.

Suprarenal. Above the kidney.

Supprarenal Gland. The adrenal gland.

Suprascapula. A bone in the pectoral girdle of certain amphibians which extends dorsally and medially from the scapula, as in the frog.

Supravital Staining. Staining by the addition of dyes to a medium containing cells which have been removed from an organism, as the study of blood cells to which neutral red or Janus green has been added.

Sural. Of or pertaining to the calf of the leg.

Surcurrent. Having winged expansions extending up the stem from the base of a leaf.

Surface Area/Volume Ratio. The ratio of the suface area of a cell, organ, or organism to its internal volume. The higher the ratio the greater the possibility for gaseous exchange and absorption of dissolved minerals. Thus the size of unicellular organisms is limited by the rate at which oxygen and carbon dioxide can diffuse into and out of the cell. The form of higher plants, especially the possession of numerous flat leaves, serves to increase the surface area/volume ratio. In this way a ratio of 30 cm^2 of surface to 1 cm^3 of tissues can be achieved. This ratio is greatly increased if intercellular spaces are taken into account.

Surface Tension Symbol γ. The property of a liquid that makes it behave as if its surface enclored in an elastic skin. The property results from intermolecular forces : a molecule in the interior of a liquid experiences a force of attraction from other molecules equally from all sides, whereas a molecule at the surface is only attracted by molecules below it in the-liquid. The surface tension is defined as the force acting over the surface per unit length of surface perpendicular to the force. It is measured in newtons per metre. It can equally be defined as the energy required to increase the surface area by one square metre, *i e.*, it can be measured in joules per metre squared (which is equivalent to N m^{-1}).

The surface tension of water is very strong, due to the intermolecular hydrogen bonding, and is responsible for the formation of drops, bubbles, and meniscuses, as well as the rise of water in a capillary tube (capillarity), and the absorption of liquids by porous substances, and the ability of liquids to wet a surface. Capillarity is very important in plants as it is largely responsible for the transport of water, against gravity, within the plant.

Surfactant (surface active agent). A substance, such as a detergent, added to a liquid to increase its spreading or wetting properties by reducing its surface tension.

Surinam Toad. An aquatic toad of South America, males of which carry the eggs attached to their back.

Surra. Trypanosomiasis of horses, camels, and other animals caused by Trypanosoma evansi, transmitted principally by biting flies.

Survival of the Fitest. Natural selection.

Susceptibility. The condition of a plant such that it is likely to succumb to attack by pathogen, Extreme susceptibility in which the host cells die soon after invasion by a pathogen, is termed hypersensitivity and this reaction in fact confers considerable resistance. Susceptibility is often found where a crop cultivar has relied on one major-gene for resistance to a particular pathogen. If a mutant of the pathoget develops that can overcome this major-gene resistance then the cultivar is often seen to have no other means of preventing the invasion and spread of the pathogen. Susceptibility, like resistance, varies according to environmental conditions. For example, excessive application of nitrogen fertilizer may lead to lavish growth that is more easily invaded by a pathogen.

Susceptible

1. Capable of being influenced or affected by an agent or environmental condition.
2. Liable to infection if exposed to the causative agent of an infections disease.

Suspended Animation. A state or condition resembling death in which vital activities, as respiration, are temporarily stopped, as in near drowning.

Suspensor. *bot.* A connecting or supporting structure, as *a* a hyphal branch which supports a conjugating isogamete, as in molds; *b*, a group of cells which places the embryo closer to a food supply, as in club mosses and gymnosperms; *c*. a chain of cells which attaches the embryo to the wall of the embryo sac, as in angiosperms.

Suspension Culture. The system of growing single cells and small cell aggregates in a liquid growth medium that is kept agitated by means of bubbling shaking, or stirring so the cells do not settle out. Microorganisms and cells derived from callus tissues may be grown in this way. Growth is maintained by providing continuous aeration and by either transferring portions of the suspension to fresh medium or replacing a part of the culture with fresh medium. Suspension cultures of plant cells derived from friable masses of callus show a similar growth curve to cultures of microorganisms in that there is a lag phase and a logarithmic phase of growth. Cells of many plant species can be induced to form embryoids (embryogeny) in suspension culture, which, if removed from the culture and given appropriate conditions, will develop into complete plants.

Suspensor. The line of cells that differentiates from the proembryo by mitosis and anchors the embryo in the parental tissue. It also conducts nutrients to the embryo.

Suspensory Ligament. A group of delicate fibers encirding the lens of the eye by which it is attached to the processes of the ciliary body.

Sustentacular Cells. Cells which serve for suspension or support, as the non-nervous cells of the olfactory epithelium and taste buds or Sertoli coils of the seminiferous tubules.

Suture. The line marking the junction of two body structures. Examples are the immovable joints between the bones of the skull and, in plants, the seam along the edge of a pea or bean pod.

[1]Swallow. A passerine bird of the family Hirundinidae, as the barn swallow (Hirundo rustica).

[2]Swallow. To pass food from the mouth cavity to the crop or stomach.

Swallow's Nest. In the Far East, the edible nest of a swiftlet composed of gumlike saliva.

Swallowtail. A large butterfly of the genus Papilio, with a backwardly projecting process on each wing. Its larva is the celery or parsley worm.

Swallowing. Deglutition.

Swamp. A region of vegetation that develops in stagnant or slow-flowing water, such as that around a lake margin. Initially there is a layer of peat supporting numerous reeds. When this builds up above the water level many other species become established, including sedges and yellow flag iris. Swamps may also develop on water-retentive clays in desert and semidesert areas.

Mangrove swamps are found along many tropical coasts. Mangroves are halophytes and grow in a tangled mass to a moderate height. The stems and the exposed roots are covered with red algae and various lichens. Stilt roots anchor them in the soft mud and help to retain silt, thus gradually enabling other species to grow.

Swan. A large, heavy-bodied, long-necked bird of the family Anatidae, especially those of the genus Cygnus, as C. columbianus, the whistling swan.

[1]Swarm

1. A large number of insects, as bees, ants, or termites in the process of swarming.

2. A large group of free-swimming or floating cells or minute organisms.

[2]**Swarm.** To collect together and leave the hive or nest to found a new colony, as the honeybee.

Swarm Cell. In the Myxomycota, an amoeba-like cell that is produced on germination of a spore. Swarm cells have two anterior whiplash flagella and lack a cell wall. Usually one, but occasionally up to four such cells emerge from one spore. They ingest food, reproduce by division, and then become gametes, in some instances becoming myxamoebae first. The gametes fuse in pairs to form a zygote that develops into the plasmodium. In adverse conditions the swarm cells can transform into microcysts.

Swarming. The sudden appearance of large numbers of individuals, as *a.* the release of swarm spores by fungi and protozoans; *b.* the appearance of free-swimming sexual individuals of the palola worm; *c.* the rapid spreading of bacteria over a moist surface, as Proteus; *d.* the departure of the queen bee with a large number of workers from the nest; *e.* the appearance of large numbers of winged termites or ants.

Swarm Spore. A motile zoospore of certain mycetozoans, especially when produced in large numbers.

[1]**Sweat**

1. To perspire or discharge sweat from a sweat gland, or the material discharged.
2. To exude moisture in small drops, as seen in green plants or in the ripening of cheese.

[2]**Sweat.** Moisture which has condensed in small droplets.

Sweat Bee. One of several species of bees which are attracted to people who are perspiring, as Halictus of the family Halictidae.

Sweat Gland. A small gland in mammalian skin that secretes sweat. The distribution of sweat glands on the body surface varies between species : they occur over most of the body surface in man and higher primates but have a more restricted distribution in other mammals.

Sweet

1. Having an agreeable taste, as that of sugar.
2. The opposite of sour or bitter.
3. Not acid, as a sweet soil.

Sweetbread. The thymus and pancreas of an animal, especially a calf, when used for food.

Sweet Gum. A tree (Liquidambar styraciflua) of the witch hazel family, or its reddish-brown wood used for furniture; also called red gum. Also the source of storax, a medicinal product.

Sweet Potato. A twining, trailing, perennial vine (Ipomoea batatas) with fleshy, adventitious roots rich in starch and sugar.

Swellfish. A puffer.

Swift. A rapidly moving animal, as *a.* the chimney swift (Chaetura pelagica), a swallowlike bird of the family Apodidae; *b.* a lizard of the genus Sceloporus; *c.* a ghost moth of the family Hepialidae.

Swiftlet. A swift of East Asia and Oceania of the genus Collocalia which produces large quantities of saliva which is used in nest building.

Swim Bladder (air bladder). An air-filled sac lying above the alimentary canal in bony fish that regulates the buoyancy of the animal. Air enters or leaves the bladder either via a pneumatic duct opening into the oesophagus or stomach or via capillary blood vessels, so that the specific gravity of the fish always matches the depth at which it is swimming. This makes the fish weightless, so less energy is required for locomotion. In lungfish it also has a respiratory function. The lungs of tetrapods are homologous with the swim bladder, which has developed its hydrostatic function by specialization.

Swimmer's Itch. Cercarial dermatitis caused by invasion of the skin by foreign schistosome cercariae.

Swimming Bell. A swimming medusa of a siphonophore; a nectocalyx.

Swine. Any member of the family Suidae, especially those of the genus Sus which comprises all true pigs. Term is applied collectively to all pigs and hogs, especially those of domestic varieties.

Swordfish. A large, ocean food fish (Xiphias gladias) of the family Xiphiidae, with an extremely long, swordlike upper jaw.

Syconium (syconus). A type of pseudocarp in which achenes are borne on the inside of a hollow receptacle. The fruit of figs (Ficus) is an example.

Syconoid. A type of canal system in sponges in which the incurrent canals parallel the radial canals, with openings called prosopyles connecting the two, as in Scypha.

Syconus. A type of composite fruit formed from a hollow fleshy inflorescence stalk inside which tiny flowers develop. Small drupes, the 'pips', are produced by the female flowers. An example is the fig.

Syllid. An epitokous, polychaete worm (Syllis ramosus) of the family Syllidae.

Sylvan. Of or pertaining to trees or woods.

Sylvatic Plague. Plague among rodents.

Symbiont. Either of two organisms living together in symbiosis.

Symbiosis. An interaction between individuals of different species. The term symbiosis is usually restricted to interactions in which both species benefit (mutualism), but it may be used for other close associations, such as commensalism. Many symbioses are obligatory (*i.e.* the participants cannot survive without the interaction); for example, a lichen is an obligatory symbiotic relationship between an alga and a fungus.

Symbiotic. Of or pertaining to symbiosis.

Symmetrical

1. Possessing or exhibiting symmetry.
2. *bot.* Regular as to number of parts as in an actinomorphic flower which has the same number of parts in each circle.

Symmetrogenic. Designating a type of binary fission in which an individual divides longitudinally giving rise to mirror image daughter cells, as in Euglena.

Symmetry. A likeness or correspondence in size, shape, or structure of parts of an organism or of a part, as a flower. Types include bilateral, radial, and universal.

Sympathetic Nervous System. Part of the autononomic nervous system. Its nerve endings release noradrenaline or adrenaline as a neurotransmitter and its actions tend to antagonize those of the parasympathetic nervous system, thus achieving a balance in the organs they serve. For example, the sympathetic nervous system decreases salivary gland secretion, increases heart rate, and constricts blood vessels, while the parasympathetic nervous system has opposite effects.

Sympatric. Describing two or more populations that could interbreed but do not usually do so because of various differences, *e.g.* in time of flowering or type of pollinator. These populations may, through natural selection, become so distinct that they may be regarded as separate species (sympatric speciation).

Sympetalae. Asteridae.

Sympetalous Having petals united, especially at their bases; gamopetalous.

Sympetaly. Condition in which the petals of a flower are united; gamopetaly.

Symphile. The subject organism in symphilism.

Symphilism. A form of symbiosis in which one organism takes care of and protects another, as when ants care for and transport aphids and in return the aphids provide honey-dew.

Symphysis. A joint that is only slightly movable; examples are the joints between the vertebrae of the vertebral column and that between the two pubic bones in the pelvic girdle. The bones at a symphysis articulate by means of smooth layers of cartilage and strong fibres.

Symplast. The continuum of cell protoplasts throughout the plant, linked by plasmodesmata. Resistance to water flow through the symplast is far greater than through the apoplast and the symplast is consequently only a secondary route for water movement.

Symplastic Growth. A type of growth in which adjacent cells grow at the same rate so that the symplast is not disrupted. Compare intrusive growth, sliding growth.

Sympodial. A method of branching in which growth is principally from lateral buds several nodes behind the apex, as in the catalpa. Compare monopodial.

Sympodial Branching. A type of growth seen in some plants, *e.g.* elm and lime, in which the apical bud withers at the end of the growing season and growth is continued the following season by the lateral bud immediately below. Compare monopodial branching.

Sympodium. The composite primary axis of growth in such plants as lime and horse chestnut. After each season's growth the shoot tip of the main stem stops growing (sometimes terminating in a flower spike); growth is continued by the tip of one or more of the lateral buds. Compare monopodium.

Symptom. Any perceptible change, usually subjective, indicative of a disease or pathological condition. Compare sign.

Synandry. A condition in which anthers are united.

Synangium. A compound fruiting unit developed from the lateral fusion of individual sporangia, as seen in some ferns, *e.g.* Marattia, and gymnosperms, *e.g.* Welwitschia.

Synantherous. A condition in which anthers are fused or joined together.

Synanthesis. A condition in which stamens and pistil mature simultaneously.

Synanthous. Condition in which flowers and leaves appear at the same time.

Synapse. The junction between two neurons. The passage of an impulse along an axon causes the secretion of a neurotransmitler substance (*e.g.* acetylcholine noradrenaline), into a space or cleft between the membrane of the axon and that of a dendrite or cell body of an adjacent neuron. The neurotransmitter diffuses across the cleft where it depolarizes the membrane of the latter, thus initiating within it a new impulse, subsequently it is destroyed by an enzyme.

Synapsid. Having a sigle temporal fenestra, with reference to the skull of mammallike reptiles of the order Synapsida and true mammals.

Synapsis. The pairing of homologous chromosomes during prophase of the first division of meiosis. The nature of the force that causes homologues to be drawn to each other is not known, but pairing is a very exact process, commencing with the pairing of the centromeres and continuing with pairing of chromomeres at various points along the length of the homologues. During the process, contraction of the chromosomes continues and they become closely coiled around each other to form bivalents.

Synapticula. Cross bars between adjacent gill bars, as in lancelets.

Synarthrosis. A type of joint lacking a joint cavity in which bones are bound firmly to each other, permitting little or no movement.

Syncarpous. Describing a gynoecium in which the carpels are fused. The degree of fusion varies from only being joined at the ovary base (semicarpous), as in the Labiatae, to fusion of the ovary and style (synstylovarious), as in the Caryophyllaceae, to fusion of the whole carpel (syncarpous), as in the Cruciferae. This fusion may or may not persist in the fruit at dispersal.

The degree of fusion of the carpels is usually taken as an indication of the degree of specialization in the flower. Compare apocarpous.

Syncarpy. The condition in which the female reproductive organs (carpels) of a flower are joined to each other. It occurs, for example, in the lactose. Compare apocarpy.

Syncope. Fainting; temporary loss of consciousness resulting from reduced blood flow to the brain.

Syncytium. A multinucleated mass of protoplasm as that compring the vegetative body of a slime mold or a striated muscle fiber. Compare coenocyte.

Syndesis. Synapsis.

Syndesmosis. A type of joint, a synarthrosis, in which bones are bound together by a fibrous membrane.

Syndetocheilic. Describing a gymnosperm stomatal complex in which the subsidiary cells are derived from the same initial as the guard cells, as occurred in the Bennettitales. Compare haplocheilic.

Syndiploidy. A doubling of the chromosome number through a fault in the mitotic process. Commonly there is either failure of spindle formation at anaphase or failure to form a dividing wall between the two daughter cells. If such cells continue to divide normally an autopolyploid segment of tissue may arise in the plant. If this develops flowers, autopolyploid seeds may result.

Syndrome. A group of symptoms and signs which, when taken together, characterize a pathological condition.

Synecology. The study of the interactions between all the living organisms in a natural community, such as an oak wood or a pond, and the effect upon them of nonliving factors in the environment. Compare autecology.

Syneresis. The contraction of a gel accompanied by exudation of a fluid, as in the coagulation of blood or milk.

Synergid. One of two or three cells or nuclei which, with the *egg*. comprise the *egg* apparatus of the female gymetophyte or embryo sac in an angiosperm.

Synergidae (synergids) The two haploid nuclei at the micropylar end of the embryo sac that do not participate in the fertilization process. Together with the *egg* nucleus they constitute the *egg* apparatus. Their function is not known and they abort soon after fertilization.

Synergism (summation)

1. The phenomenon in which the combined action of two substances (*e.g.* drugs or hormones) produces a greater effect than would be expected from adding the individual effects of each substance.

2. The combined action of one muscle (the synergist) with another (the agonist) in producing movement. Compare antagonism.

Synergistic. Of, pertaining to, or involving synergism.

Syngamy. The union or fusion of gametes in sexual reproduction : Fertilization.

Syngen. A specific mating type, as occurs in certain ciliates, conjugation being restricted to members of the opposite type.

Syngenesious. Describing an androecium in which the anthers are fused, as in composite plants. Compare adelphous.

Synizesis. A contracture or closure, as the constriction of the pupil of the eye or condensation of chromatin at the side of a nucleus during synapsis.

Synkaryon. A fusion nucleus as that in protogoans following conjugation or in a zygote following fertilization.

Synoecy. The complicated interrelationships between organisms living together in complex communities.

Synoekete. Guest.

Synonym. *taxonomy*. One of two or more scientific terms which are applied to the same taxon.

Synonomy. A complete list of scientific names applied to a taxon, preferably with data as to author, date of publication, reference, and type locality.

Synovia. Synovial fluid, a clear, viscous fluid normally present in a synovial cavity of a joint, a tendon sheath, or a bursa.

Synovial Membrane. The membrane that lines the ligament surrounding a freely movable joint (such as that at the hip or elbow). It secretes a fluid (synovial fluid) that lubricates the layers of cartilage forming the articulating surfaces of the joint.

Synsacrum. In birds, a bone consisting of the fused posterior thoracic, lumbar, sacral, and some caudal vertebrae.

Synsepaly. The condition in which the calyx is composed of fused or united sepals; gamosepaly.

Synthesis. The building up or production of a compound by bringing together or combining simpler elements or constituents, as the synthesis of proteins by plants.

Syntype. Any one of two or more specimens or other material (descriptions, illustrations, etc.) designated by an author in the original publication of the name of a taxon. As a taxon can only have one type, lectotype can subsequently be chosen from a group of syntypes to serve as the nomenclatural type.

Syphilis. Disease of humans caused by Treponema pallidum; transmission occurs primarily by sexual contact. The first symptom of infection is the development of a sore (chancre), usually in the genital region; later, secondary lesions develop, and finally the bones, heart, and nervous system may become involved.

Syrinx. The sound-producing organ of a bird, situated at the lower end of the trachea where it splits into the bronchi. It has a complex structure with a number of vibrating membranes.

Syrup also Sirup

1. A thick, sweet liquid.
2. A concentrated fruit juice.
3. A sweetened medicinal product.

System

1. A methodical arrangement of objects or units.
2. *biol. a.* A group of organs or structures which function together as a unit, as the root system of a

plant or the digestive system of an animal. *b.* The orderly arrangement of taxonomic groups, as the binomial system of nomenclature.

Systematics. The study of the diversity of organisms and their natural relationships. It is sometimes used as a synonym for taxonomy. The term biosystematics describes the experimental study of diversity, especially at the species level. Biosystematic methods include breeding experiments, biochemical work (chemosystematics), and cytotaxonomy.

Systemic Arch. In the embryo of a tetrapod, the fourth aortic arch which, in the adult, becomes the main source of the blood supply to all parts of the body other than the head. In amphibians and reptiles both right and left arches are present in adults. In birds only the right arch is present in adults and in mammals only the left arch is present in adults.

Systemic Circulation. The circulation of blood through arteries to the body tissues and back through veins to the heart. Compare pulmonary circulation.

Systole. The phase of the heart beat during which the ventricles of the heart contract to force blood into the arteries. Compare diastole.

Systole

1. *physiol.* The contraction phase of the heartbeat. Compare diastole.
2. In protozoa, the contraction of contractile vacuole and discharge of its contents.

Syzygy

1. The union of gamonts in pairs in certain protozoans, as Eimeria.
2. The end-to-end union of two sporodins (trophozoites), as in gregarines.

T

2,4,5-T (2,4,5-trichlorophenoxyacetic acid). A synthetic auxin of the phenoxyacetic acid type with three substituted chlorine atoms. It has mainly proved of use as a selective weedkiller and as a defoliant. However, contamination with the highly toxic chemical dioxion has led to measures to restrict its use.

Tabasheer. A siliceous concretion in the joints of bamboo.

Table. A thin, flat plate of bone, as that on the surfaces of a cranial bone.

Tabula. A horizontal, calcareous plate traversing certain cavities in a millepore or stony coral.

Tachina Fly. A depterous insect of the family Tachinidae whose larvae parasitize the larvae of other insects, as Winthermia.

Tachyblastic. Developing immediately, with reference to eggs. Compare opsiblastic.

Tachypnea. Excessive rapidity of respirations.

Tachytalic. Evolving rapidly with resultant rapid speciation.

Tactic. Of or pertaining to a taxis.

Tactic Movement. Taxis.

Tactile. Of or pertaining to the sense of touch.

Tactile Organ. A sensory receptor which responds to touch or contact, as Meissenger's corpuscle in man.

Tadpole. The larva of a frog or toad, an aquatic form with gills; a pollywog.

Taenia

1. A band or bandlike structure.
2. A tapeworm of the genus Taenia.

Taeniola. An endodermal ridge in the planula larva of a scyphozoan.

Tagged. Bearing an identifying element or compound which enables a specific substance (atom or compound) to be traced, as CO_2 containing heavy oxygen used in experiments involving photosynthesis.

Tagma pl. **Tagmata**. A division of the body of an arthropod, as the head, thorax, abdomen, or cephalothorax.

Taiga. A northern, coniferous forest, especially one in Eurasia.

Tail

1. *zool.* The elongated, posterior portion of the body of an animal, as *a.* in vertebrates the caudal extension of the vertebral column with its muscles and associated structures; *b.* in birds, a group of feathers, attached fanlike, extending caudally over the pygostyle; *c.* in invertebrates, any long, flexible, terminal appendage extending caudally.
2. A *anat.* slender, terminal portion of an organ or structure, as the tail of the pancreas.

Tailed

1. *zool.* Having a tail.
2. *bot.* Having a long, taillike appendage, as the caudal appendage of an anther.

Tail Fan. In various crustaceans, a swimming organ consisting of the telson and two uropods.

Tail Fin. The caudal fin, as in fishes.

Take All. A disease of grasses and cereals caused by the fungus Gaeumannomyces (Ophiobolus) graminis. The pathogen survives in the soil on crop debris and can infect the corp at any stage. The dense mycelium on the roots and stem bases gives them a typical blackened appearance. If the plants survive until ear emergence the ears have little grain and appear bleached and are therefore called 'white-heads'.

Takin. A goat antelope (Budorcas) of the highlands of central Asia.

Talon. A sharp claw, especially that of a bird of prey.

Talonid. The posterior portion of the crown of a lower molar tooth, bearing two cusps, the hypoconid and entoconid.

Talus. A tarsal bone which articulates with the tibia and fibula; astragulus.

Tamandua. An arboreal anteater (Tamandua tetradactyla) of Central and South America.

Tamarind. A tropical tree (Tamarindus indica) or the fruit it produces which is widely used in the Far East.

Tambour. A drumlike device used in recording changes in pressure.

Tanager. A brightly colored passerine bird of the family Thraupidae, as the scarlet tanager (Piranga olivacea).

Tandem. One after another, a damselflies when mating.

Tangerine. A small, round orange, with reddish-orange color, easily removable peel, and segments which separate easily.

Tangoreceptor. A touch receptor; a receptor which is stimulated by physical contact, as Meissner's corpuscle; a tactile organ.

Tannic Acid. A tannin obtained from nut galls, used medicinally as an astringent.

Tannin. One of a group of complex organic chemicals commonly found in leaves, unripe fruits and the break of trees. Their function is uncertain though the unpleasant taste may discourage grazing animals. Some tannins have commercial uses, notably in the production of leather and ink.

Tapetum

1. *bot.* The inner nutrient layer of *a.* the sporangium of ferns; *b.* the pollen sac of angiosperms; *c.* the inner integument of an embryo sac.
2. *zool. a.* A postretinal membrane in the indirect eye of an arthropod. *b.* A light reflecting layer in the choroid of the eye, as the tapetum lucidum of elasmobranchs, tapetum fibrosum of ungulates, and tapetum cellulosum of carnivores and lower primates. *c.* A layer of nerve fibers in the roof and lateral wall of a lateral ventricle of the brain.

Tapeworm. A parasitic flatworm of the subclass Cestoda with a body consisting of a scolex and a chain of proglottids. Adults live in the intestine of vertebrates; larvae live in intermediate hosts.

Taphrinales. An order of the Hemiascomycetes containing many plant parasites, with most of the 105 species being placed in the genus Taphrina. There are three other genera. These fungi commonly induce hyperplasia, as in peach leaf curl, caused by T. deformans, and witches' broom of birch, caused by T. betulina. The Taphrinales form a limited dikaryotic mycelium that gives rise to asci. The ascospores reproduce asexually by budding before giving rise again to hyphae.

Tapioca. A starchy preparation obtained from the root of the cassava.

Tapir. A large, almost tailless ungulate of the family Tapiridae inhabiting Central and South America and Southeast Asia, as Tapirus terrestris, the Brazilian tapir.

Taproot. The primary root of a plant which grows directly downward, giving off lateral branches.

Tarantula

1. Any of a number of large, hairy spiders of the family Theraphosidae, including the genera Dugesiella and Eurypelma of the southwestern United States.
2. The wolf spider (Lycosa tarantula) of Europe.

Tardigrade. A water bear, an invertebrate of the class Tardigrada, which includes a number of minute, aquatic or semiaquatic animals of uncertain affinities variously considered to be a phylum, an order of Arachnida, or a class of the Arthropoda. Common genera are Echiniscus and Macrobiotus.

Target Organ. *endycrin.* An organ or structure upon which a hormone has a specific effect.

Tarpon. A large, marine, game fish (Tarpon atlanticus) of the family Megalopidae, of the Atlantic coast.

Tarsal (tarsal bone). One of the bones that form the ankle (tarsus) in terrestrial vertebrates.

Tarsal Glands. The Meibomian glands of the eyelid, sebaceous glands whose ducts open within the inner border of each lid.

Tarsal Plate. A plate of dense connective tissue forming the supporting framework of an eyelid.

Tarsus. The ankle (or corresponding part of the hindlimb) in terrestrial vertebrates, consisting of a number of small bones (tarsals). The number of tarsal bones varies with the species : humans, for example, have seven.

Tartaride. A schizomid, an arachnid of the order Schizomida.

Tasmanian Devil. A small, carnivorous marsupial (Sarcophilus harrisii) of Tasmania, with an exaggerated reputation for ferocity.

Tassel. The male or staminate inflorescence of maize and related plants.

Taste Bud. A small sense organ in most vertebrates, specialized for the detection of taste. In terrestrial animals taste buds are concentrated on the upper surface of the tongue. They are sensitive to four types of taste : sweet, salt, bitter, or sour. The taste bud transmits information about a particular type of taste to the brain via nerve fibres. The four types of taste bud show distinct distribution patterns on the surface of the human tongue.

In fishes, taste buds are distributed over the entire surface of the body and provide information about the surrounding water.

Tattler. A sandpiper (Heteroscelus incanum), the wandering tattler.

Tatuasa. The giant armadillo (Priodontes gigas) of Brazil.

Tautog. The blackfish (Tautoga onitis), an edible fish of the East Coast.

Tautonym. A specific or infraspecific name that exactly repeats the generic name, *e.g.* Magnolia magnolia. This is not allowed in botanical nomenclature but is, however, acceptable in zoology.

Taxales. An order of gymnosperms containing five extant genera (including Taxus, the yews) and about 20 species all in the family Taxaceae. They are often included within the order Coniferales but differ from conifers in having solitary ovules borne on short terminal shoots. The Taxales also have a distinct fossil record going back to the Triassic.

Taxis (tactic movement) The movement of a cell (*e.g* a gamete) or a microorganism in response to an external stimulus. Certain microorganisms have a light-sensitive region that enables them to move towards or away from high light intensities (positive and negative phototaxis respectively).

Many bacteria move in response to chemical stimuli (chemotaxis); a specific example is aerotaxis, in which atmospheric oxygen is the stimulus. Tactic movements are restricted to cells that possess cilia, flagella, or some other means of locomotion. The term is usually not applied to the movements of higher animals. Compare kinesis; tropism.

Taxometrics. Numerical taxonomy.

Taxon. Any named taxonomic group of any rank in the hierarchical classification of organisms. Thus the taxa Papilionidae, Lepidoptera, Insecta, and Arthropoda are named examples of a family, order, class, and phylum, respectively.

Taxonomic. Of or pertaining to taxonomy.

Taxonomic Characters. Features, such as form, physiology, structure, and behaviour, that are assessed in isolation from the rest of the plant by taxonomists, in order to make comparisons and interpretations. It is important to distinguish between characters and character states. For example, leaf width may be a character, while leaves 4 mm wide are an expression of that character, *i.e.* its character state Characters are often referred to as 'good' or 'bad' but this is strictly relative. Thus a good diagnostic character, such as compound leaves in a group of plants that mainly have entire leaves, would be bad for separating taxa in a group in which leaf divisions were either variable or often compound.

Taxonomy. The study of the theory, practice, and rules of classification of living and extinct organisms. The naming, description, and classification of a given organism draws on evidence from a number of fields. Classical taxonomy is based on morphology and anatomy. Biochemical taxonomy studies similarities in the structure of certain proteins and nucleic acids. Cytotaxonomy compares the size, shape, and number of chromosomes of different organisms. Numerical taxonomy uses mathematical procedures to assess similarities and differences and establish taxonomic groups.

Taxus (yew; family Taxaceae). Genus of conifers with erect, solitary ovules surrounded by fleshy cup-like red arils with a sweet taste. The whole plants are highly poisonous (containing the alkaloid taxine) except for the red arils of the seeds. T. baccata is native in western Europe and is notable for its longevity; some specimens planted in churchyards in Britain and in France are believed to be about 1000 years old. It is the only genus of the family in Europe. There are six or seven species, distributed through the northern temperate zone.

TCA Cycle (tricarboxylic acid cycle, citric acid cycle, Krebs' cycle). A cyclic sequence of reactions, found almost universally in aerobic organisms, in which the acetyl portion of acetyl CoA is oxidized to carbon dioxide and hydrogen ions. The energy released by this oxidation is principally conserved by the concominant reduction of NAD and flavoprotein. The reduced cofactors eventually provide energy for ATP formation via the respiratory chain and oxidative phosphorylation.

Many different substrates can feed into the TCA cycle. Pyruvate, from the breakdown of glucose, feeds into the cycle by an oxidative decarboxylation to form acstyl CoA; the enzyme is the pyruvate dehydrogenase complex.

The TCA cycle is not simply catabolic in function. It is in fact an amphibolic pathway, combining both anabolic and catabolic functions. The amino acids glutamate, aspartate, alanine, and glycine arise directly from the TCA cycle, while many other amino acids, the hexose and pentose sugars, the purines and pyrimidines, and the porphyrin-based molecules are indirectly formed from TCA cycle intermediates. Certain enzymatic reactions, termed anaplerotic reactions, produce TCA cycle intermediates to replace those removed by synthetic pathways. An example is the formation of oxaloacetate by the carboxylation of pyruvate.

t **Distribution.** The ratio of the deviation, *d*, to the estimated standard deviation, *s*. It is used in experiments where the number of observations is small (31 or less and hence 30 or less degrees of freedom) and consequently the estimated standard deviation may differ widely from the true standard deviation. To find whether any deviation is significant, its probability is looked up in 'Student's' *t* tables, which take the number of degrees of freedom (N) into account. The greater the value of N, the smaller the value of *t* for any given level of probability.

Tea. The dried leaves of the shrub Camellia (Thea) sinensis, extensively cultivated in Asia and used in the preparation of a caffeine- and tannin-containing beverage.

Teacher Bird. The ovenbird.

Teak. The wood of the tree Tectona grandis, noted for its beauty and durability, an important commercial wood of East Asia.

Teal. One of several species of small, short-necked, surface-feeding ducks of the genus Anas.

Tear. A drop of the secretion of the lacrimal gland.

Teat. An elongated protuberance through which the young of mammals suck or draw milk from the udder or mammary gland.

Tectin. Pseudochitin, a substance forming the skeleton of radiolarians.

Tectorial Membrane. A thin, jellylike membrane which overlays and is in contact with the hair cells of the organ of Corti of the inner ear.

Tectum. A roof or covering.

Teeth. Plural of Tooth.

Tegmen pl. **Tegmina**

1. A coat or covering; an integument.
2. The leatherlike covering of the calyx of a crinoid.
3. The thickened, hardened, front wing of an orthopteran.

Tegmenum

1. A covering.
2. *zool.* *a.* The surface layer of the shell plate of a chiton. *b.* In vertebrates, the dorsal portion of the cerebral peduncles of the midbrain.
3. *bot.* A layer of scales which encloses a bud.

Tegument. An integument.

Tela. A weblike tissue or structure.

Tela Choroidea. A membranous structure lined with ependymal epithelium which forms the roof of the third and fourth ventricles of the brain.

Teleceptor. A distance receptor, as the eye, ear, or nose; a teloreceptor.

Telegony. An erroneous belief that mating with a male influences the future offspring of that female even though subsequent matings are with other males.

Telencephalon. The anterior portion of the embryonic forebrain from which the rhinencephalon, corpora striata, and cerebral cortex develop.

Teleoptile. A mature or adult type of feather. Compare neoptile.

Teleost. Any fish of the class Osteichthyes (Teleostomi), characterized by possession of a bony skeleton.

Teleostei. The major subclass of the Osteichthyes (bony fish), containing about 20 000 species. Teleosts have colonized an extensive variety of habitats and show great diversity of form. The group includes the eel seahorse, plaice, and salmon. They have been the dominant fish since the Cretaceous period (about 70 million years ago).

Teleostomi. The 'true' fish (Osteichthyes), *i.e.* those with a terminal mouth, in contrast to the shark-like fish (Chondrichthyes) which have the mouth positioned underneath a substantial rostrum. Some authors consider the (subgrade) Teleostomi to include the class Osteichthyes as well as the class of fossil Acanthodii.

Teleutosorus (telium). A sorus in which teleutospores develop.

Teleutospore (teliospore). A dark two-celled thick-walled binucleate spore formed towards the end of the growing season by rust and smut fungi. Teleutospores develop in a black sorus, the teleutosorus or telium, and are the form in which the fungus overwinters. The two nuclei in each cell fuse and the zygote nuclei then undergo meiosis so that on germination a haploid promycelium grows from each cell. This subsequently forms basidiospores. The teliospores of smut fungi are often termed brand spores or chlamydospores.

Teliomycetes (Hemibasidiomycetes). A class of the Basidiomycotina containing those fungi in which a sorus (teleutosorus or telium) develops in place of a basidiocarp and produces resting spores (teleutospores) that act as probasidia. It contains the two orders Uredinales and Ustilaginales. Some classifications include the Tremellales in this class.

Teliosorus. A telium.

Teliospore. A heavy-walled, two-celled spore of the resting type produced late in the growing season by certain rusts and smuts. It gives rise to basidiospores at the beginning of the next season.

Telium pl. Telia. The fruiting body of rusts and smuts in which teliospores are formed; a teliosorus.

Teloblast Cell. In protostomes, one of the two cells derived from the fourth blastomere from which the mesoderm develops.

Telocentric. Describing a chromosome that has the centromere at, or very close to, one end so that only one chromosome arm is visible. Compare acrocentric, metacentric.

Telodont. With extremely large mandibles, as the stag beetle.

Telolecithal. Designating ova in which a large amount of yolk is concentrated at the vegetal pole, as in the eggs of reptiles and birds.

Telome. A single terminal segment of a branching axis, with reference to the evolutionary development of plants.

Telome Theory. The proposition that certain plant organs are derived from ized for storage. Swollen taproots are produced by many biennial plants, *e.g.* carrot (Daucus carota).

Telophase. The fourth and final phase of mitosis and meiosis, during which the spindle disappears, nucleoli reappear, the nuclear membranes start to develop around the two groups of daughter chromosomes/chromatids, and the chromosomes return to their extended state in which they are no longer visible. The nuclei then enter a resting stage as they were before division occurred.

Telopodite. A sickle-shaped copulatory structure on the gonopod of a diplopod in the base of which sperm are stored.

Telotaxis. A type of taxis in which an animal responds to only one of several stimuli.

Telotroch

1. In a trochophore, a ring of cilia which encircles the embryo just above the anus.

2. A free-swimming individual produced by a stalked ciliate.

Telson

1. In crustaceans, the median, terminal portion of the abdomen, as in the caryfish.
2. In arachinds, *a.* the terminal spine of the king carb; *b.* the curbed, dorsal spine or sting of a scorpion.
3. The terminal abdominal segment in a primitive insect or an insect embryo.

Temperate Phase. A DNA phage that does not necessarily induce lysogeny of an infected bacterial cell. Instead the phage DNA may be incorporated into the bacterial chromosome, where it replicates along with the bacterium. A bacterium thus infected is described as lysogenic.

Temperature Inversion. Atmospheric condition in which the typical lapse rate is reversed and temperature increases vertically through a given layer. In the troposphere an inversion layer marks conditions of great stability, *i.e.* a region in which vertical motion is strongly damped, with an absence of turbulence. An inversion acts as a ceiling, preventing further upward convection, and is generally the limit for cloud development. Marked and persistent inversions occur at lower levels, with subsiding air in major antityclonic cells, such as the Azores high-pressure zone and cold anticyclones over continents.

Temperature Range. Extent of diurnal or seasonal (annual) temperature variation. Generally the highest annual range of temperature is experienced in higher latitudes, especially over 65° N, which reflects the continental influences of N. America and Asia. Tropical land masses tend to have the highest diurnal temperature ranges, which in the equatorial zone are much higher than the annual variations. Annual temperature ranges in general are particularly moderated by maritime influences.

Template. A pattern or mold which serves as a guide or base for work to be performed.

Temple. The region of the head above the zygomatic arch.

Temporal. Of or pertaining to the temple or temporal bone.

Temporal Bone. A bone forming a portion of the side and base of the cranium, composed of four portions : tympanic, squamous, mastoid, and petrous.

Temporary Stain. A type of stain used for immediate observation through the light microscope. Such stains often damage the section, or the colour of the stain fades after a short time For example, when plant sections are stained with Schultze's solution and mounted in 50% glycerol, the stain eventually causes swelling and dissolves the walls. Some specimens can be mounted directly in the staia, for example, when using ruthenium red. Compare permanent stain.

Temulentous. With jerky, irregular movements, as those of an intoxicated person.

Tenaculum

1. *zool.* A clasping or holding structure, as *a.* a glandular, adhesive structure on sea anemones; *b.* the structure which clasps the furcula in springtails; *c.* in fishes, a ligamentous structure which holds the eyeball in place.
2. *bot. a.* A holdfast in certain algal. *b.* A structure surrounding the ostiole of an ascusin certain fungi.

Tendon. A thick strand or sheet of tissue that attaches a muscle to a bone. Tendons consist of collagen fibres and are therefore inelastic : they ensure that the force exerted by muscular contraction is transmitted to the relevant part of the body to be moved.

Tendril. A modified leaf, leaflet, branch, or inflorescence of a climbing plant that coils around suitable objects, such as other nearby plants, and helps support and elevate the plant. Examples are the branch tendrils of white bryony (Bryonia dioica), the leaf tendrils of yellow vetchling (Lathyrus aphaca), and the inflorescence tendrils of virginia creepers (Parthenocissus). The tendrils of some species terminate in disclike suckers while others, *e.g.* those of grapevines (Vitis), resemble climbing roots in being negatively phototropic and hence growing into dark cracks on the support.

Tension

1. The act of stretching or state of being stretched; as muscle tension.
2. The partial pressure of a gas.

Tentacle

1. In many invertebrate animals; a long, slender, flexible structure, often bearing sense receptors, used to obtain information about the immediate environment and often to obtain food.
2. In corals, zoanthids, and anemones, a movable, tubular extension of the body cavity; tentacles are arranged in a ring around the mouth.
3. In cephalopods, a movable modification of the soft body; tentacles surround the mouth and are sometimes studded with sucker discs.

Tentacular Bulb. In coelenterates, an enlargement at the base of a tentacle which functions in digestion and nematocyst formation, as in various medusae. It may bear ocelli and other sensory structures.

Tentaculum. A tentaclelike organelle located between the feathery membranelles in certain loricate protozoans.

Tent Caterpillar. One of several moths whose larvae construct a tentlike nest which is used as a shelter, as Malacosoma americanum, the Eastern tent caterpillar.

Tentillum. A branch of a tentacle.

Tentorium

1. *zool.* The endoskeleton of the head of an insect.
2. *anat.* A fold of the dura mater located between the cerebral hemispheres and the cerebellum. Also called tentorium cerebelli.

Tent Pole. In certain gymnosperms, an extension of the female gametophyte towards the pollen chamber. It is seen in Ginkgo biloba and is also characteristic of many fossil genera.

Teosinte. A tall grass (Euchlaena mexicana) of Mexico and Central America, related to maize.

Tepal. A division of the perianth when petals and sepals are indistinguishable from each other.

Tephigram. Diagram showing the vertical variation in properties of the atmosphere, *i.e.*, temperature and humidity are plotted as a function of pressure, with lines indicating dry and saturated adiabatic lapse rates. The changes in temperature and humidity of lifted air parcels can be compared against the environment (surrounding air) curve revealing the stability or instability of the air mass and the level at which condensation will occur in the uplifted air.

Teratology. The study of malformations and abnormal growth.

Tercel. The male of certain hawks, especially the peregrine falcon; also tercelet.

Terebra. The serrated, boring or piercing ovipositor or sting of an insect, as that or various hymenopterans.

Terete. Smooth, cylindrical, and tapering as, for example, a grass stem.

Tergite. A sclerite of the tergum.

Tergum pl. **Terga**

1. The dorsal surface of a body somite or segment, as in arthropods.
2. One of a pair of plates covering the anterior lateral surface of barnacle.

Terminal

1. Pertaining to, placed at, or forming an end or extremity.
2. *bot.* Located at or growing from the apex of a branch or stem, as a bud or flower.
3. *zool. a.* Being the last of a series. *b.* Located at the extreme end of a body or structure.

Terminology. A system of special names or terms used in a specific field; nomenclature.

Termitarium. A complex structure which houses a termite colony.

Termite. Any of a number of wood-eating insects of the order Isoptera; a white ant.

Termone. A sex-determinig chemotactic substance in protozoa.

Tern. A gull-like bird of the family Laridae comprising the genus Sterna and related genera.

Ternate. In threes; trimerous.

Terpene. Name given to hydrocarbons that are composed of two or more isoprene units. They may be linear or cyclic molecules or combinations of both, and include important biological compounds such as vitamins A,E, and K, carotenoids, phytol, gibberellic acid, natural rubber, and some lipids.

Terpenoid. Any of a large class of compound derived from multiples of the unsaturated hydrocarbon, isoprene. They inculde the terpenes, which are all hydrocarbons. Terpenoids based on one, two, three, or four isoprene subunits are called hemiterpenoids (*e.g.* apiose), monoterpenoids (*e.g.* camphor), sesquiterpenoids (*e.g.* zingiberine), and diterpenoids (*e.*g. phytol) respectively.

The terpenoids are a very diverse class of compounds. They may be cyclic, *e.g.* cannabidiol, or acyclic, *e.g.* phytol, a precursor of chlorophyll. Many give the characteristic odour or flavour to a plant oil, *e.g.* limonene (lemon oil), pinene (pine oil), and menthol (mint oil). The fat-soluble vitamins A, E, and K are terpenoids as are the ubiquinones and plastoquinones and the growth substances gibberellic acid and abscisic acid. The carotenoids (tetraterpenoids) and sporopollenin, gutta-percha, and natural rubber (polyterpenoids) are further examples of this group.

Terrapin. One of a number of freshwater turtles, especially the diamondback terrapin (Malaclemys terrapin), highly esteemed for its flesh; also the painted terrapin (Chrysemys picta) and Spanish terrapin (Clemmys leprosa).

Terrarium. An enclosure for keeping terrestrial organisms.

Terra Rossa. A type of intrazonal soil rich in lime (calcimorphic) from the underlying limestone. It is a clayey soil with a low humus content and is bright red colour results from large amounts of iron oxides. It may be found in regions of Spain, southern France, and southern Italy. Compare rendzina.

Terrestrial

1. Adapted to and living on land; not aquatic.
2. *bot* Growing on the ground.

Terricolous. Living or dwelling in or on the ground.

Territory. A fixed area that an animal or group of animals defends against intrusion from others of its species. Outside the territory (which may contain food sources, hiding places, and nesting sites) others are not threatened. Many mammals indicate their territory boundaries with scent markings, while birds sing territorial songs that repel would-be intruders. Animals in neighbouring territories normally respect each other's boundaries, which reduces overt aggression. Some animals are territorial only at certain times of the year, usually the breeding season (courtship).

Tertain. Occurring every other day, as tertain malaria, with reference to chills.

Tertiary. The first period of the Cenozoic era from about 65 to 2 million years ago. It began with the Palaeocene epoch, which was followed by the Eocene, Oligocene, Miocene, and Pliocene (Pleiocene) epochs. The climate was tropical to the end of the Oligocene, becoming cooler and dries towards the end of the period as the oceans contracted and the present mountain ranges were formed. Abundant plant fossils have been found, many showing similarity to modern-day plants. Changes in the distribution of the flora can be related to changes in climate throughout the era.

Tertiary Period A major division of the Cenozoic Era comprising the Pliocene, Miocene, Oligocene, Eocene, and Paleocene epochs characterized by the rise of modern mammals and flora.

[1]Test. *zool.*

1. A shell or covering of various animals, as that of testaceans or echinoids.
2. The tunic of a tunicate.
3. A girdlelike prototroch of a trochophore, as in various mollusks.

[2]Test. A trial, examination, or procedure, used to identify or to determine the presence or absence of, or the amount of a substance; to detect alterations in function; or to determine a specific condition or situation, as a test for blood sugar, liver function test, or pregnancy test.

Testa. The protective outer covering of a seed, derived from the integuments of the ovule after fertilization. In primitive forms the outer integument may remain fleshy and the inner become lignified to form a sarcotesta and schlerotesta respectively. In more advanced forms both the integuments fuse and become hard and dry except for a small unthickened area at the micropyle, which facilitates radicle emergence at seed germination. In some species the outer surface of the testa becomes covered with mucilage, hairs, or fibres to aid seed dispersal. The fibrous nature of the cotton seed has long been exploited commercially.

Testa. The outer covering or coat of a seed.

Testacean. A rhizopod protozoan of the order Testacea, characterized by possession of a shell or test, as Arcella.

Testaceous

1. Of or pertaining to a shell or test.
2. Brick red or brownish yellow in color.

Test Cross. A cross between an individual of uncertain genetic constitution and a homozygous recessive. The latter is often a parent, in which case the test cross is a specific form of backcross. The purpose of a test cross is to ascertain the unknown genotype. For example, if T (tall peas) is dominant to *t* (short peas) then any all peas (T_) could be either TT or T*t*. If T_ were test crossed to *tt* and all the offspring were tall then the second allele could be assumed to be T. Alternatively, if there were any short (*tt*) peas among the offspring the second allele must be *t*.

Testis (testicle). The reproductive organ in male animals in which spermatozoa are produced. In vertebrates there are two tests; as well as sperm, they produce steroid hormones (androgen). In most animals the testes are within the body cavity but in mammals, although they develop within the body near the kidneys, they come to hang outside the body cavity in a scrotum. Most of the vertebrate testis is made up of a mass of seminiferous tubules, in which the sperms develop. It is connected to the outside by means of the vas deferens.

Testicle. A testis.

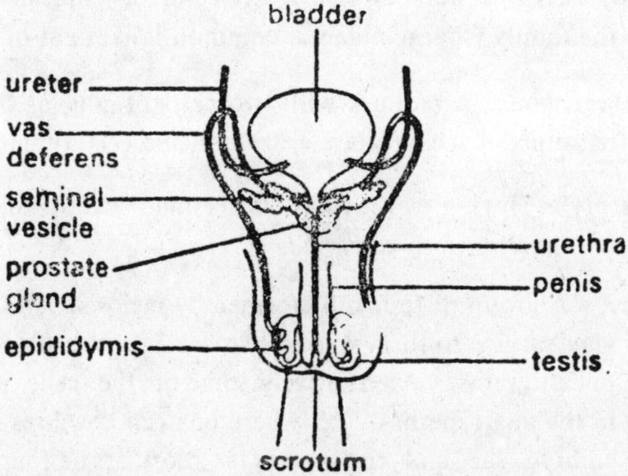

Human male reproductive system

Test of Significance. A way of finding whether the results obtained from an experiment differ from the hypothesis the experiment was constructed to test because of sampling error or because the original hypothesis is invalid.

Testosterone An androgenic hormone produced by the mammalian testis.

[1]**Testudinate.** A turtle; a chelonian.

[2]**Testudinate.** Arched like the carapace of a turtle.

Tetanus. Disease of humans and other animals that follows infection, usually via a wound, by the bacterium Clostridium tetani. This organism is resident in the gut of animals, so that contamination of a wound with manure or manured soil gives greatest risk of infection. C. tetani produces a powerful neurotoxin which causes uncontrollable muscle contraction; the first muscles to be affected are those of the neck and jaw (hence the alternative name 'lockjaw'). In untreated cases death from exhaustion may occur.

Tetany. A condition characterized by painful, tonic spasms of muscles due to lowered blood calcium and elevated pH.

Tetra. Any of a number of brightly-colored, tropical fishes of the family Characinidae, a common inhabitant of aquaria.

Tetrabranchiate. A mollusk with two pairs of gills, as the pearly nautilus, of the subclass Tetrabranchia (Nautiloidea).

Tetracotyle. Having two regular suckers and two pseudosuckers, with reference to cercariae.

Tetrad. A group of four cells formed by meiosis. All four cells may survive to form spores, as occurs in the formation of pollen grains. Alternatively some of the cells abort, as in the angiosperm ovule, where one cell develops into the embryo sac and the remainder abort. The four cells of the tetrad may remain joined together. This provides a useful system for the study of the nature and extent of recombination, a procedure termed tetrad analysis. The shape of the tetrad, *e.g.* whether it is linear tetrahedral, tetragonal, or rhomboidal can be a useful taxonomic character and is a major factor determining pollen morphology.

Tetaad Analysis. The genetic analysis of the four cells resulting from a meiotic division in order to gain information on the nature and extent of recombination. Tetrad analysis is only possible when the meiotic products remain together in groups (tetrads) This does occur in certain lower plants notably ascomycete fungi, *e.g.* Neurospora, and some bryophytes, *e.g.* the livewort Sphaerocarpus.

Tetradynamous. Having four long staments and two short stamens, as do the flowers of plants in the family Cruciferae.

Tetrafossate. With four suckers on the scolex, with reference to tapeworms.

Tetragonal. Having four angles.

Tetramerous (4-merous). Describing flowers in which the parts of each whorl are inserted in fours, or multiples of four, as in the willowherbs (Epilobium) and members of the Cruciferae.

Tetrandrous. Possessing four stamens.

Tetrapetalous. Possessing four petals.

Tetraploid. An organism or cell with four times the haploid number of chromosomes. The fusion of diploid gametes will result in the formation of a tetraploid. Such gametes initially arise because of the failure of homologous chromosomes to separate at meiosis. Alternatively a tetraploid segment of a plant may arise because of the failure of chromatids to separate at mitosis. If this segment develops reproductive structures then diploid gametes will be formed.

Tetraploidy. Possessing four times the normal haploid number of chromosomes.

Tetrapod. A vertebrate animal with four limbs. Tetrapods include amphibians, reptiles, birds, and mammals. The skeleton of the limbs of all tetrapods is based on the same five-digit pattern.

Tetrapterous. Having four wings or winglike appendages.

Tetrarch. A type of xylem which has four rays extending outward from the center of the vascular cylinder.

Tetrasepalous. Having four sepals.

Tetrasomic. In aneuploidy, having four of one pair of chromosomes. Chromosome number is $2n+2$.

Tetrasporangium. A sporangium in which four spores (the tetraspores) are formed. It is seen in some of the red algae, *e.g.* Polysiphonia.

Tetraspore

1. One of four spores of a tetrad.
2. A nonmotile, asexual spore formed in group of four, as in the red algae.

Tetrastichous. Four-ranked; arranged in four vertical rows, said of flowers.

Tetraxon. A sponge spicule having four rays radiating from a common point but not in the same plane; tetractine, quadriradiate.

Texas Fever. An infectious disease of cattle caused by a protozoan (Babesia bigemina) transmitted by a tick. Also called redwater fever, hemoglobinuric fever, tick fever.

Thalamus

1. (in anatomy). Part of the vertebrate forebrain that lies above the hypothalamus. It relays sensory information to the cerebral cortex and is also concerned with the translation of impulses into conscious sensations.
2. (in botany) receptacle.

Thalessa. A large ichneumon fly (Megarhyssa macrurus) with an extremely long ovipositor by which eggs are laid in the larva of the pigeon tremex.

Thallophyta. A former division containing all nonanimal organisms without differentiated stems, leaves, and roots, *i.e.*, the algae, fungi, lichens, and bacteria. It was a feature of older classifications but has largely been replaced by more detailed systems that recognize the fundamental differences between these groups. In some recent classifications the Thallophyta (or Thallobionta) is retained as a subkingdom of the Plantae in distinction to the Embryophyta.

Thallophyte

1. Any plant of the Thallophyta, formerly a taxon which included the algae and fungi.
2. A simple plant; one lacking true roots, stems, or leaves.

Thallose. With a simple, undifferentiated plant body.

Thallus. A relatively undifferentiated plant body with no true roots, stems, leaves, or vascular system. It is found in the algae, lichens, and bryophytes and in the gametophyte generation of pteridophytes.

Thanatoid. Resembling death.

Thanatosis. Feigning death.

Theca

1. *zool.* A sheath or covering, as *a.* the skeletal cup of a coral; *b.* an armor of plates in pelmatozoans (extinct echinoderms); c. a structure enclosing a hydranth or gonophore in colonial coelenterates; *d.* a sheath enclosing an ovarian follicle.
2. *bot.* A capsule, spore case, or similar enclosing structure.

Thecate. Possessing a theca, with reference to hydrozoans.

Thecodont. Designating a type of dentition in which the teeth are set in sockets in the jaw bones.

Thecosomata (shelled pteropods; phylum Mollusca, class Gastropoda). Order of opisthobranch gastropods which have a planktonic mode of life, aided by fins or lobes on the foot. The mantle cavity is large and the shell may be coiled spirally. Individuals are small in size and are ciliary feeders.

Thelephora (family Thelophoraceae). Genus of fungi in which the fruit bodies are variously shaped, according to species; they may be more or less branched, are typically leathery in texture, and bear a well-developed, wrinkled or smooth hymenium T. terrestris ('earth fan') forms fan-shaped fruit bodies 3—8 cm across, erect or horizontal, reddish to brown, often in clusters. They are common in conifer woods and heaths.

Thelephorous. Bearing nipplelike prominences or projections.

Thelytoky. Obligatory parthenogenesis, such that populations consist entirely of females, with, occasional functionless males. It is the only genetic system in which fertilization (the union of egg and sperm) is eliminated completely. Evolution In thelytokous species can therefore take place only by favourable mutations occurring in a single individual, and persisting in the line descending from that individual.

Thenar

1. The palm of the hand.
2. The fleshy prominence at the base of the thumb.

Theraspid. One of an extinct group of mammallike reptiles of the Triassic period thought to be ancestral to modern mammals.

[1]**Therian.** Of or pertaining to the subclass Theria which includes the true mammals.

[2]**Therian.** Any member of the Theria, comprising mammals which bring forth their young alive and possess mammary glands with nipples.

Thermal. Used as a noun, the term refers to air that rises in a column over some localized heat source; it rises through the atmospheric environment as a result of its reduced density. Intense heating over land (and particularly over some types of surface) results in adiabatic expansion and uplife. When thermals rise to condensation level short-lived clouds (*e.g.*, fair-weather cumulus) may form. Continued strong thermals can result in growth of the cloud to larger cumulus or cumulonimbus. When the upward growth reaches a stable layer, the cloud top may spread laterally.

Thermal Stratification. *Limnology.* A condition in deep lakes following the spring overturn in which layers of water differing in temperature exist.

Thermoduric. Capable of enduring high temperatures, with reference to bacteria.

Thermography. A medical technique that makes use of the infrared radiation from the human skin to detect an area of elevated skin temperature that could be associated with an underlying cancer. The heat radiated from the body varies according to the local blood flow, thus an area of poor circulation produces less radiation. A tumour, on the other hand, has an abnormally increased blood supply and is revealed on the thermogram (or thermograph) as a 'hot spot'. The technique is used particularly in mammography' the examination of the infrared radiation emitted by human breasts in order to detect breast cancer.

Thermolabile. Changed or destroyed by heat, said of enzymes.

Thermoluminescence. Luminescence produced in a solid when its temperature is raised. It arises when free charge carriers, trapped in a solid as a result of exposure to ionizing radiation, unite and emit photons of light. The process is made use of in thermoluminesceut dating, which assumes that the number of charge carriers trapped in a sample of pottery is related the length of time that has elapsed since the pottery was fired. By comparing the luminecence produced by heating a piece of pottery of unknown age with the luminescence produced by heating similar materials of known age, a fairly accurate estimate of the age of an object can be made.

Thermoluminescent Dating. Thermoluminescence.

Thermonasty. A nastic movement in response to a change in temperature. For example when subjected to a temperature increase of between 5 and 10°C, Crocus flowers open in a few minutes due to a relative increase in growth rate on the inner side of the petals.

Thermoperiodicity. The effects of changes in temperature between day and night periods upon plant activity, especially growth.

Thermoperiodic Response. The response of a plant to a diurnal fluctuation in temperature. For example, growth of tomato plants is best when a certain day/night temperature regime is experienced. Meristematic activity and extension growth are often affected by thermoperiodicity

Thermophilic. Describing microorganisms that require high temperatures (45 – 65°C) for growth. Such organism are found in rottin g vegetable matter and hot springs. Compare mesophilic, psychrophilic.

Thermophyllous. Producing leaves in summer.

Thermophyte. A heat-tolerant plant.

Thermoreceptor. A sensory receptor which is stimulated by changes in temperature, as an end bulb of Krause or brush of Ruffini.

Thermostable. Not readily affected by heat; resistant to heat up to 100°C.

Thermotropism. The bending of a part of a plant in response to heat.

Therophyte. One of Raunkiaer's life-form categories, being a plant that completes its life cycle rapidly during periods when conditions are favourable and survives unfavourable conditions (*e.g.* cold, heat, or competition) as seed; it is thus an annual or ephemeral plant. Therophyters are very typical of desert environments and cultivated land. Compare chamaeophyte; crytpophyte; hemicryptophyte; and phanerophyte.

Thiamin (thiamine, vitamin B_1). A substituted pyrimidine joined through a methylene bridge to a substituted thiazole. In its active form, thiamin pyrophosphate, it acts as a coenzyme in reactions involving the transfer of aldehyde groups in carbohydrate metabolism. Thiamin is synthesized by plants but not by some microorganisms or most vertebrates, which thus require it in the diet.

Thigh The portion of the lower extremity or hindlimb between the pelvic girdle and knee.

Thigmotaxis (stereotaxis). Change in direction of locomotion in a motile organism or cell made in response to a tactile stimulus (touch), where the direction of movement is determined by the direction from which the stimulus is received. It may inhibit movement, causing the organism to come into close contact with a surface. Thigmotaxis is commonly observed in insects.

Thigmotropism (haptotropism). The growth of an aerial plant organ in response to localized physical contact. For example, when a tendril of sweet pea touches a supporting structure, it curves in the direction of the support and coils around it.

Thin-layer Chromatography. A widely used, fairly fast chromatographic technique for separating the components of mixtures. A glass plate is covered with a thin layer of cellulose, silica gel, or alumina. This represents the solid stationary phase. A line is scratched on the base of the plate and a small spot of the mixture is applied to the base line using either a wire loop or a capillary tube. The plate is then suspended in a suitable solvent (the mobile phase), which rises up the plate by capillary action, carrying and separating the mixture into its constituents The remainder of the procedure is similar to that used in paper chromatography.

Thiobacteriales. Formerly, an order containing the sulphur bacteria and the photosynthetic bacteria. Bacteria once placed in this order are now placed in either the Beggiatoales or Pseudomonadales.

Thiourea. A chemical, with the formula NH_2CSNH_2, widely used to stimulate germination in seeds that have a light requirement. It is believed to act by increasing gibberellin levels.

Thoracic. Of or pertaining to the thorax.

Thoracic Duct. The main collecting vessel of the lymphatic system, running longitudinally in front of the backbone. The thoracic duct drains its lymph into the superior vena cava.

Thoracic Vertebrae. The vertebrae of the upper back, which articulate with the ribs. They lie between the cervical vertebrae and the lumbar vertebrae and are distinguished by a number of articulating facets for attachment of the ribs. In man there are 12 thoracic vertebrae.

Thorax. The anterior region of the body trunk of animals. In vertebrates it contains the heart and lungs within the rib cage. It is particularly well-defined in mammals, being separated from the abdomen by the diaphragm. In insects the thorax is divided into an anterior prothorax, a middle mesothorax, and a posterior metathorax, each of which bears a pair of legs; the hindmost two segments also both carry a pair of wings. In other arthropods, especially crustaceans and arachnids, the thorax is fused with the head to form a cephalothorax.

Thorn. A sharply pointed woody structure formed from a modified reduced branch and connected to the vascular system of the plant. Examples are those of the hawthorn (Crataegus monogyna) and sole or blackthorn (Prunus spinosa). Compare spine, prickle.

Thorn Forest. Forest.

Thrasher. A thrushlike bird of the family Mimidae, as the brown thrasher (Toxostoma rufum).

Thread

1. The coiled tube of a nematocyst.
2. A spirally coiled structure within a thread cell of a hagfish.
3. Any of a number of natural filaments, especially those produced by spinnerets.

Thread Cell (nematoblast; cnidoblast). A specialized cell found only in the ectoderm of the Coelenterata. It contains a nematocyst, a fluid-filled sac within which lies a long hollow coiled thread. When a small sensory projection (cnidocil) on the surface of the thread cell is touched, *e.g.* by prey, the thread is shot out and adheres to the prey, coils round it, or injects poison into it. Numerous thread cells on the tentacles of jellyfish produce their sting.

Threonine. A polar amino acid with the formula $CH_3CH(OH)CH(NH_2)COOH$ (illustration at amino acid). The biosynthetic pathway of threonine follows that of methionine from aspartic acid to the formation of homogentisic acid, at which point the two pathways diverge. Breakdown occurs via glycine and acetyl CoA. Isoleucine is synthesized from threonine.

Threshold (in physiology). The minimum intensity of a stimulus that is necessary to initiate a response.

Thrips. A minute insect of the order Thysanoptera.

Throat

1. *bot.* The opening into a gamopetalous corolla; the point of junction between the tube and limb.
2. *anat.* *a.* The anterior portion of the neck containing the lower portion of the pharynx, larynx, and portions of the trachea and esophagus. *b.* In common usage, the fauces and pharynx.

Thrombin. An enzyme that catalyses the conversion of fibrinogen to fibrin.

Thrombocyte

1. In mammals, a blood platelet.
2. In vertebrates below mammals, a spindle cell of the blood.

Thromboplastin. A substance released from disintegrating blood platelets and injured tissue which, in the presence of calcium ions, converts prothrombin to thrombin.

Thrombosis. The formation of a thrombus.

Thrombus. A blood clot formed within a blood vessel or the heart.

Throwback. A reversion to an ancestral type.

Thrum. Heterostyly.

[1]**Thrush.** One of a number of small to medium-sized passerine birds of the family Turdidae, as Hylocichla mustelina, the wood thrush.

[2]**Thrush.** *med.* A throat infection caused by a fungus (Candida albicans).

Thumb. The pollex, the short first digit on radial side of the hand; the corresponding digit in other animals.

Thylacine. A carnivorous marsupial (Thylacinus cynocephalus), of Tasmania, also called the Tasmanian wolf.

Thylakoid. Any one of the layers making up the grana in chloroplasts. It consists of a channel surrounded by a pigmented membrane.

Thyme. A low shrub (Thymus) of the mint family, with aromatic leaves used in seasoning.

Thymine. A pyrimidine derivative and one of the major component bases of nucleotides and the nucleic acid DNA.

Thymus. An organ, present only in vertebrates, that is concerned with development of lymphoid tissue and hence the antibody producing white blood cells (lymphocytes) and the immune response. In mammals it is a bilobed organ in the region of the lower neck, above and in front of the heart. It shrinks in size after sexual maturity and is therefore believed to function only during early life.

Thyrocalcitonin. Calcitonin.

Thyroid. Of, pertaining to, produced by, or located near the thyroid gland.

Thyroid Gland. A bilobed endocrine gland in vertebrates, situated in the base of the neck. It secretes two iodine-containing hormones, thyroxine and triiodotyrosine, which control the rate of all metabolic processes in the body and influence physical development. Growth and activity of the thyroid is controlled by a hormone, thyrotrophin (or thyroid-stimulating hormone), secreted by the anterior pituitary gland.

Thyrotrophin. A thyroid-stimulating hormone (TSH) produced by the anterior lobe of the pituitary. Also thyrotropin.

Thyrse. A complex densely branched infloresence the individual branches of which are dichasia. An example is that of the horse chestnut (Aesculus hippocastanum).

Thyroxine. The principal hormone of the thyroid gland.

Thysanopteran. Any insect of the order Thysanoptera, which includes the thrips. fringe-winged insects with conelike mouth parts, as Thrips tabaci, the onion thrips.

Thysanuran. A primitive, wingless insect of the order Thysanura which includes the bristletails, as the silverfish (Lepisma) and firebrat (Thermobia).

Tibia

1. In a tetrapod vertebrate, the anterior long bone of the lower hind limb (the 'shin' bone).
2. In an insect, the long and often narrow segment of the leg that articulates proximally with the femur and distally with the tarsus. The tibia contains the muscles that control the tarsi. The musculature operating the tibia is found in the femur, and acts through the agency of a tendon.

Tibiofibula. The fused tibia and fibula as in the frog.

Tibiotarsus. The tibia and some fused tarsals comprising the principal leg bone of a bird, located between femur and tarsometatarsus.

Tick

1. A bloodsucking arachnid of the order Acarina comprising two families, the Argasidae (soft ttcks) and Ixodidae (hard ticks). They parasitize warm-blooded animals, are annoying pests, and serve as reservoirs and transmitting agents for the causative agents of a number of diseases affecting man and domestic animals.
2. A louse fly.

Tickbird. The oxpecker, an African bird (Buphagus) which feeds on ixodid,ticks, especially those infesting the rhinoceros.

Tick Fever. Any of a number of diseases resulting from the bite of a tick, as Rocky Mountain spotted fever, Colorado tick fever, relapsing fever, Texas fever, and tularemia.

Tidal

1. Of, pertaining to, or associated with tides, as tidal rhythms.
2. Periodically rising or falling, or flowing in or out, as tidal air.

Tide. A periodic increase in the pH of urine (alkaline tide), as occurs following ingestion of food.

Tiedemann's Bodies. Nine vesicles located on the inner margin of the ring canal of a starfish; they produce amebocytes.

Tiger. A large, carnivorous mammal (Panthera (Felis) tigris) of the cat family, widely distributed throughout southern Asia.

Tiger Beetle. One of a number of brightly colored, predaceous beetles of the family Cicindelidae, especially those of the genus Cincidela.

Tiger Cat

1. A marsupial (Dasyurus maculatus) of southern Australia.
2. The ocelet.
3. The margay.

Tight Junction. Region of the cell surface, of variable size, and situated just below the apical border where the membranes of adjacent cells are fused to form a pentalaminar structure. In simple epithelial layers tight junctions often form a continuous layer (the zonula occludens). Their function appears to be the provision of areas of contact between cells of enhanced permeability and low electrical resistance. They occur in tissues such as the blood-brain barrier and cardiac muscle, where such features are advantageous.

Tigrolysits. Chromatolysis or dissolution of Nissl bodies in a nerve cell.

Tiller. A shoot that develops from axillary or adventitious buds at the base of a stem, often in response to injury of the main stem. Tillering is seen when the trunk of a tree is lopped, as in the practice of coppicing. It is also characteristic of the growth of grasses, giving, the tufted appearance of many species.

Timber Line (Waldgrenze). The more or less clearly defined region at high altitudes or latitudes beyond which normal dense tree growth does not occur. The trees growing between the timber line and the tree line tend to be dwarfed and deformed and are termed elfin forest.

Time-lapse Photography. A form of cine photography used to record a slow process, such as plant growth. A series of single exposures of the object is made on cine film at predetermined regular intervals. The film produced is then projected at normal speeds and the process appears to be taking place at a most unusual rate.

Tinder Fungus. Common name for the fruit bodies of Fomes fomentarius. These are hoof-shaped; the upper surface is pale brown or greyish-brown with concentric furrows, while the tubes on the underside are pale becoming brown. The spore print is white. In Britain tinder fungus is found on birch trees and occurs only in Scotland; in N. Europe and the USA it is common on beech and other trees.

Tine. A slender, pointed process, as the prong of an antler.

Tip. The extreme end of a structure; the apex or summit.

Tissue. A collection of similar cells organized to carry out one or more particular functions. For example, in animals nervous tissue is specialized to perceive and transmit stimuli. An organ, such as a lung or kidney, contains many different types of tissues.

Tissue Culture. The growth of the tissues of living organisms outside the body in a suitable culture medium. Culture (or nutrient) media contain a mixture of nutrients either in solid form (*e.g.*, in agar) or in liquid form (*e.g.* in physiological saline). Tissue culture has proved to be invaluable for gaining information about factors that control the growth and differentiation of cells.

[1]Tit. Titmouse.

[2]Tit. Teat; Nipple.

Titre

1. The number of infectious virus particles present in a suspension.
2. A measure of the amount of antibody present in a sample of serum, given by the highest dilution of the sample that results in the formation of visible clumps with the appropriate antigen.

Toad. One of a number of tailless, leaping amphibians of the order Salientia, most of which are dry-skinned terrestrial forms except during the breeding season. True toads belong to the family Bufonidae, as Bufo americanus.

Toadfish. A small, bottom-living, venomous, marine fish of the family Batrachoididae, as Opsanus tau of the Atlantic coast; also called oysterfish.

Toadstool. A poisonous, inedible mushroom.

Tobacco. One of several species of solanaceous plants of the genus Nicotiana, especially N. tabacum, whose leaves are widely used for smoking and chewing.

Tobacco Mosaic Disease. A disease of tobacco plants caused by a virus. It was the first disease for which a filterable agent was found to be the causative agent (Iwanowski, 1892) and its virus was the first to be purified in crystalline form (Stanley, 1935).

Tobacco Mosaic Virus (TMV). A rigid rod-shaped RNA-containing virus that causes distortion and blistering of leaves in a wide range of plants, especially the tobacco plant. It is transmitted by insects when they feed on plant tissue. TMV was the first virus to be discovered.

Tobacco Rattle. Disease which occurs in tobacco, tomato, potato, and other plants. Symptoms vary with the nature of the plant infected. The causal agent is a virus which consists of two entirely separate particles, both of which must be present in the plant for replication of the complete virus to occur.

Tocopherol (vitamin E). A terpenoid-like substance found in high concentrations in certain seeds, notably cereals. It is believed to prevent the oxidation of lipids and so prolong seed viability. In a few species applications of tocopherol have been shown to replace the vernalization requirement. Deficiency in certain animals appears to cause infertility.

Toe

1. A digit of the foot.
2. A process on the foot of a rotifer.

Tolerance. The act of tolerating or enduring, as tolerance of shade or of a drug. In ecology, the degree of tolerance is expressed by the prefixes steno-, meaning narrow, and eury-, meaning wide.

Tolerate. To bear, withstand, or endure without injury or harm.

Tollen's Reagent. A reagent used in testing for aldehydes. It is made by adding sodium hydroxide to silver nitrate to give silver(I) oxide, which is dissolved in aqueous ammonia (giving the complex ion $[Ag(NH_3)_2]^+$). The sample is warmed with the reagent in a test tube. Aldehydes reduce the complex Ag^+ ion to metallic silver, forming a bright silver mirror on the inside of the tube (hence the name silver-mirror test). Ketones give a negative result.

Toluidine Blue. A general purpose alkaline aniline stain commonly used to give an even coloration to the specimen and distinguish it from the embedding material. It is frequently used to stain the 1 μm sections cut on ultra-microtomes as an adjunct to transmission electron microscope studies.

Tomato. A solanaceous garden plant (Lycopersicon esculentum) or the fruit it produces.

Tomentose Describing a surface densely coveted in short hairs, such as that of the leaves of hoary mullein (Verbascum pulverulentum).

Tomentulose. Finely or delicately tomentose.

Tomentum. A fine, densely-matted pubescence or woollike haisiness.

Tomium. The cutting edge of the bill of a bird.

Tomite. A free-swimming, nonleeding stage in the life cycle of certain holotrich protozoans that follows the protomite stage.

Tomography. The use of X-rays to photograph a selected plane of a human body with other planes eliminated. The CAT (computerized axial tomography) scanner is a ring-shaped X-ray machine that rotates through 180° around the horizontal patient, making numerous X-rays measurements every few degrees. The vast amount of informotion acquired is built into a three-dimensional image of the tissues under examination by the scanner's own computer. The patient is exposed to a dose of X-rays only some 20% of that used in a normal diagnostic X-ray.

Tomont. A stage in the life cycle of a holotrich protozoan in which multiple division occurs, resulting in the formation of many small, ciliated individuals. Usually occurs in encysted forms.

Tone (tonus). The state of sustained tension in muscles that is necessary for the maintenance of posture. In a tonic muscle contraction, only a certain proportion of the muscle fibres are contracting at any given time; the rest are relaxed and recovering for subsequent contractions. The fibres involved in tone contract more slowly than the fast fibres used for rapid responses by the same muscle. The porportions of slow and fast fibres depends on the function of the muscle.

Tongue

1. In vertebrates, a muscular structure in the mouth, usually movable and protrusable, which functions in foodgetting, manipulation, tasting, and swallowing. It may also serve other functions, as touch, olfaction, and sound production.

2. In invertebrates, a comparable organ, as *a.* the hypopharynx of a grasshopper; *b.* the coiled proboscis of a moth or butterfly; *c.* the labium of a honeybee.

3. *bot.* A ligule or ligula.

Tongue Bar. In lancelets, a secondary gill bar which divides each primary gill cleft.

Tongue Worm

1. A pentastomid.

2. An acorn worm or enteropneustid.

Tonoplast. The membrane separating the cell vacuole from the protoplasm. It has the same structure as the palsma membrane and mediates between the protoplasm and the vacuolar sap.

Tonsil. A mass of lymphoid tissue, several of which are situated at the back of the mouth and throat in higher vertebrates. In humans there are the palatine tonsils at the back of the mouth, lingual tonsils below the tongue, and pharyngeal tonsils (or adenoids) in the pharynx. They are concerned with the production of lymphocytes and therefore with defence against infection.

Tonus. Tone.

Tooth. Any of the hard structures in vertebrates that are used principally for biting and chewing food but also for attack, grooming, and other functions. In fish and

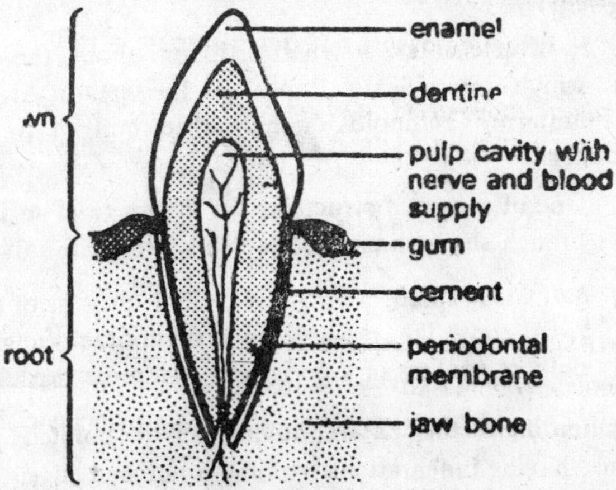

Section through an incisor tooth

amphibians the teeth occur all over the palate, but in higher vertebrates they are concentrated on the jaws. They evolved in cartilaginous fish as modified placoid scales, and this is reflected in their structure : a body of bony dentine with a central pulp cavity and an outer covering of enamel on the exposed surface (crown). The portion of the tooth embedded in the jawbone is the root (illustration).

In mammals there are four different types of teeth, specialized for different functions (canine; incisor; molar; premolar). Their number varies with the species (dental formula).

Tooth pl. **Teeth**

1. A vertebrates, a hard cornified or calcified structure in the mouth used primarily for cutting and mastication of food, but also functioning as offensive and defensive weapons, for grasping and holding prey, and for injecting venom. A true tooth, as in a

mammal, consists of a root, neck, and crown, the crown consisting of a surface layer of enamel overlying a layer of dentine, the whole enclosing a pulp cavity.

2. In invertebrates, a structure in or about the mouth which resembles a tooth, as the teeth of Aristotle's lantern of echinoids or the gastric mill of a crustacean.

3. One of a pair of structures on the hinge of a lamellibranch shell which function in locking the valves.

4. *bot.* *a.* A small, pointed, marginal process of a leaf. *b.* A toothlike process, as in the toothed fungi. *c.* A pointed process of a peristome of a moss capsule.

Toothed. Bearing teeth; dentate; having small pointed projections; having indentations forming a notched edge.

Toothed Fungi. Fungi of the family Hydnaceae in which the hymenium covers the surfaces of downward-projecting spines or teeth.

Tooth Shell. A burrowing marine gastropod of the class Scaphopoda, a Dentalium, with a long, pointed shell open at both ends.

Tope. A small shark (Galeorhinus galeus) of European waters.

Topotype. A specimen of a species collected at the type locality.

Tormogen Cell. A hypodermal cell in insects which produces the articular membrane of the setae.

Tornaria Larva. The pelagic, ciliated larva of various enteropneustans which bears a marked resemblance to the auricularia larva of echinoderms.

Tornote. A sponge spicule, lance-headed at each end.

Torpedo Ray. An electric ray of the genus Torpedo.

Torpid. Inactive; dormant; lacking in energy, as a hibernating animal.

Torpor. A state of sluggishness or inactivity, as in estivation : Suspended Animation.

Torques. A collarlike structure of hair, feathers, or modified integument which encircles the neck, usually of a distinctive color or structure.

Torsalo. The larva of Dermatobia hominis, a skin bot.

Torsion. A turning or twisting, as occurs in snails when the visceral mass is twisted on the head-foot.

Tortoise. A turtle, especially a land turtle, as Testudo, the giant land tortoise of the Galapagos Islands or Gopherus of the southern states.

Torula. One of the false or pseudoyeasts which cause undesirable fermentations.

Torulus. A socket which lodges the basal end of the antenna of an insect.

Torus. The thickened central part of the pit membrane in the bordered pits of many gymnosperms, consisting of primary cell wall material. The torus is believed to act as a valve, blocking the pit when there is an inequality of pressure on either side of the pit, as is the case when an adjacent tracheary element is damaged.

Touch. The tactile sense; the sense of feeling.

Toxic. Of or pertaining to a poison; poisonous.

Toxin. A poison produced by a living organism, especially a bacterium. An endotoxin is released only when the bacterial cell dies or disintegrates. An exotoxin is secreted by a bacterial cell into the surrounding medium. In the body a toxin acts as an antigen, producing an immune response.

Toxoid. A toxin which has been modified by physical or chemical agents so that its toxic properties are lost but its antigenic properties remain intact, as the toxoids of tetanus and diphtheria.

Toxoplasmosis. Disease of humans or other animals caused by the protozoon Toxoplasma gondii. Although a very wide range of animals can be infected by T. gondii, overt symptoms of disease are not common. When they do occur the symptoms are variable; death may occur rapidly if the lungs or brain become involved.

TPN. NADP.

Trabant. Satellite.

Trabecula. A barlike structure extending across a lumen or lacuna. For example, in some plants extensions of the secondary wall thickening from trabeculae across the lumina of xylem tracheids.

Trace Element. An element which is essential for normal activities of an organism, but required only in minute amounts, as *a.* for plants, boron, cooper, zinc, and manganese; *b.* for animals, aluminum, boron, cooper, zinc, silicon, cobalt, iodine, fluorine, manganese, selenium, and possibly others.

Tracer. A radioactive isotope or other substance whose course can be traced within the body or in biochemical reactions.

Trace Fossil. Fossil.

Trachea

1. The windpipe in air-breathing vertebrates: a tube that conducts air from the throat to the bronchi. It is strengthened with incomplete rings of cartilage.
2. An air channel in insects and most other terrestrial arthropods. Tracheae occur as ingrowths of the body wall. They open to the exterior by spiracles and branch into finer channels (tracheoles) that terminate

in the tissues. Pumping movements of the abdominal muscles cause air to be drawn into and out of the tracheae.

Trachea

1. Vessel; a tube-like series of non-living cells in the xylem of a plant, supplying mechanical support and involved in the transport of water and salts.
2. One of the cuticular tubes that make up the respiratory system of an insect. The tracheae ramify throughout the body, terminating in fine, intracellular branches (tracheoles).
3. In air-breathing vertebrates, the 'windpipe', leading from the throat and dividing into two bronchii, which enter the lungs.

Tracheal. Of, pertaining to, or resembling a trachea.

Tracheal Gill. A gill containing trachea and tracheoles, as in the nadias, larvae, and pupae of aquatic insects, as dragonflies and mayflies.

Tracheal System. A respiratory system in which air is conveyed through minute tubes (trachea, tracheoles) to the tissues, as in various terrestrial arthropods, as insects, spiders.

Tracheary. Of or pertaining to xylem elements which resemble animal tracheae, as tracheids and vessel members.

Tracheary Element. A water-conducting cell in the xylem, *i.e.* a vessel element or tracheid. The secondary cell walls of the tracheary elements show various types of thickening (illustration). Annular and spiral patterns of thickening allow further extension of the tracheary element and tend to be found in protoxylem. The other forms of thickening are seen in metaxylem. Although bryophytes do not posses xylem, some do possess water-conducting cells known as hydroids. Some consider these are also tracheary elements.

Tracheid. A type of cell occurring within the xylem of conifers, ferns, and related plants. Tracheids are elongated and their walls are usually extensively thickened by deposits of lignin. Water flows from one tracheid to another through unthickened regions (pits) in the cell walls. Compare vessel element.

Tracheole. One of the numerous, minute branches of a trachea in an arthropod.

Tracheophyta. A group (division) of the plant kingdom containing all plants possessing organized vascular tissue. This classification is an alternative to other classifications, which divide vascular plants into the Pteridophyta and Spermatophyta. The Tracheophyta comprises the subdivisions Psilopsida (mostly extinct), Lycopsida, Sphenopsida, and Pteropsida.

Tracheophyte. Any plant of the division Tracheophyta which includes the vascular plants comprising the ferns and fernlike plants and the seed plants.

Trachoma. Chronic disease of the human eye which is probably the greatest single worldwide cause of loss of sight. It is caused by Chlamydia trachomatis (once believed to be a virus). Initially, inflammation of the surface of the eye causes blurring of vision, and this may be followed by scarring of the cornea which may lead to total blindness. The disease is commonest in India, the Middle East, and parts of Africa.

Trachycarpous. Rough-skinned, with reference to fruits.

Trachyspermous. Possessing a rough coat, with reference to seeds.

Tract

1. A pathway or course, as the alimentary tract.
2. A bundle or group of nerve fibers in the spinal cord or brain.

Tractellum. The anterior flagellum or a flagellate, used primarily for pulling.

Traction The act of drawing or pulling.

Tragacanth. A gum with marked water-absorbent properties obtained from various Asiatic plants of the genus Astragulus.

Tragus

1. *anat*. *a*. A process anterior to and projecting over the external acoustic meatus. *b*. A hair of the external acoustic meatus.
2. *zool*. In insectivorous bats, a flap that can be drawn over the ear; an earlet.

Trama. The central tissue in the gill of a fungus, consisting of loosely packed hyphae.

Transaminase. An enzyme which catalyzes a transamination reaction.

Transamination. A biochemical reaction in amino acid metabolism in which an amine group is transferred from an amino acid to a keto acid to form a new amino acid and keto acid. The coenzyme required for this reaction is pyridoxal phosphate.

Trans Arrangement (repulsion). The situation in which an individual is heterozygous for two linked genes (either two units of function or two mutations in the same functional unit), and the recessive (or mutant) allele of one gene is on the same chromosome as the dominant (or normal) allele of the other gene. The homologous chromosome will thus possess the dominant allele of the first gene and the recessive allele of the second gene. If the recessive alleles are in the same functional unit then their effects will show in the phenotype because there is no unchanged functional unit to mask them. If they are in different functional units, then the phenotype will be normal. This is the basis of the *cis-trans* test. Compare *cis* arrangement.

Transcription. The process in living cells in which the genetic information of DNA is transferred to a molecule of messenger RNA (mRNA) as the first step in protein synthesis (also genetic code). Transcription takes place in the cell nucleus or nuclear region An enzyme (transcriptase) proceeds along the DNA strand and assembles the nucleotides necessary to form a complementary strand of mRNA. Compare translation.

Transduction. The transfer of genes from one bacterium to another by the action of a temperate bacteriophage acting as a vector (transmitting agent). It occurs when a phage excises from a bacterial genome in a faulty manner, taking some of the bacterial genes with it and leaving some of its own behind. The transferred genes (the transducing material) are incorporated into the bacterial genome of a new host cell and result in the transduced cell showing a permanent genetic change. Abortive transduction is sometimes seed, in which the transferred genes do not become incorporated into the genome but remain as a plasmid in the cell. The recipient bacterium then only shows the new properties until the plasmid is lost from the cell. Transduction occurs naturally at low frequency but this can be increased substantially under laboratory conditions. It is an important tool in genetic engineering.

Transect. A straight line across an expanse of ground along which ecological measurements are taken, continuously or at regular intervals. Thus an ecologist wishing to study the numbers and types of organisms at different distances above the low-tide line might sample at five-metre intervals along a number of transects perpendicular to the shore.

Transection. A cut or section made across the long axis of a structure.

Transferase. Any enzyme that catalyses reactions in which a functional group is transferred from a donor to an acceptor molecule. Six classes of transferase are distinguished, including enzymes that transfer phosphate groups (phospho transferases or kinases) and enzymes that transfer acyl groups (*e.g.* phosphate acyltransferase, which catalyses the transfer of an acyl group from phosphate to coenzyme A).

Transfer Ribonucleic Acid (transfer-RNA, tRNA). Generic term for a group of small RNA molecules, each composed of 70-80 nucleotides arranged in a clover-leaf pattern stabilized by hydrogen bonding. They are responsible for binding amino acids and transferring these to the ribosomes during the synthesis of a polypeptide (*i.e.* during translation). At the ribosomes, which are attached to the messenger-RNA (mRNA), the 'reading frame' indicates the three mRNA nucleotides that form the next triplet codon in the sequence : whichever tRNA molecule carries the complementary anticodon can associate with the ribosome such that the amino acid that it bears can be joined on to the end of the growing polypeptide.

Transformation *genetics*. A process by which bacteria grown on a nutrient medium containing a transforming principle (DNA) extracted from killed bacteria are transformed or changed to a different type, such involving the transfer of genetic material.

Transformer. *ecol.* An organism, as a nitrate or nitrite bacterium, which converts simpler substances into compounds which can be used by plants in the synthesis of more complex compounds, as proteins.

Transfusion. The introduction of whole blood, plasma, or saline solution into a blood vessel of the body.

Transfusion Tissue. The tissue immediately surrounding at least part of the vascular bundles in the leaves of gymnosperms, *e.g.* Pinus. Transfusion tissue is composed of tracheids (transfusion tracheids) with conspicuous bordered pits, and parenchyma cells (transfusion parenchyma) containing tanin-like substances and sometimes starch. The main function of the transfusion tissue is believed to be the transport of materials between the vascular bundles and the mesophyll.

Transition. A mutation caused by substitution in the DNA of one purine base for the other, or one pyrimidine for the other. Hence adenine might replace guanine and *vice versa*, or thymine might replace cytosine and *vice versa*. It is thought that mutagens such as 5-bromouracil induce transitions. Compare transversion.

Transition Region

1. The part of the plant body between the stem and the root in which there are intermediate arrangements of the tissues. Vascular transition takes place in this region, ensuring continuity of vascular tissues throughout the plant.
2. An intercalary meristem located between the blade-like portion and the narrow stemlike portion of the plant body in the Laminariales (an order of brown algae).

Translation. The polymerization of amino acids into a polypeptide chain whose structure is determined genetically. This process occurs on a ribosome and involves several small proteins, mRNA, and tRNA. The sequence of amino acids in the chain is specified by that of the nucleotides in the mRNA (these being read as codons, *i.e.* in groups of three), and this in turn follows the sequence of nucleotides in the DNA.

Translator. A structure at the tip of fused anthers on certain flowers to which masses of pollen grains become attached, as in the milkweed.

Translocation

1. The movement of dissolved substances within a plant, usually from the site of synthesis or uptake to centres of growth or storage.

2. A change in the arrangement of genetic material, altering the location of a chromosome segment. The most common forms of translocations are reciprocal, involving the exchange of chromosome segments between two non-homologous chromosomes. A chromosomal segment may also move to a new location within the same chromosome or in a different chromosome, without reciprocal exchange; these kinds of translocations are sometimes called transpositions.

3. The movement of soil materials in solution or in suspension from one horizon to another.

Transmigration. The movement from one place to another, as ions across a cell membrane.

Transmitting Tissue (conducting tissue). The specialized thin-walled tissue that constitutes the central part of the style in some angiosperms, through which the pollen tube grows down to the funiculus. It may be involved in self-incompatibility systems.

Transmutation. The change of a species or type to another : Evolution.

Transparent. Permitting the passage of light rays; capable of being seen through.

Transpiration. The removal of moisture from the soil by plant roots, its translocation up the stem to the leaves, and its evaporation through the stomata. The flow of water through the plant is known as the transpiration system. It reduces leaf temperatures and is thought to be important for mineral absorption and translocation within plants. The process imposes a number of environmental requirements upon plants; for example, wilting and desiccation result from an insufficient supply of water.

Transpiration Stream. The flow of water from the roots to the leaves via the xylem vessels that is caused by transpiration at the leaf surface.

[1]Transplant. To remove and place in another location where growth may take place, as seedlings or tissue.

[2]Transplant. A piece of tissue or a part of an organism which is removed and transferred to another site, either in the same individual (autoplastic or homoplastic transplant) or in another individual (heteroplastic transplant).

Transport. The movement of substances from one place to another.

Transposition. A change in position, especially the reversal or transfer to the opposite side.

Transudate. The product resulting from transudation.

Transudation. The passage of a substance through pores of a membrane or interstices of a tissue, as blood plasma through a capillary wall.

Transversion. A mutation caused by the substitution of a purine base for a pyrimidine base (or vice versa) in the DNA. Compare transition.

Trap. *bot.* A structure which imprisons an insect or small organism, as the modified leaf of an insectivorous plant.

Trap Crop. Any crop planted in or around another crop to attract pests away from the more valuable crop. Trap crops are usually heavily treated with pesticides, burnt, or ploughed in.

Trap Flower. A prison flower.

Trap Hairs. Hairs which prevent an insect from leaving a flower or leaf.

Trauma

1. An injury or wound, especially one induced by a physical agent, as a cut, bruise, or burn.
2. A severe psychic or emotional shock.

Traumatic. Of, pertaining to, or resulting from trauma.

Traumatic Acid. A straight chain dicarboxylic acid, formula $COOHCH:CH(CH_2)_8COOH$. It has been isolated from green bean pods and is believed to act as a wound hormone.

Traumatism

1. An abnormal condition resulting from trauma.
2. *bot.* An abnormal growth resulting from injury.

Traumatropism. The abnormal sensitiveness of certain plant structures to injury.

Tread. To copulate or to cover, with reference to male birds.

Tree

1. A woody, perennial plant with a single main axis or trunk which bears branches.
2. Something resembling a tree in shape or form.

Tree Fern. One of a number of giant ferns with well-developed, treelike trunks, as those of the families Cyatheaceae and Marattiaceae.

Treehopper. One of a number of small, leaping insects of the order Homoptera with a well-developed pronotum giving them a humpbacked appearance, as the buffalo treehopper (Ceresa bubalus).

Tree Line (Baumgrenze). The more or less clearly defined region at high latitudes (the taiga/tundra boundary) or high altitudes (the subalpine/alpine boundary) beyond which trees do not grow. Occasionally inverted tree lines are seen in which trees do not grow below a certain line as, for example, in frost hollows. The limits to tree growth are presumably set by some climatic factor though it is by no means certain which particular factor is operating. Numerous theories have been advanced based on different climatic variables such as heat, light, or carbon dioxide deficiency, excessive wind or snow depth, etc. A recent theory suggests that, beyond the tree line, leaves become desiccated in winter because the summer growing season is not long enough to allow the leaves to mature fully and resist water stress. Compare timber line.

Tree of Heaven. A rapid-growing Asiatic tree (Ailanthus altissima) with ill-smelling staminate flowers.

Tree Shrew. A small, arboreal, rodentlike mammal of the family Tupaiidae, of Southeast Asia, considered to be the most primitive of primates, as Tupaia, Ptilocercus.

Trematoda. A class of parasitic flatworms (Platyhelminthes) comprising the flukes, such as Fasciola (liver fluke). Flukes have suckers and hooks to anchor themselves to the host and their body surface is covered by a protective cuticle. The whole life cycle may either occur within one host or require one or more intermediate hosts to transmit the infective eggs or larvae. Fasciola hepatica, for example, undergoes larval development in a land snail (the intermediate host) and infects sheep (the primary host) when contaminated grass containing the larvae is swallowed.

Trematode. A parasitic flatworm of the class Trematoda; a fluke.

Tremellales. An order of the Hymenomycetes containing fungi that produce gelatinous basidiocarps, hence the common name gelatinous or jelly fungi. These number about 200 species (26 genera) and are usually found growing on dead wood. They have characteristic rounded basidia divided by septa into four cells. Typical examples are witches' butter (Exidia glandulosa) and the yellow brain fungus (Tremella mesenterica). In some classifications the Tremellales are included in the Teliomycetes.

[1]**Trephine.** An instrument for making an opening into the skull.

[2]**Trephine.** To perforate the skull with a trephine.

Triacylglycerol (triglyceride). An ester of glycerol and three long-chain carboxylic acids or fatty acids. Triacylglycerols may be triesters of either the same fatty acid, or more commonly of two or three different fatty acids (mixed triacylglycerols). The most common fatty acids found in triacylglycerols are palmitic, stearic, oleic, and linolenic acids.

Triacylglycerols are synthesized from glycerol phosphate and fatty acyl CoAs. The glycerokinase that phosphorylates glycerol is a soluble enzyme, but the other enzymes of triacylglycerol synthesis are associated with the microsomes. Breakdown of triacylglycerols to glycerol and free fatty acids is achieved by the action of lipases.

Triacylglycerols are important energy storage molecules especially in seeds, many of which (*e.g.* rape, linseed, castor bean, coconut) are important commercially as sources of fats and oils. Fats and oils are solid and liquid triacylglycerols respectively.

Triad. A closely associated or related group or set of three objects, things, or individuals.

Triadelphous. With stamens arranged in three bundles or sets.

Triandrous. Possessing three stamens.

Triarch. Designating a protoxylem with three rays.

Triassic. The earliest of the three periods of the Mesozoic Era, which began 225 million years ago and lasted 40 million years. As a result of the mass extinctions of the late Palaeozoic, Triassic communities contained many new faunal and floral elements. Among these were the ammonites, modern corals, various molluscs, the dinosaurs, and certain gymnosperms.

Triassic Period. The first and earliest period of the Mesozoic era, characterized by the rise of giant reptiles.

Tribe. A category used in the classification of plants and animals that consists of several similar or closely related genera within a family. For example the Bambuseae, Oryzeae, Paniceae, and Aveneae are tribes of grasses.

Tribocytic Organ. A glandular, adhesive organ in holostome flukes located immediately posterior to the acetabulum, as in strigeids.

Tricamerous. Having three loculi, said of fruits.

Tricarboxylic Acid Cycle. Krebs cycle.

Tricarinate. Having three keels or angles.

Tricarpellate. Having three carpels.

Triceps. A muscle with three heads, as the triceps brachii.

Trichite. A tubular trichocyst containing a coiled thread.

Trichocyst

1. One of the numerous oval or rod-shaped structures in the ectoplasm of various ciliates which function as defensive or anchoring structures.
2. A hairlike structure in certain cryptomonads and chloromonads capable of being discharged; an ejectosome.

Trichogen. A cell in the hypodermis of an insect which gives rise to a hair or seta.

Trichogyne. A receptive, often hairlike, uni- or multicellular structure that projects from the female sex organ in some algae, ascomycetes, and lichens. It serves to attract and receive the male gamete or nucleus prior to fertilization.

Trichome. A hairlike projection from a plant epidermal cell. Examples include root hairs and the stinging hairs of nettle leaves.

Trichopteran. Any insect of the order Trichoptera which includes the caddis flies.

Trichothallic. Designating growth of a filamentous thallus, as in certain brown algae.

Trichothallic Growth. A form of growth seen in certain brown algae, *e.g.* Ectocarpus and Cutleria, in which cell division is restricted to well defined intercalary regions.

Tricolpate. Describing a pollen grain having three colpi, as is commonly found amongst most dicotyledon species.

Trichotomous. In three parts or divisions; three-forked.

Triclad. A free-living, turbellarian flatworm of the order Tricladida with a three-part gastrovascular cavity, as Planaria, Dugesia.

Tricolpate. With three grooves, with reference to pollen grains.

Tricostate. With three ribs or costae.

Tricuspid. With three cusps or leaflets.

Tricuspid Valve. A valve, consisting of three flaps, situated between the right atrium and the right ventricle of the mammalian heart. When the right ventricle contracts, forcing blood into the pulmonary artery, the tricuspid valve closes the aperture to the atrium, thereby preventing any backflow of blood. The valve reopens to allow blood to flow from the atrium into the ventricle. Compare mitral valve.

Tricuspid Valve. A heart valve located between the right atrium and right ventricle.

Tricussate. On groups of three; ternate, with reference to whorls of leaves.

Tridactyl. With three digits; tridigitate.

Trident. Tridentate.

Tridentate. With three teeth, toothlike processes or points.

Tridigitate. With three digits or fingerlike processes; tridactyl.

Tridynamous. With six stamens (three long, three short).

Trifoliate. Describing a compound leaf having three leaflets arising from the same point, such as the clovers (Trifolium) and wood sorrels (Oxalis).

Trigeminal Nerve. The fifth cranial nerve (V) consisting of three main divisions, the ophthalmic, maxillary, and mandibular. On its root is the semilunar or Gasserian ganglion.

Triglyceride (triacylglycerol). An ester of glycerol (propane-1,2,3-triol) in which all three hydroxyl groups are esterified with a fatty acid. Triglycerides are the major constituent of fats and oils and provide a concentrated food energy store in living organisms as well as cooking fats and oils, margarines, soaps, etc. Their physical and chemical properties depend on the nature of their constituent fatty acids. In simple triglycerides all three fatty acids are identical; in mived triglycerides two or three different fatty acids are present.

Trigonal. Triangular.

Trigonid. A weil-developed triangular area on a lower molar tooth.

Trihybrid. An organism that is heterozygous for three genes. *e.g.* AaBbCc. Trihybrid crosses, especially of the type AaBbCc × aabbcc, are commonly used devices in chromosome mapping. By comparing the frequencies of the phenotypes, the chromosomal arrangements of the three genes A/a, B/b, and C/c can be deduced. This is technically easier than setting up three dihybrid crosses AaBb × aabb, AaCc × aacc, and BbCc × bbcc, which would only achieve the same result.

Trilete. Triradiate scar.

Trilobate. With three lobes.

Trilobite. An extinct marine arthropod belonging to the class Trilobita (some 4000 species), fossils of which are found in deposits dating from the Precambrian to the Permian period (590-280 million years ago). Trilobites were typically small (1-7 cm long); the oval flattened body comprised a head (covered by a semicircular dorsal shield) and a thorax and abdomen, which were protected by overlapping dorsal plates with a raised central part and flattened lateral portions, presenting a three-lobed appearance. The head bore a pair of antenna-like appendages and a pair of compound eyes; nearly all body segments bore a pair of Y-shaped (biramous) appendages—one branch for locomotion and the other fringed for respiratory exchange. Trilobites were bottom dwelling scavengers.

Trilobite Larva. The larva of the king crab.

Trilocular. Having three cavities or compartments.

Trimerous (3-merous). Describing flowers in which the parts of each whorl are inserted in threes or multiples of three. This arrangement is characteristic of many monocotyledons.

Trimorphic. Existing or occurring in three types or forms.

Trioecious. Producing staminate, pistillate, and perfect flowers on different plants within a species.

Ttriose Phosphate. A three-carbon phosphorylated sugar. Two commonly occurring triose phosphates are glyceraldehyde 3-phosphate and dihydroxyacetone phosphate (DHAP), which are both intermediates in the synthesis and breadown of glucose. In glycolysis the triose phosphates are formed by the splitting of fructose bisphosphate, while in glucose synthesis they are formed from phosphoglyceroyl phosphate. Interconversion of these two triose phosphates is catalysed by the enzyme triose phosphate isomerase.

Triose phosphates are important in other metabolic processes. Glycerol is formed from DHAP, and glyceraldehyde 3-phosphate is an intermediate in the pentose phosphate pathway.

Triphosphopyridine Nucleotide. NADP.

Ttripinnate. Describing a bipinnate leaf in which the secondary leaflets are further subdivided, as occurs in certain ferns.

Triple Fusion. In angiosperms, the union of *a.* one of the sperm nuclei of a pollen tube with an ovum which gives rise to a diploid zygote and, *b.* the other sperm nucleus with the two endosperm nuclei to form the triploid endosperm of a seed. Also called double fertilization.

Triplet. A sequence of three nucleotides on a DNA or messenger RNA molecule. Most of the 64 possible triplets (genetic code) code for amino acids (codon). However a few act as 'start' signals while others act as 'stop' signals to begin and end a polypeptide chain (nonsense triplets).

Triploblastic. Describing an animal having a body composed of three embryonic cell layers : the ectoderm, mesoderm, and endoderm. Most multicellular animals are triploblastic; the coelenterates, which are diploblastic, are an exception.

Triploid. An organism, tissue, or cell that possesses three complete sets of chromosomes per nucleus. A triploid may arise from the fusion of a haploid and a diploid nucleus, or from the fusion of three haploid nuclei. Triploid organisms are normally infertile, since meiosis results in gametes that have more or less than the normal haploid number of chromosomes. The endosperm tissue of angiosperms is typically triploid (or pentaploid in some monocotyledons).

Triploidy. The condition in which an individual has three of each kind of chromosome, chromosome number=3n.

Tripterous. Three-winged, said of fruits and seeds.

Triquetrous. Having three salient angles, said of triangular stems with convex sides.

Triradiate. Having three rays or radiating parts.

Triradiate Scar. A scar on the surface of a spore that marks the point at which it was jointed to the other three spores making up the tetrad. Triradiate scars are seen when the tetrad shows tetrahedral symmetry. It is conspicuous because the spore wall is fairly thin at this pont while the rest of the wall is thickened with cutin. In the megaspores of Selaginella kraussiana the archegonia break through the megaspore wall at this point. Spores bearing a triradiate scar are termed trilete.

Tristichous. Arranged in three vertical rows.

Trisomic. An organism with an extra chromosome in addition to the normal complement, *i.e.* $2n+1$. Trisomy typically arises when a normal gamete (n) fuses with one containing an extra chromosome ($n+1$). The extra chromosome may be a simple copy of one of the chromosomes (primary trisomic) an isochromosome (secondary trisomic), or may include parts of two nonhomologous chromosomes (tertiary trisomic). Trisomics often have abnormal phenotypes and are frequently less fertile than diploids.

Tristichous. Describing a form of alternate leaf arrangement in which successive leaves arise 120° around the circumference of the stem giving three vertical rows of leaves.

Tritonymph. The last of three stages in the development of certain mites.

Triturate. To crush or pulverize; to grind to a powder.

Triungulin. The free-living, first larval stage of strepsipterans and certain coleopterans which undergo hypermetamorphosis.

Trivalent. The temporary association of three homologous chromosomes in a triploid or trisomic organism. Such associations are observed between mid prophase and late metaphase of the first meiotic division.

Trivium

1. In asteroids, the three arms opposite the madreporite.
2. In holothuroids, the three ambulacral areas forming the ventral surface.

TRNA. Transfer RNA.

Trochal. Resembling a wheel.

Trochanter

1. Any of several bony knobs on the femur of vertebrates to which muscles are attached.
2. The second segment of an insect's leg, between the coxa and the femur.

Trochal Disc. The flattened, ciliated, anterior end of a rotifer.

Trochanter

1. One of two large processes on the proximal end of the femur.
2. The second segment in the leg of an arthropod, located between the coxa and femur.

Trochlea. A puffeylike structure, as *a.* process at the distal end of the humerus : *b.* a ligamentous ring in the orbit through which passes the tendon of the superior oblique muscle.

Trochlear Nerve. The 4th cranial nerve (IV) supplying the superior oblique muscle of the eye.

Trochophore. The ciliated, free-swimming, pear-shaped larva of a number of invertebrate groups, especially annelids and mollusks; a trochosphere.

Trochosphere. A trochophore larva.

Trochus. The inner, ciliated ring of a trochal disc of a rotifer.

Troglobiont. A cave-dweller, an organism which spends a portion of or its entire life in caves.

Troglobiotic. Pertaining to cave life.

Trongon. A tropical bird of the family Trogonidae, noted for its brilliant plumage.

Trombiculid. A mite of the family Trombiculidae which includes the red bugs or chiggers.

Tropane Alkaloids. A group of alkaloids derived from the amino acid ornithine. The include hyoscyamine and its stereoisomer atropine, both solanaceous alkaloids. These are prepared from Datura stramonium (thorn apple) and Atropa belladonna (deadly nightshade) respectively. The cocane alkaloids, derived from the leaves of Erythroxylum coca and E. novagranatense (coca), are also examples.

Trophallaxis

1. The mutual exchange of food between adults and larvae, as in certain hymenopterans.
2. The transfer of secretions which serve as food and regulatory substances between adults and young, as in termite colonies.

Trophi

1. The mouthparts of an insect including their appendages.

2. The sclerotized jaws of a rotifer located on the inner wall of the pharynx or mastax.

Trophic

1. Pertaining to growth or nutrition.
2. Pertaining to that which influences growth and development or stimulates functional activity, as a trophic hormone.

Trophic Level. A step in the transfer of food or energy within a chain. There may be several trophic levels within a system, for example producers, (autotrophs), primary consumers (herbivores), and secondary consumer (carnivores); further carnivores may form fourth and fifth levels. There are rarely more than five levels since usually by this stage the amount of food or energy is greatly reduced.

Tropical Air. Air masses whose characteristic originate from a tropical source. Broadly, these comprise :

(*a*) maritime tropical air, originating over oceans; and

(*b*) continental tropical air, originating over land masses, and especially over N. Africa and the Middle East. Movements of these air masses pole-ward, with modification of their original characteristics, can have marked influence on weather in mid latitudes.

Tropism (tropic movement). Directional response by a plant to a stimulus. It may be positive or negative (*i.e.* toward or away from the source of the stimulus). The plant may respond by growth or turgor changes so that parts of it bend towards, away from, or at right angles to the direction of the stimulus. The suffix 'tropism' is used in relation to responses to particular stimuli, *e.g.* 'photo-tropism' is a response to light, 'geotropism' to gravity, and 'chemotropism' to a chemical substance.

Trophoblast. The surface layer of cells of a mammalian blastocyst from which the chrorion develops.

Trophocyte

1. A nutritive cell or one that stores food, as those of the fat body of an insect.
2. A nurse cell.

Trophoderm

1. The portion of the trophoblast which comes in contact with the uterine endometrium.
2. In mammals, the serosa or extraembryonic somatopleure.

Trophont. A vegetative stage in the development of certain parasitic ciliates.

Tropopause. Boundary separating a lower layer of the atmosphere (troposphere), in which air temperature generally decreases with height, from the layer above (stratosphere), in which temperature remains constant or increases with height. The altitude of the tropopause varies from an average of 10·12 km over the poles (occasionally descending to 8 km or below) to 17 km over the equator, according to season, and changes over short periods.

Tropophyte. A plant that is adapted to survive in a climate where there are alternating wet and dry seasons, by having a resting phase during the dry season. For example, many trees in monsoon forests shed their leaves in the dry season.

Trophosome. Collectively, the nonsexual structures of a hydrozoan Coelenterate.

Trophozoite. The vegetative phase in the life cycle of a protozoan during which asexual reproduction occurs.

Trophozooid. A gastrozooid.

Tropic. Of or pertaining to a tropism.

Tropical. Of or pertaining to the tropics.

Tropism. An involuntary response to a stimulus exhibited by plants and sedentary animals in which a bending, turning, or growth occurs, as a phototropism, geotropism, or hydrotropism. The response may be positive (towards) or negative (away from) the stimulus. Compare taxis.

Troposphere. The layer of the atmosphere between the Earth's surface and the tropopause, within which the air temperature on average decreaes, with height at a rate of about 6.5° C/km, though variations that sometimes occur include inversions (temperature increase with height within some limited layer). Most of the atmospheric turbulence and weather features occur in this layer, which contains almost all the atmospheric water vapour and most of the aerosols in suspension in the atmosphere (although there is also an important aerosol layer at about 22 km).

Tropophilous. Thriving under alternating environmental conditions, as dry-moist habitats or hot-cold seasons.

Trumpeter. Any of several animals which makes a trumpetlike sound, as *a.* a large, long-legged South American bird of the family Psophiidae; *b.* the trumpeter swan; *c.* several marine fishes, as the trumpeter perch; *d.* a breed of domestic pigeons.

Truncate

1. Having a square end, or appearing as though the apex or tip of a tapering structure has been broken or cut off.
2. Lacking a normal tip or apex.

True Fungi. Eumycota.

Truffles. Tuberales.

Truncate. Describing a leaf that is squared off at the apex.

Truncus Arteriosus

1. In lungfishes and amphibians, the anterior end of the conus arteriosus.
2. In vertebrate embroys, the tube leading from the bulbus arteriosus to the aortic sac and aortic arches.
3. The ventral aorta.

Trunk

1. *bot.* The main stem of a tree.
2. *anat* and *zool. a.* The body without head or limbs; the torso. *b.* The thorax and abdomen of an arthropod. *c.* The main portion of a structure, as a nerve trunk. *d.* A proboscis, as that of an elephant.

Trypanosome. Any flagellate protozoan of the genus Typanosoma, including blood parasites infesting man and other vertebrates, the causative agents of a number of diseases, as African sleeping sickness, Chaga's disease, surra, nagana, and dourine.

Trypanosomiasis. Any disease or condition resulting from infection with trypanosome.

Trypsin. An enzyme that digests protein (protease). It is secreted in an inactive from (trypsinogen) by the pancrease into the duodenum. There, trypsinogen is acted on by an enzyme (enterokinase) produced in the duodenum to yield trypsin. The active enzyme plays an important role in the digestion of proteins in the anterior portion of the small intestine.

Trypsinogen. The precursor or zymogen of trypisn secreted by the pancreas.

Tryptophan. A nonpolar aromatic amino acid with the formula $C_8H_6NCH_2CH(NH_2)COOH$ (illustration at amino acid).

Tryptophan is synthesized via the shikimic acid pathway and broken down to alanine and acetyle CoA.

As with the other aromatic amino acids, tryptophan is the precursor of many aromatic compouncs. Examples are the auxin indoleacetic acid and certain of the indole alkaloids, such as strychine and yohimbine.

Tsetse Fly. One of a number of species of bloodsuckings, African flies of the genus Glossina which act as vectors of trypanosomes.

TSH. Thyroid-stimulating hormone, a thyrotrophic hormone secreted by the anterior lobe of the pituitary.

Tutara. A primitive, rhynchocephalian reptile (Sphenodon punctatum) of New Zealand.

Tube

1. Any hollow, cylindrical structure.
2. *bot.* The basal portion of a calyx or corolla in a synsepalous or sympetalous flower.
3. *anat.* The uterine or auditory tube.
4. *zool.* A cylindrical burrow or house constructed by various invertebrates, as tube worms.

Tube Cell (tube nucleus). One of the cells contained within the microspore of gymnosperms, the other being the generative cell and the prothallial cell or cells. In Cycas it enters the haustorial pollen tube but its function is uncertain. In angiosperms the cell at the tip of the pollen tube that precedes the generative nuclei is sometimes termed the tube cell but it is more often called the vegetative nucleus.

Tube Nucleus. A nucleus at the tip of a pollen tube which functions in the growth and development of the tube.

Tuber. A swollen underground stem or root in certain plants. It enables the plant to survive the winter or dry season and is also a means of propagation. A stem tuber, such as the potato, forms at the end of an underground stem. Each tuber represents several nodes and internodes. The following season several new plants develop from the terminal and axillary buds (eyes). Root tubers, such as those of the dahlia, are modified food-storing adventitious roots and may also give rise to new plants.

Tuberales (truffles). An order of the Discomycetes in which the ascocarps are formed underground and resemble tubers. It contains about 35 genera and 230 or so species, many of which are edible. Certain species are often found under particular trees, *e.g.*, Tuber melanosporum (the European truffle), which grows under oaks. They are thus thought to be mycorrhizal.

Tubercle. A small, rounded prominence or excrescence, as *a. anat.* that on the crown of a molar tooth or on a bone; *b. bot.* a nodule on the root of a legume; *c. med.* a specific lesion produced by a tubercle bacillus.

Tuberculate (verrucose). Having a surface covered with small warty projections as, for example, the rind of ridge cucumbers. Pollen covered in wartlike structures (verrucae). *e.g.*, that of ivy (Hedera helix), is normally described as verrucate.

Tuberculosis. Infectious disease which affects humans and other animals. In humans the commonest from of the disease is pulmonary tuberculosis (consumption, phthisis); the causal agents are usually Mycobacterium tuberculosis or M. bovis. Infection occurs by inhalation of the pathogen, and lesions known as tubercles develop in the lungs. Tuberculous lesions may also develop in other areas of the body, *e g.* the liver or the bones. In untreated cases the mortality rate may be very high. Domestic animals, particularly cattle and pigs, may also contract tuberculosis Tuberculosis in cattle used to be very common in Britain, but is now much less so due to strict control measures; bovine tuberculosis is now a notifiable disease. Certain types of wild animals (especially badgers) can contract bovine tuberculosis and are believed to be able to transmit the infection to cattle; this has led to the extensive slaughter of badgers in certain areas of Britain.

Tuberculum. A tubercle.

Tuberiferous. Producing or bearing tubers.

Tuberoid. Resembling a tuber, as the thick, fleshy roots of certain orchids.

Tuberosity. A prominence on a bone; a large tubercle.

Tuberous. Pertaining to, resemoling, bearing, or producing tubers.

Tube Worm. One of a number of polychaete annelids which live in tubes which they rarely leave, as those of the orders Sabellidae and Serpulidae (fan worms and feather duster worms).

Tubicolous. Tube-dwelling; living in a tube.

Tubifacient Secreting or constructing a tube.

Tubule. A small tube of a minute, tube-shaped structure.

Tubuloalveolar. Possessing both secretory tubules and alveoli, with reference to compound glands.

Tubulose. Tubular; made up or tubular structures.

Tufted. Bearing or possessing a tunt; growing in tufts or clusters.

Tularemia. An infectious disease caused by a bacillus (Pasteurella tularensis) acquired by handling infected animals or through the bite of an arthropod. Also called rabbit fever.

Tulip. A European bulbous herb (Tulipa) of the lily family, cultivated for its showy, single flowers.

Tumblebug. A scarab beetle, as Canthon or Deltochilum, which feeds on dung. Working in pairs, tumblebugs roll pieces of dung into a ball, bury it, and, deposit their eggs in or on it. Also called dung beetles.

Tumbler. A variety of domestic pigeon which tumbles or somersaults in flight.

Tumefacient. Swollen; tending to produce swelling.

Tumid. Swollen, inflated, distended.

Tumour. Abnormal growth of new tissue that occurs anywhere in the body. Such a growth may be harmless or benign, *e.g.* a wart. Alternatively it may be malignant, destroying the tissue upon which it grows. It may also invade other tissues through the process of metastasis, in which cells sloughed off from the tumour are carried to other parts of the body.

Tumour-inducing Principle. A plasmid carried by the bacterium Agrobacterium tumefaciens, which causes crown gall dis-disease in plants. The plasmid ls necessary for the transformation of normal host tissue into tumour tissue. It is believed that this brought about by the incorporation of the plasmid into the plant genome. Tissue removed from crown gall tumours can be grown in culture without the addition of auxin and cytokinin.

Tuna. A large food and game fish of the family Thunnidae, order Percomorphi, as Thunnus, Neothunnus, Euthynnus. Also called tuna fish, tunny.

Tundra. A major regional community (biome) in which the vegetation is poor, the few species being mainly lichens, mosses, heaths, sedges, grasses, and some her baceous plants, but no trees. It is a region of cold desert, the temperature rarely exceeding 10°C. The topsoil is frozen for about nine months of the year and the subsoil is subjected to permafrost. The plants are thus subjected both to extreme cold and physiological drought as the soil water is frozen. The topography, type of soil, degree of shelter, etc. give rise to differences in vegetation from one locality to another. Arctic tundra is found north of the tree line of North America and Eurasia in a band of varying width circling the Arctic Ocean. In the Antarctic, there are only small scattered areas of arctic vegetation consisting of mosses and lichens on some of the islands.

Tung Oil. A fixed oil obtaned from the nuts of the tung oil tree (Aleurites fordii) of central and western China; an important drying oil.

Tunic. A coat or covering, as *a. bot*, the investing covering of a bulb or the integument of a seed; *b. zool.* the covering (test) of a tunicate.

Tunica

1. An enveloping coat or covering; a tunic.
2. One of the three layers comprising the wall of a blood vessel.

[1]Tunicate. Any member of the subphylum Urochordata (Tunicata); a sea squirt.

[2]Tunicate or Tunicated

1. Possessing a tunic.
2. Possessing concentric layers, as the bulb of an onion.

Tunicine. A polysaccharide resembling cellulose, present in the tunic of tunicates and in tubes housing sessile hemichordates.

Tunica-corpus Theory. A concept of the organization and development of the apical meristem, in which the meristematic region is differentiated into an outer peripheral layer or layers, termed the tunica, and an inner mass of cells, termed the corpus. The tunica is characterized by chiefly anticlinal divisions and the corpus mainly by periclinal divisions. The corpus gives rise to the interior part of the plant body and the tunica differentiates the outer layers including the epidermis. Compare histogen theory.

Tunny. A tuna.

Tur. A Caucasian wild goat (Capra caucasica) of the central region.

Turbellaria. A class of free-living flatworms (Platyhelminthes) comprising the planarians, which occur in wet soils, fresh water, and marine environments. Their undersurface is covered with cilia, used for gliding over stones and weeds. Planarians can also swim by means of undulations of the body.

Turbellarian. A free-living flatworm of the class Turbellaria.

Turbid. Cloudy, not clear.

Turbidimetry. Determination of the number of bacteria by estimation of the degree of turbidity of a suspension.

Turbot. A European flounder (Scopthalmus maximus), a highly esteemed food fish.

Turgid

1. Abnormally swollen, distended, or inflated.

2. Tightly drawn or stretched by pressure from within.

Turgor. The condition in a plant cell when its vacuole is distended with water, pushing the protoplasm against the cell wall. In this condition the osmotic pressure forcing water in is balanced by pressure exerted by the cell wall. Turgidity assists in maintaining the rigidity of plants; a decrease in turgidity leads to wilting. Compare plasmolysis.

Turgor Movement. Movement resulting from changes in turgor pressure, as the opening and closing of stomata.

Turgor Potential. Pressure potential.

Turgor Pressure. In calculations of osmotic pressure, the hydrostatic pressure exerted by the contents of the cell against the cell wall.

Turion

1. A winter bud, covered with scale leaves and mucilage, that is produced by certain aquatic plants, such as frogbit. Turions become detachad and remain dormant on the pond or lake bottom during the winter before developing into new plants the following season.
2. Sucker.

Turnip. A biennial herb (Brassica rapa) with edible root and leaves.

Turreted. Having the shape of a turret; long-spired, as certain gastropod shells.

Turtle. Any reptile of the order Chelonia including both terrestrial and aquatic forms with a body enclosed in a shell composed of a dorsal carapace and a ventral plastron.

Tusk

1. A greatly elongated and enlarged tooth, as that seen in the elephant, walrus, wild boar, and other mammals.
2. Any large, projecting tooth.

Twig. A small branch, as that of a tree, nerve, or blood vessels.

Twin

1. One of two individuals both at the same birth of the same parent.
2. One of a pair of similar structures.

Twine. To coil or twist about a structure.

Twiner. A plant whose stem twines about an object for support.

Twining. Winding about or twisting together; growing in a spiral fashion about an object, characteristic of certain climbing plants.

Twinning

1. The production of twins.
2. The production of twin objects, as kernels of a nut.

Two-dimensional Analysis. A technique used to separate mixtures of closely related molecules. One method involves two-dimensioual paper chromatography, in which a chromatogram produced by a solvent running in one direction is then subjected to a second separation by placing the chromatogram at right angles in a second solvent. Another method involves separation by electrophoresis followed by paper chromatography.

Tyloses. Bladder-like ingrowths that protrude into the tracheary elements of older wood eventually causing blockage. They originate from adjacent parenchyma cells via paired pits in the cell walls. Tyloses often become filled with tannins, resins, gums, or various pigments, so giving the heartwood its characteristic darker colour. These substances also help to preserve and strengthen the wood, while some of the pigments are important commercially as dyes (*e.g.* haematoxylin). Tyloses are sometimes found in the vessels of herbaceous plants, in which their function is unclear. They may act to seal off damaged vessels.

Tylosis pl. **Tyloses.** A bladderlike outgrowth of a parenchyma cell which grows into and plugs a water-conducting element of wood.

Tymbal. A vibrating structure in the sound-producing organ of a cicada; a timbal.

Tympanic. Of or pertaining to the tympanum or tympanic cavity.

Tympanic Cavity. The cavity of the middle ear; the tympanum or eardrum.

Tympanic Membrane

1. The drum membrane, which separates the external acoustic meatus from the tympanic cavity.
2. In common usage, the eardrum.

Tympanum

1. The middle ear; the tympanic cavity or eardrum.
2. In birds, a resonating chamber in the bronchotracheal type of syrinx.
3. In insects, the auditory organ or eardrum, as that on the first abdominal segment in a locust.

Type. An individual or a group of individuals which serves as a basis for the name of a taxonomic category (taxon), as a specimen which bears the name of a species.

Type Specimen. The specimen used for naming and describing a species or subspecies. If this is the original specimen collected by the author who named the species it is termed a holotype. The type specimen is not necessarily the most characteristic representative of the species. The term type is also used of any taxon selected as being representative of the rank to which it belongs. For example, the genus Solanum (potato) is said to be the type genus of the family Solanaceae.

Typhlosole

1. A longitudinal infolding of the wall of the intestine in annelids or in isopods.
2. The spiral valve of a cyclostome or elasmobranch.

Typhoid Fever. Acute disease of humans, caused by the bacterium Salmonella typhi. Infection occurs by ingestion of the pathogen, commonly in contaminated drinking water. The pathogen invades the lymphoid tissue of the small intestine. Symptoms include fever, skin rash, and diarrhoea or constipation. The disease can be fatal if untreated.

Typhus. An infectious disease caused by rickettsias transmitted by arthropods, as epidemic typhus, transmitted by the human body louse; endemic (murine or shop) typhus transmitted by the rat flea; scrub typhus, transmitted by the chigger.

Typhus Fevers. Fevers that are caused by rickettsias. Classical (epidemic or louse-borne) typhus is an acute disease of humans caused by Rickettsia prowazekii. The infection is carried by lice. Symptoms include fever, muscular pains, headache, malaise, and later a rash. Similar diseases are caused by other species of Rickettsia.

Tyrian Purple. A highly prized purple dye obtained from the adrectal glands of certain gastropods (Murex, Purpura, Mitra) and used by the ancient Greeks and Romans.

Tyrogenous. Produced by or originating in cheese.

Tyrosinase. An enzyme which catalyzes the formation of melanin from tyrosine.

Tyrosine. An aromatic polar amino acid with the formula $HOC_6H_4CH_2CH(NH_2)COOH$ (illustration at amino acid). The biosynthesis of tyrosine is similar to that of phenylalanine, diverging only in the last few reaction steps. Breakdown to acetyl CoA and fumaric acid occurs via phenylalanine. Like phenylalanine, tyrosine is a precursor of the isoquinoline alkaloids. It is also a precursor of various phenolic inhibitors, *e.g.* coumaric acid.

Tyrothricin. An antibiotic polypeptide mixture isolated from soil bacteria of the Tyrothrix type effective against gram-positive bacteria, some fungi, and protozoans.

U

Uakari. A bald-headed monkey of the gene. Cacajao of the Amazon forests.

Uniquitous. Widespread; occurring everywhere.

Uniquinone. Coenzyme Q.

Udder. A large, pendulous mammary gland, espcially one with two or more teats, as in the cow.

UDP. Nucleoside diphosphate sugars.

Ulcer. A break in the continuity of an epithelium of the skin or mucous membrane accompanied by degeneration and necrosis of underlying tissues.

Uliginose

1. Swampy; oozy.
2. Inhabiting or growing in swamps.

Ulna

1. The medial bone of the forearm in man.
2. The corresponding bone in the forelimb of other tetrapods.

Ulnare. In birds, the posterior of the two carpal bones in the wing; in mammals, the triquetral or cuneiform bone, a carpal bone.

Ulotrichous. Having woolly, curly hair.

Ulotrichales. An order of the Chlorophyceae containing unbranching filamentous algae (*e g.* Ulothrix). Each cell of the filament contains cne bandlike chloroplast around its periphery and cell division is in one direction only. Asexual reproduction is by zoospores of various kinds while sexual reproduction varies from isogamy to the well developed oogamy seen in Cylindrocapsa.

Ultracentrifuge. A high-speed centrifuge used to measeure the rate of sedimentation of colloidal, particles or to sepaiate macromolecules, such as proteins or nucleic acids, from solutions. Ultracentrifuges are electrically driven and are capable of seeds up to 60000 rpm.

Ultrafiltration. Filtering utilizing filters by which particles of colloidal size can be seprated from those of molecular size in true solutions.

Ultramicroscope. A form of microscope that reveals the presence of particle's that cannot be seen with a normal optical microscope. Colloidal particles, smoke particles, etc., are suspended in a liquid or gas in a cell with a black background and illuminated by an intense cone of light that enters the cell from the side and has its apex in the field of view. The particles then produce diffraction-ring systems, appearing as bright specks on the dark background.

Ultramicroscopic. Not capable of being seen by an ordinary microscope.

Ultrasonics. The study and use of pressure waves that have a frequency in excess of 20 000 Hz and are therefore inaudible to the humans ear. Ultrasound is used in medical diagnosis, particularly in conditions such as pregnancy, in which X-rays could have a harmful effect.

Ultrastructure (fine structure). Structural details of cells below the limit of resolution of the light microscope and only revealed by the electron microscope.

Ultraviolet Radiation (UV). Electromagnetic radiation having wavelengths between that of violet light and long X-rays, *i.e.* between 400 nanometres and 4 nm. In the range 400—300 nm the radiation is known as the near ultraviolet. In the range 300—200 nm it is known as the far ultraviolet. Below 200 nm it is known as the extreme ultraviolet or the vacuum ultraviolet, as absorption by the oxygen in the air makes the ure of evacuated apparatus essential. The sun is a strong emitter of UV radiatlon but only the near UV reaches the surface of the earth as the ozone in the atmosphere absorbs all wavelengths below 290 nm.

Most UV radiaiton for practical use is produced by various types of mercuryvapour lamps. Ordinary glass absorbs UV radiation and therefore lenses and prisms for use in the UV are made from quartz.

Ulvales. An order of the Chlorophyceae containing pseudoparenchymatous thalloid algae (*e.g.* Ulva), characteristically found in marine and brackish waters. The sheetlike thallus is formed by division in two planes of a filament that initially resembles those of the Ulotrichales. The Ulvales are consequently often placed in this order. There is an isomorphic alternation of generations in some species.

Umbel. A type of racemose inflorescence in which stalked flowers arise from the same point on the flower axis, resembling the spokes of an umbrella. An involucre (cluster) of bracts may occur at the point where the stalks emerge. This arrangement is characteristic of the family Umbelliferae (*e.g.* carrot. hogweed, parsley, parship), in which the inflorescence is usually a compound umbel.

Umbellate. Pertaining to or producing umbels.

Umbelliferous. Producing or bearing umbels.

Umbellule. A secondry umbel or umbellet; a small umbel.

Umber Bird. Umbrette.

Umbilical Cord. The cord that connects the embryo to the placenta in mammals. It contains a vein and two arteries that carry blood between the embryo and placenta. It is severe after birth to free the newly born animal from the placenta, and shrivels to leave a scar, the navel, on the animal.

Umbelliferae (Apiaceae). A dicotyledonous family containing about 2500—3000 species in about 300 genera and commonly known as the carrot family. Its members are distinguished by their characteristic infloresence, the umbel, a feature that made them one of the first natural families to be clearly recognized. Most umbellifers are herbaceous and have hollow internodes and often a characteristic odour. The fruit is dry and usually ridged and many are used as species, such as caraway (Carum carvi) and coriander (Coriandrum sativum). Species used as herbs include parsley (Petroselinum crispum) and fennel (Foeniculum vulgare), while the carrot (Daucus carota) and parsnip (Pastinaca sativa) are important roots crops.

Umbilicate. Having a depression in the center resembling an umbilicus.

Uucoupling Agent. Any chemical that uncouples the process of respiration from that phosphorylation. For example, in glycolysis the formation of 3-phosphoglycerate from 3-phosphoglyceroyl phosphate normally yields two molecules of ATP. However arsenate prevents the formation of ATP at this point. Arsenate also acts as an uncoupling agent in oxidative phosphorylation. Many other uncouplers of oxidative phosphorylation are known, most of which contain an aromatic rind and an acldic group. Examples are 2,4-dinitrophenol (DNP) and dicumarol. DNP has been used to investigate many aspects of plant physiology. For example, in research on phloem transport it has been shown that DNP inhibits translocation of assimilates. This implies there is some energy-requiring metabolic component in phloem transport and that the process is not purely due to osmotic potential and turgor pressure. DNP has also been used to investigate the theory that the respiratory climacteric that occurs during fruit ripening is due to the accumulation of natural uncoupling agents (uncoupling agents promote respiration as they cause a build-up of ADP).

Umbilicus

1. *zool. a.* The navel, a round depressed scar in the midventral line of the abdomen marking the point of attachment of the umbilical cord. *b.* A depression or opening in the shell of certain gastropods about which the whorls coil. *c.* One of two openings in the quill of a feather : the inferior umbilicus at the tip of the quill, the superior umbilicus at junction of rachis and quill.
2. *bot.* The hilum of a seed.

Umbo pl. **Umbones.** A boss; a rounded prominence or protuberance, as *a.* that on the valve of a bivalve marking the oldest portion of the shell; *b.* the central portion of the tympanic membrane; *c.* the posterior beak of the ventral valve of a brachiopod.

Umbonate. Bearing a conical or rounded boss or umbo.

Umbracticolous. Inhabiting shady places.

Umbraculiferous. Bearing an umbrellalike structure.

Umbracumorm. Shaped like an umbrella.

Umbraculum. The wavy, pigmented margin of the iris in the eye of certain mammals, as the camel.

Umbrageous. Providing shade.

Umbrella

1. The saucer-shaped body of a medusa or jellyfish; the bell.
2. Ectoderm cells located anterior to the prototroch in the development of a trochosphere.

Unau The two toed sloth (Choloepus didactylus) of tropical America.

Underfur. The dense, soft fur of animals composed of short, closely packed hairs among which are interspersed longer and coarser hairs which form the surface covering.

Undulant. Characterized by undulations or up and down movements.

Undulant Fever. An infectious disease affecting domestic animals and man caused by bacteria of the genus Brucella; brucellosis; malta fever.

Undulate. Possessing a wavy surface or margin; repand.

Undulipodia. A collective name for flagella and cilia, favoured by certain authorities because these organelles have the same (9+2) structure. The distinction between them has been an arbitrary one based on length and number.

Ungulate A herbivorous mammal with hoofed feet (unguligrade). Ungulates are grouped into two orders : Artiodactyla and Perissodactyla.

Unguligrade. Describing the gait of ungulates (*e.g.* horses and cows), in which only the tips of the digits (*i.e.* the hooves) are on the ground and the rest of the foot is off the ground. Compare digitigrade; plantigrade.

Ungual. Pertaining to, resembling, or possessing a hoof, claw, or nail.

Ungufigrade. A type of foot posture in which an animal walks on hoofs, as a horse or cow.

Uniaxial. Having a single axis.

Unicellular. Describing tissues, organs, or organisms consisting of a single cell. For example, the reproductive organs of some algae and fungi are unicellular. Unicellular organisms, *e.g.* bacteria, protozoans and certain algae and fungi, are sume times placed in a separate kingdom, the Protista. Compare acellular; multicellular.

Unilocular Sporangium. A sporangium that is not divided and comprises only one locule or compartment. Unilocular sporangia are seen in the sori of the brown alga Laminaria.

Unicorn. An arwhal.

Unicuspid. Having a single point or cusp.

Uniflagellate. Having a single flagellum.

Unifoliate. Designating a compound leaf which has been reduced to a single leaf, usually the enlarged terminal leaflet, as in the orange.

Unigeneric. Monogeneric; composed of a single genus, with reference to a family.

Unijugate. Having a single pair of leaflets.

Unilobar. Having a single to be.

Unilocular. Having a single chamber, cavity, or loculus.

Uninuclear. Possessing only one nucleus.

Unionid. A freshwater clam or mussel of the family Unionidae, common throughout the Mississippi valley, as Unio, Amblema.

Uniovular. From one egg; monozygotic.

Uniparous. Having one offspring at a time.

Unipetalous. Having a corolla of one petal.

Unipolar

1. Having a single pole.
2. Having a single process, as a unipolar neuron.

Unipotent. Giving rise to only one type of cell or tissue.

Uniramous Lacking an exopodite, with reference to crustacean appendages.

Uniseptate. With a single septum or partition.

Uniseriate. With a single row of cells.

Unisexual. Describing animals or plants with either male or female reproductive organs but not both. Most of the more advanced animals are unisexual but plants are often hermaphrodite. Flowers that contain either stamens or carpels but not both are also described as unisexual.

Unistratose. Possessing one layer.

Unit. A specified measure of a physical quantity, such as length, mass, time, etc., specified multiples of which are used to express magnitudes of that physical quantity. For scientific purposes previous systems of units have now been replaced by SI units.

Unit Character. *genetics*. A trait or character which differs from others by a single gene difference; a trait whose inheritance can be accounted for on the basis of a single pair of genes.

Unitypic. Monotypic; of a single type.

Univalent

1. Unpaired at meiosis, as a chromosome which is lacking its synaptic mate.

[1]Univalve. Having one valve.

[2]Univalve. A mollusk with a univalve shell, as a gastropod.

Universal. All-inclusive, wide-spread, all-embracing.

Universal Donor. In blood transfusion, an individual whose blood is of the group O type and can be received by those of all blood groups.

Universal Recipient. One whose blood is of group AB and Rh positive.

Universal Symmetry. Symmetry as that possessed by spherical organisms in which any plane passing through the center would divide the body into two similar halves.

Universal Veil. A membrane that encloses the developing fruiting body of many basidiomycete fungi. It ruptures as the stalk elongates, the remnants forming the volva at the base of the stalk and the flecks of tissue seen on the upper surface of the cap.

Univoltine. Having one brood a year, as various insects and most birds.

Unsealed. With margins of the carpels not coherent.

Urachis. An embryonic cord or tube which connects the tip of the urinary bladder with the allantoic stalk.

Uracil. A pyrimidine derivative and one of the major component bases of nucleotides and the nucleic acid RNA.

Urate. A salt of uric acid.

Urceolate. Urn-shaped; expanded below and constricted near the mouth.

Urea (carbamide). A white crystalline water-soluble solid, $CO(NH_2)_2$. Urea is the major end product of nitrogen excretion in mammals, being synthesized by the urea cycle. Urea is synthesized industrially from ammonia and carbon dioxide for use in urea-formaldehyde resins and pharmaceuticals, as a source of nonprotein nitrogen for ruminant livestocks, and as a nitrogen fertilizer.

Urea Cycle (ornithine cycle). The series of biochemical reactions that converts ammonia to urea during the excretion of metabolic nitrogen. Urea formation occurs in mammals and, to a lesser extent, in some other animals. The liver converts ammonia to the much less toxic urea, which is excreted in solution in urine.

Uranium—Lead Dating. A group of methods of dating certain rocks that depends on the decay of the radioisotopes uranium—238 to lead—206 (half-life 4.5×10^9 years) or the decay of uranium—235 to lead—207 (halflife 7.1×10^8 years). One form of uranium—lead dating depends on measuring the ratio of the amount of helium trapped in the rock to the amount of uranium present (since the decay $^{238}U \rightarrow ^{206}Pb$ releases eight alpha-particles). Another method of calculating the age of the rocks is to measure the ratio of radiogenic lead (^{206}Pb, ^{207}Pb, and ^{208}Pb) present to nonradiogenic lead (^{204}Pb). These methods give reliable results for ages of the order 10^7—10^9 years.

Uranyl Acetate. A widely used electron stain suitable for high-resolution transmission electron microscopy. It stains nucleic acids and proteins thus enhancing the contrast obtained in observations of membranes and membrane-bound organelles.

Urease. An enzyme which catalyzes the conversion of urine to ammonia and CO_2.

Uredinales. An order of the Teliomycetes containing the rust fungi, which number over 5000 species in about 126 genera. The teliospore is terminal, and the basidiospores develop on sterigmata and are actively discharged from the promycelium. Compare Ustilaginales.

Uredospore (urediospore). A dikaryotic spore formed in a spore cluster (a uredosorus or uredium) by certain rust fungi. The uredospores of Puccinia graminis are formed on the main host, wheat, and are responsible for the characteristic rusty streaks of infected plants. On release they infect more wheat plants.

Uredinium. A rust-colored pustule (sorus) formed on a wheat plant infected by the rust fungus. It produces uredospores.

Urediosorus. A uredinium.

Uredospore. A dikaryotic, one-celled spore formed in the uredinium of certain rusts, as the wheat rust; also urediospore, urediniospore.

Ureotelic. Term applied to animals in which urea is the principal nitrogenous product excreted in the urine, as amphibians, mammals. Compare ammonotelic, uricotelic.

Ureter. The duct in vertebrates that conveys urine from the kidney to the bladder.

Urethra. The duct in mammals that conveys urine from the bladder to be discharged to the outside of the body. In males the urethra passes through the penis and is joined by the vas deferens; it therefore also serves as a channel for sperm.

Urial. A wild sheep (Ovis vignei) of central Asia. Also called shapu.

Uric Acid. The end product of purine breakdown in most primates, birds, terrestrial reptiles, and insects and also (except in primates) the major form in which metabolic nitrogen is excreted. Being fairly insoluble, uric acid can be expelled in solid form, which conserves valuable water in arid environments. The accumulation of uric acid in the synovial fluid of joints causes gout.

Urinary. Of or pertaining to urine or to the structures which secrete, store, or convey urine.

Urinary Bladder. A reservoir in which urine is stored.

Urinary System. The organs concerned with the formation and excretion of urine; in mammals, the kidneys, ureters, bladder, and urethra.

Urinate. To discharge urine.

Uridine Diphosphate. Nucleoside diphosphate sugars.

Urine. The aqueous fluid formed by the excretory organs of animals for the removal of metabolic waste products. In higher animals, urine is produced by the kidneys, stored in the bladder, and excreted through the urethra or cloaca.

Apart from water, the major constituents of urine are one or more of the end products of nitrogen metabolism —ammonia, urea, uric acid, and creatinine. It may also contain various inorganic ions, the pigments urochrome and urobilin, amino acids, and purines. Precise composition depends on many factors, especially the habitat of a particular species : aquatic animals produce copious volumes; terrestrial animals need to conserve water and produce much less (about 1.0-1.5 litres per day in humans).

Uriniferous. Conveying urine, as uriniferous tubule.

Urn

1. *bot.* The lower portion of the base of a pyxis.
2. *zool* A ciliated vase-or funnel-shaped, excretory structure present in the body cavity of sipunculids, echiurids, and some holothuroids.

Uronic Acids. A class of sugar acids in which the carbon atom carrying the primary hydroxyl group (*i.e.* the CH_2OH end of the molecule) is oxidized to a carboxyl group ($COOH$). Uronic acids are biologically the most important group of the sugar acids and are common constituents of polysaccharides. For example, glucuronic acid, derived from glucose, is a common constituent of gums and mucilages. Galacturonic acid is a component of pectic substances while mannuronic acid is found in the seaweed gum alginic acid.

Urinogenital. Urogenital.

Urochordate. Any chordate of the subphylum Urochordata comprising mostly sessile forms with an enveloping covering or tunic; a tunicate, ascidian, or sea squirt.

Urochrome. A pigment present in normal urine and responsible for its colour.

Urodele. A tailed amphibian of the class Caudata (Urodela), as a newt or salamander.

Urodeum. In birds and monotremes, the portion of the cloaca which receines the ureters and reproductive ducts.

Urongenitap

1. Of or pertaining to the urinary and reproductive organs.
2. Functioning as both an excretory and reproductive structure, as a urogenital papilla, pore, or sinus.

Urogenital System. The organs which comprise the urinary and reproductive systems; urinogenital system.

Urogomphus. A fixed and unjointed cercus in an insect larva.

Urohypophysis. A neurosecretory structure located at the posterior end of the spinal cord in fishes; also called urophysis.

Uropod. One of a pair of appendages located on either side of the telson in various crustaceans, as the lobster.

Uropygial Gland. An oil gland located at the base of the uropygium in birds; also called preen gland.

Uropygid. A whip scorption, an arachind of the order Uropygi.

Uropygium. In birds, a pointed prominence at the posterior end of the body containing the caudal vertebrae and pygostyle. It supports the tail feathers.

Urosome. The hind body of a copepod, consisting of one or two thoracic segments and the abdomen.

Urostyle

1. A rodlike bone composed of fused caudal vertebrae present in frogs and toads.
2. The posterior end of the vertebral column which extends into the dorsal flange of a homocercal tail in fishes.

Ursine. Of or pertaining to bears or the bear family, Ursidae.

Urticaceous. Of or belonging to the family Urticaceae, a family of herbs, shrubs, and trees which includes the nettles.

Urticaria. Inflammation of the skin characterized by redness, development of welts and wheals, and intense itching; hives; nettle rash.

Urticating. Causing urticaria, as urticating caterpillars whose poison hairs or spines cause a dermatitis.

Uta. An iguanid lizard of the genus Uta of western North America.

Ustilaginales. An order of the Teliomycetes containing the smut fungi, which number about 850 species in some 48 genera. The teliospore (the brand or smut spore) is not terminal and basidiospores develop directly on the promycelium rather than on sterigmata. The basidiospores are not actively discharged. Compare Uredinales.

Utrical (bladder)

1. An ovoid compartment lined with sensitive hairs that serves to trap and digest small animals. It is seen in species of Utricularia (bladderworts) and is a modification of the leaf.
2. An indehiscent bladder-like fruit formed by certain plants in the Chenopodiaceae and Amaranthaceae. It is a type of achene.

Uterine. Of or pertaining to the uterus.

Uterine Bell. A structure at the posterior end of an acanthocephalan into which eggs are drawn which functions as a sorting device returning immature ova to the body cavity.

Uterine Horns. The anterior portions of a bipartite or bicornate uterus; also called cornua.

Uterine Milk. A uterine secretion which bathes developing embryos, as in the opossum.

Uterus (womb). The organ of female mammals in which the embryo develops. Paired in most mammals but single in humans, it is situated between the bladder and rectum and is connected to the fallopian tubes and to the vagina. The linning shows cyclical changes (menstrual cycle; oestrous cycle) associated with egg production and provides a thick spongy layer in which the fertilized egg becomes embedded. The outer wall of the uterus is thick and muscular; by contracting, it forces the fully grown fetus through the vagina to the outside.

Utricle

1. *anat*. *a*. A saclike structure in the internal ear which contains the maculae utriculi, sensory receptors for position and movement. *b*. A small pocket in the prostatic portion of the male urethra.
2. *bot*. *a*. An air bladder of a seaweed. *b*. A bladderlike structure in certain fungi, as Atriplex. *c*. A small, bladderlike one-seeded fruit, as in a sedge.
3. A utriculus.

Utricular. Of or pertaining to a utricle or utriculus; inflated; saclike; bladderlike; utriculate.

Utriculate. Utricular.

Uvea. The pigmented, vascular coat of the eye, comprising the choroid, ciliary body, and iris; the tunica vasculosa, the middle layer.

Uvula. A pendant, fleshy, conical structure hanging from the free border of the soft palate.

Urchin

1. A sea urchin.
2. A hedgehog.

Uterine Milk. A uterine secretion which bathes developing embryos, as in the opossum.

Uterus (womb). The organ of female mammals in which the embryo develops. Paired in most mammals but single in humans, it is situated between the bladder and rectum and is connected to the fallopian tubes and to the vagina. The lining shows cyclical changes (menstrual cycle, oestrous cycle) associated with egg production and provides a thick spongy layer in which the fertilized egg becomes embedded. The outer wall of the uterus is thick and muscular; by contraction it forces the fully grown fetus through the vagina to the outside.

Utricle

1. [illegible]. A saclike structure in the internal ear which contains the [illegible] receptors for position and movement. 2. A small pocket in the prostatic region of the male urethra.

3. [illegible]. An air bladder or [illegible]. A bladderlike structure in certain [illegible], as [illegible] [illegible].

[illegible]

[illegible]

[illegible]

[illegible]

[illegible]

V

Vaccination

1. Inoculation with a vaccine in order to develop immunity against a specific disease.
2. Inoculation with the virus of vaccinia in order to develop immunity against smallpox.

Vaccine. A liquid preparation of treated disease-producing microorganisms or their products used to stimulate an immune response in the body and so confer resistance to the disease (immunization). Vaccines are administered orally or by injection (inoculation). They take the form of dead viruses or bacteria that can still act as antigens, live but weakened microorganisms (attenuation), specially treated toxins, or antigenic extracts of the microorganism.

Vaccinia. Cowpox, a virus disease of cows transmissible to man by contact or vaccination.

Vacuolar. Pertaining to, resembling, or composed of vacuoles.

Vacuolated. Containing vacuoles or cavities.

Vacuole. A space within the cytoplasm of a living cell that is filled with air, water or other liquid, sap, or food particles. In plant cells there is usually one large vacuole; animal cells usually have several small ones.

Vacuome. The vacuoles of a cell together with their cell sap.

Vagal. Of or pertaining to the vagus nerve.

Vagina. The tube leading from the uterus to the outside. Sperm are deposited in the vagina during copulation and the fully developed fetus is born through it. In a number of mammals the vagina may be sealed when the animal is not sexually receptive and only open during oestrus. Its lining produces mucus, which prevents friction and the entry of infective organisms.

Vaginal. Of or pertaining to the vagina.

Vaginate. Sheathed; enclosed within a sheath.

Vagus Nerve. The tenth cranial nerve : a paired nerve that supplies branches to many major internal organs. It carries motor nerve fibres to the heart, lungs, and viscera and sensory fibres from the viscera.

Valine. A nonpolar amino acid with the formula $(CH_3)_2CHCH(NH_2)COOH$ (illustration at amino acid). Valine is synthesized from pyruvate via α-ketoisovalerate. The degradation of valine is extremely complex, leading eventually to proprionyl CoA and thence to succinyl CoA. Methionine, leucine, and isoleucine also degrade to proprionyl CoA; the last sequence of reactions to succinyl CoA is thus common to all four amino acids.

Vallate. Surrounded by a depression outside of which is an elevated rim, as the vallate papillae of the tongue.

Vallecula. A shallow groove, channel, or depression.

Vallecular Canal. A longitudinal channel in the stem internode of Equisetum and some of its fossil relatives, positioned radially opposite a longitudinal furrow (valley) between the stem ridges. The vallecular canals are arranged roughly between the vascular bundles. Compare carinal canal.

Valvate. Describing sepals and petals that meet but do not overlap in the bud. Compare imbricate.

Valve

1. (in anatomy). Any of various structures for restricting the flow of a fluid through an aperture or along a

tube to one direction. Valves in the heart (mitral valve; tricuspid valve), veins, and lymphatic vessels consist of two or three flaps of tissue (cusps) fastened to the walls. The cusps are flattened to the walls to allow the normal passage of blood or lymph, but a reverse flow causes them to block the vessel or aperture, so preventing further backflow.

2. (in botany) *a.* Any of the parts that make up a capsuleor other dry fruit that sheds its seeds. *b.* One of the two halves of the cell wall of a diatom.

Valvula. A little valve or fold.

Valvulae Conniventes. Circular folds (plicae conniventes) in the small intestine of a vertebrate.

Vampire. One of several bloodsucking bats of the genera Dasmodus and Diphylla of Central and South America. False vampires comprise the genera Vampyrus and Phyllostomus.

Vampire Fish. The candiru (Vandellia cirrhosa), a small, bloodsucking catfish of the Amazon which invades the urogenital openings of vertebrates. It is the only vertebrate parasite of man.

Vanadium. A rare element, symbol V, at. no. 23, absent in most animals but highly concentrated in ascidians, as Ciiona.

Vanadocyte. A green cell in the blood of an ascidian in which vanadium is bound to hydrosulfuric acid.

Vane

1. *zool.* The flat, expanded portion of a feather; web.
2. *bot.* A vexillum.

Vanilla. A climbing orchid (Vanilla planifolia) of tropical America, whose fruits, vanilla beans, are the source of vanilla flavoring extract.

Variance. Symbol V or σ^2. The square of the standard deviation. The mean square is the estimated variance.

Variant. An individual or group which differs from others of its own type.

Variation. The differences between individuals of a plant or animal species. Variation may be the result of environmental conditions; for example, water supply and light intensity affect the height and leaf size of a plant. Differences of this kind, acquired during the lifetime of an individual, are not transmitted to succeeding generations since the genes are not affected. Variations due to differences in genetic constitution are inherited (continuous variatian; discontinuous variation). Wide genetic variation Improves the ability of a species to survive in a changing environment, since the chances that some individuals will tolerate a particular change are increased. Such individuals will survive and transmit the advantageous genes to their offspring.

Varicellate. Having small and indistinct ridges or varices, said of shells.

Varicose. Swollen, knotted, tortuous, as a varicose vein.

Variegated. Having streaks or patches of different colors, with reference to leaves.

Variegation. The occurrence of patches or streaks of different coloured tissues in a plant organ, usually a leaf or petal. It may be due to infection, particularly viral infection, mineral deficiency, or physiological or genetic differences between the cells. The variegated petals of certain tulip varieties (*e.g.*, Rembrandt tulips) are due to a virus infection. The variegated leaves of Coleus are caused in groups of cells developing different pigment combinations. This is a form of somatic variegation and heritable differences between different coloured parts of the leaf are not evident. In contrast the variegated leaves of, for example,

Pelargonium are due to genetic variation arising from mutation.

Variety. A category used in the classification of plants and animals below the species level. A variety consists of a group of individuals that differ distinctly from but can interbreed with other varieties of the same species. The characteristics of a variety are genetically inherited. Examples of varieties include breeds of domestic animals and the races of man.

Variola. Smallpox.

Variole. A small pit or foveola.

Varix pl. Varices

1. *zool.* A transverse ridge across the whorls of various gastropod shells marking the former position of the outer lip.
2. *med.* A tortuous and dilated vein.

Varus. Turned abnormally inward, with reference to the lower extremity.

Varve. A stratum in the bottom deposits of a lake consisting of two layers, one formed in the spring, the other in the winter.

Varve Dating A method used to determine the age of a particular sediment and of the fossils that it contains. A varve is a layer of sediment that has been deposited in a glacial lake by the melt waters in spring and summer. Because the particles brought down in the spring are much coarser than those deposited later in the year, annual layers can be distinguished. Varves were formed in the Pleistocene when the ice was retreating, and by counting them, the chronology for parts of northern Europe has been established.

Varying Hare. Snowshoe rabbit.

Vas pl. Vasa A vessel or canal : a duct.

Vas Afferens pl. Vasa Afferentia. An afferent vessel, as that leading to a lymph node.

Vasa Vasorum. Small blood vessels supplying the wall of an artery or vein.

Vascular

1. Of or pertaining to vessels conducting a fluid.
2. Supplied with or containing vessels or ducts, especially blood vessels.

Vascular Bundle (fascicle). A long continuous strand of conducting (vascular) tissue in seed plants and pteridophytes that extends from the roots through the stem and into the leaves. It consists of xylem and phloem, which are separated by a cambium in plants that undergo secondary thickening.

Vascular Cambium. A lateral meristem, found in those vascular plants exhibiting secondary growth, that gives rise to secondary xylem and secondary phloem mostly by periclinal cell divisions. The vascular cambium contains fusiform initials, which give rise to the radial (ray) system of the secondary tissues. Compare phellogen.

Vascular Cylinder. The stele of a root or stem.

Vascularization. The formation and development of blood vessels in a tissue or organ.

Vascularized. Supplied with blood vessels.

Vascular Plants. All plants possessing organized vascular tissue. They may be grouped in a single division, axial system, and ray initials, which give ris to the the Tracheophyta, or separated into two divisions, the Pteridophyta and Spermatophyta.

Vascular Ray. A radial extension of the vascular cambium in the stem of a woody plant.

Vascular System

1. *zool.* In vertebrates, the cardiovascular or circulatory system; in echinoderms, the lacunar system.

2. *bot.* The water- and food-conducting system of a vascular plant.

Vascular Tissue (vascular system). The tissue that conducts water and nutrients through the plant body in higher plants (ferns and seed plants). It consists of xylem and phloem. Since the xylem and phloem tissues are always in close proximity to each other, distinct regions of vascular tissue can be identified (vascular bundle). The possession of vascular tissue has enabled the higher plants to attain a considerable size and dominate most terrestrial habitats.

Vascular Transition. Transition region.

Vasculum. A metal container used for collecting botanical specimens.

Vas Deferens. One of a pair of ducts carrying sperm from the testis (or epididymis) to the outside, in mammals through the urethra.

Vasectomy. Removal of a portion of the vas deferens.

Vas Efferens. Any of various small ducts carrying sperm. In reptiles, birds, and mammals they convey sperm from the seminiferous tubules of the testis to the epididymis; in invertebrates they carry sperm from the testis to the vas deferens.

Vasoconstriction. The reduction in the internal diameter of blood vessels, especially arterioles or capillaries. The constriction of arterioles is mediated by the action of nerves on the smooth muscle fibres of the arteriole walls and results in an increase in blood pressure.

Vasodepressor. That which brings about a lowering of blood pressure by dilatation of blood vessels, as a vasodilator nerve.

Vasodilation (vasodilatation). The increase in the internal diameter of blood vessels, especially arterioles or capillaries. The vasodilation of arterioles is mediated by the action of nerves on the smooth muscle fibres of the arteriole walls and results in a decrease in blood pressure.

Vasomotor. Pertaining to or regulating constriction (vasoconstriction) or dilatation (vasodilatation) of blood vessels, as a vasomotor nerve.

Vasomotor Nerves. The nerves of the autonomic nervous system that control the diameter of blood vessels. Vasoconstrictor nerves decrease the diameter (vasoconstriction); vasodilator nerves increase it.

Vasopressin (antidiuretic hormone; ADH). A hormone, secreted by the posterior pituitary gland, that stimulates absorption of water by the kidneys and thus controls the concentration of body fluids. Vasopressin is produced by specialized nerve cells in the hypothalamus of the brain and is transported to the posterior pituitary in the bloodstream. Deficiency of ADH results in a disorder known as diabetes insipidus, in which large volumes of urine are excreted; it is treated by administration of natural or synthetic hormone.

Vasotomy. The cutting of or making an incision into the vas deferens.

Vector. An animal, usually an insect, that passively transmits disease-causing microorganisms from one animal or plant to another or from an animal to man. Compare carrier.

Vector Tissue. A special tissue in leeches which serves as a pathway for sperm passing to the ovisacs.

Vegetable

1. Of, pertaining to, or of the nature of a plant.
2. Derived from plants, as a vegetable oil.

[2]Vegetable. A plant, especially a herbaceous plant which is cultivated for food, or the edible portion of such a plant.

Vegetal

1. Of or pertaining to plants.
2. Pertaining to growth and nutrition; vegetative.

Vegetalized. *embryol.* A condition in which the animal pole is weakened and the vegetal pole becomes dominant.

Vegetal Pole. In an ovum, the pole opposite the animal pole, characterized by accumulation of yolk.

Vegetation

1. All the plants of an area or region.
2. *med.* A plantlike growth, as a vegetation on a heart valve.

Vegetative

1. Resembling a plant, with respect to nutrition and growth.
2. Pertaining to stem and leaf development in contrast to flower and seed development.
3. With respect to reproduction in plants, nonsexual in contrast to sexual development.
4. Inactive, as the vegetative nucleus.

Vegetative Nucleus (vegetative cell). The large nucleus formed within the pollen grain of angiosperms along with one or two smaller generative nuclei. After germination of the pollen grain it migrates to the tip of the pollen tube where it may be termed the tube nucleus. It is thought to control the growth and development of the pollen tube penetrates the nucllus penetrates the nucellus.

Vegetative Propagation (vegetative reproduction)

1. A form of asexual reproduction in plants whereby new individuals develop from specialized multicellular structures (*e.g.* tubers, bulbs) that become detached from the parent plant. Examples are the production of strawberry plants from runners and of gladioli from daughter corms. Artificial methods of vegetative propagation include grafting (graft), budding and making cuttings.
2. Asexual reproduction in animals, *e.g.* budding in Hydra.

Vegetative Reproduction (vegetative propagation). A form of asexual reproduction in which specialized multicellular organs formed by the parent become detached and generate new individuals. Such parts may include bulbs, corms, gemmae, rhizomes, stems, tubers, etc. The regenerative capacities of various plant organs have been exploited through a number of techniques used in agriculture and horticulture to multiply stocks. These methods include budding, layering, air-layering, cutting, and pegging, and may be enhanced by the careful control of microclimate or by growth regulators.

Vegetative Stage. In protozoans, the trophozoite which reproduces asexully.

Veil

1. *zool. a.* A velum. *b.* A caul.
2. *bot.* A velum.

Vein

1. A blood vessel that carries blood towards the heart. Most veins carry deoxygenated blood (the pulmonary

vein is an exception). The largest veins are fed by smaller ones, which are formed by the merger of venules. Veins have thin walls and a relatively large internal diameter. Valves within the veins ensure that the flow of blood is always towards the heart. Compare artery.

2. A vascular bundle in a leaf.

3. Any of the tubes of chitin that strengthen an insect's wing.

Veination. Venation.

Velamen. A whitish spongy sheath of dead empty cells that surrounds the aerial roots of epiphytic plants, such as orchids. It absorbs any surface water on the roots.

Velar. Of or pertaining to a velum.

Velarium. A structure resembling a velum present in certain scyphozoan medusae.

Velate. Having a veil or velum.

Veliger. The free-swimming larva of certain mollusks characterized by possession of a velum.

Velum

1. A thin, membranous structure which resembles a curtain or veil, as the shelflike structure which projects inwardly from the margin of the bell in hydromedusae.

2. *anat.* The soft palate.

3. *bot.* *a.* A membrane extending from the stalk to the pileus in certain fungi, as Amanita. *b.* A protective membrane covering the sporangium in quillworts.

Velutinous. Velvety; covered with a fine, silky pubescence.

Velvet. A soft, highly vascular skin which covers the antlers of deer during the growth period and is sloughed off when development is complete.

Vena Cava. Either of the two large veins that carry deoxygenated blood into the right atrium of the heart. The precaval vein (anterior or superior vena cava) receives blood from the head and forelimbs; the postcaval vein (posterior or inferior vena cava) drains blood from the trunk and hindlimbs.

Venation

1. The arrangement of veins (vascular bundles) in a leaf. The leaves of dicotyledons have a central main vein (midrib) with side branches that themselves further subdivide to form a network (net or reticulate venation). The leaves of monocotyledons have parallel veins (parallel venation).

2. The arrangement of the veins in an insect's wing, which is often important in classification.

Venereal. Pertaining to or related to sexual intercourse.

Venesection. Taking blood from the body by cutting into a vein; phlebotomy.

Venin

1. A mixture of venoms from various snakes.

2. The poisonous principle in a venom. Also venene.

Venom. A toxic substance produced by various animals, as fishes, snakes, lizards, spiders, ticks, scorpions, centipedes, and insects. Its toxic principle may be a neurotoxin, neurocytolysin, hemolysin, hemocoagulin, proteolysin, or cytolysin.

Venomous. Poisonous; capable of inflicting, a poisonous bite, sting, or injury.

Venous

1. Of or pertaining to a vein or veins.

2. Designating blood carried by veins.

Vent. An outlet, as the anal or cloacal opening in certain vertebrates, as fishes and birds.

Venter. The swollen flask-shaped base of an archegonium that contains the megaspore.

Ventilation. *physiol.* The process of renewing or supplying fresh air to the lungs.

Ventilator. A worker in a bee colony which, by fanning with its wings, aids in ventilating the nest or hive.

Ventral. Describing the surface of a plant or animal that is nearest or next to the ground or other support, *i.e.*, the lower surface. In bipedal animals, such as man, it is the forward-directed (anterior) surface. Compare dorsal.

Ventral Canal Cell. One of the products that is formed along with the egg cell when the primary ventral cell of an archegonium divides. It has no cell wall and lies at the base of the neck. When the archegonium is mature the ventral canal cell becomes mucilaginous and may produce chemicals to attract the male gametes.

Ventral Placentation. Marginal placentation.

Ventral Suture. The line of fusion where the margins of the megasporophyll join to form the characteristic tubular shape of the ovary as found in angiosperms. This is often one of the first lines of weakness along which dehiscence occurs at fruit ripening.

Ventricle

1. A chamber of the heart that receives blood from an atrium and pumps it into the arterial system. Amphibians and fish have a single ventricle, but mammals, birds, and reptiles have two, pumping deoxygenated blood to the lungs and oxygenated blood to the rest of the body, respectively.
2. Any of the four linked fluid-filled cavities in the brain of vertebrates. One of these cavities is in the

medulla oblongata, two are in the cerebral hemispheres (cerebrum), and the fourth is in the posterior part of the forebrain. The ventricles contain cerebrospinal fluid filtered from the blood by the choroid plexus.

Ventricose. Inflated, swollen, protruding outward on one side.

Ventricous. Ventricose.

Ventricular

1. Of or pertaining to a ventricle.
2. Bulging or protruding.

Ventricular Folds. The false vocal folds in the larynx of a mammal.

Ventriculus

1. *zool.* The midgut or midintestine (stomach) of an insect.
2. The gizzard or stomach of a bird.

Ventrose. Having a belly or a bellylike protrusion; pot-bellied.

Venule A small blood vessel that receives blood from the capillaries and transports it to a vein.

Venus's flower-basket. A genus of hexactinellid sponges (Euplectella) with a cylindrical skeleton of siliceous fibers resembling spun glass, from waters off the coasts of Southeast Asia.

Venus's Girdle. A ctenophore (Cestum venerum) with a long, ribbonlike body.

Verdant. Covered with green vegetation.

Verdin. A small titmouse (Auriparus flaviceps).

Verge. The male copulatory organ of certain invertebrates, as a snail.

Vermicide. An agent which kills or destroys worms, especially parasitic worms.

Vermicular. Wormlike, resembling a worm in form or activities.

Vermiculate. Vermicular; wormlike.

Vermiculated

1. Infested with worms.
2. Having cavities resembling the burrows of worms.

Vermiculose. Vermicular.

Vermiform. Shaped like a worm.

Vermiform Process. The appendix in man.

Vermin

1. Any of the various small animals that infest the bodies or the habitations of man and domestic animals, especially cockroaches, bedbugs, fleas, lice, mites, mice, or rats.
2. Any animal which preys upon game.

Verminous. Pertaining to, infested with, or caused by vermin.

Vermis. A small median lobe of the cerebellum.

Vernacular. Local; characteristic of a locality.

Vernacular Name. The common or local name of an animal or plant.

Vernal

1. Of or pertaining to spring.
2. *ecol.* Late spring.

Vernalin. A hypothetical plant growth substance that, it has been suggested, is formed in meristematic regions of a plant subjected to cold. Experiments that apparently show this substance can be transmitted to other plants by grafting have probably failed to separate the effects of photoperiod from those of vernalization. Thus the transmitted flower stimulus could be florigen rather than vernalin. Other experiments suggest that, if such a substance is formed, it is only transmitted to other cells by cell division. Thus if one apex on a plant is locally vernalized, the other apices remain unvernalized. It is probable that there is no one substance formed by vernalization and that the biochemical basis of vernalization is different in different cold-requiring species. Thus applying gibberellin to seeds replaces the vernalization requirement in some species but not others. Other substances that have partly or completely replaced the vernalization requirement in different species include auxin, kinetin, RNA, and vitamin E.

Vernalization. The application of a cold treatment to germinating seeds or seedlings to ensure flowering. Many plants, including winter cereals, will not flower unless subjected to a period of chilling early in their development. Winter cereals are therefore sown in the autumn for flowering the following year. However, if germinating seeds are artificially vernalized they can be sown in the spring for flowering the same year.

Vernation (ptyxis). The pattern of folding and rolling of leaves in a bud. Many types of vernation are recognized (illustration), which may be useful diagnostically. The leaf margins may be rolled forwards to the upper side of the leaf (involute) or rolled backwards to the adaxial surface (revolute). The margin of one side may be wrapped around the other (convolute) or each leaf may be folded in a U-shape, enclosing the next youngest leaf (conduplicate). There may be many longitudinal folds in the lamina (plicate), as in certain palms, or the lamina may be rolled from apex to base (circinate), as seen in most ferns. Compare aestivation.

Vernicose. Shiny; appearing as though polished, said of leaves.

Verruca. A wart or wartlike elevation.

Verrcuose. Warty; bearing wartlike elevations.

Versatile Describing an anther that is joined to the filament about half way along its length and can move relatively freely.

Versicolor

1. Possessing various colors; variegated; partly colored.
2. Changeable in color.

Vertebra. Any of the bones that make up the vertebral column. In mammals each vertebra typically consists of a main body, or centrum, from which arises a neural arch through which the spinal cord passes, and transverse processes projecting from the side. There are five groups of vertebrae, specialized for various functions and varying in number with the species. In man, for example, there are 7 cervical vertebrae, 12 thoracic vertebrae, 5 lumbar vertebrae, 5 fused sacral vertebrae, and 5 fused caudal vertebrae (forming the coccyx).

Vertebral. Of or pertaining to a vertebra or the vertebral column; composed of vertebrae.

Vertebral Canal. The canal within the vertebral column formed by the vertebral foramina of successive vertebrae which lodges the spinal cord, meninges, cerebral spinal fluid, and roots of the spinal nerves.

Vertebral Column (backbone; spinal column; spine). A flexible bony column in vertebrates that extends down the long axis of the body and provides the main skeletal support. It also encloses and protects the spinal cord and provides attachment for the muscles of the back. The vertebral column consists of a series of bones (vertebra) separated by discs of cartilage (intervertebral discs). It articulates with the skull by means of the atlas vertebra, with the ribs at the thoracic vertebrae, and with the pelvic girdle at the sacrum.

Vertebrata (Craniata). The largest subphylum of the Chordata, comprising all those animals with backbones (vertebral column). The replacement of the rigid notochord by the more flexible backbone has permitted vertebrates a greater degree of movement and subsequent improvement in the sense organs and enlargement of the brain. The brain is enclosed in a skeletal case, the cranium. There are seven extant classes : Agnatha (jawless fishes), Elasmobranchii (cartilaginous fishes), Osteichthyes (bony fishes), Amphibia, Reptilia, Aves (birds), and Mammalia.

[1]Vertebrate. Possessing a backbone spinal or vertebral column).

[2]Vertebrate. Any chordate of the subphylum Vertebrata (Craniata), comprising all animals with a vertebral column (cyclostomes, fishes, amphibians, reptiles, birds, and mammals).

Vertex

1. The highest point, summit, or apex.
2. The top of the head.

Vertical

1. Of or pertaining to a vertex.
2. Upright; perpendicular to the horizontal plane.
3. Lengthwise or in the direction of the long axis.

Verticillaster (false whorl). The arrangement, resembling a complete whorl of flowers, that results when two dichasia form opposite each other at a node on an extended rachis. It is seen in members of the Labiatae, for example the white dead-nettle (Lamium album).

Verticil. A whorl; a circle of similar parts, as leaves, petals, or inflorescences arising from a point on an axis.

Verticillastrate. Arranged in clusters resembling whorls.

Vervet. An African monkey Cercopithecus pygeryth us), a guenon, related to the green monkey.

Vesicle. A small, usually fluid-filled, membrane-bound sac within the cytoplasm of a living cell. Vesicles form part of the Golgi apparatus.

Vesicular. Of, pertaining to, or composed of vesicles.

Vesicular-arbuscular Mycorrhiza. A form of endotrophic mycorrhiza in which the fungus lives between the cells of the cortex and forms temporary hyphal projections that penetrate the cortical cells. The projections may simply be swollen vesicles or may consist of finely branched masses called arbuscules. Many grasses and crop plants form such as sociations and the fungi involved are often species of Pythium or Endogone. When soil nutrients are in short supply plants forming such mycorrhizae fare better than uninfected plants.

Vesiculate

1. Covered with vesicles; containing vesicles.
2. Bearing wings with reference to pollen grains.

Vespiary. The nest of any of the social wasps (yellow jackets, hornets) or the colony inhabiting it.

Vespine. Of, pertaining to, or resembling a wasp or wasps.

Vessel

1. (in botany). A tube within the xylem composed of joined vessel elements. Vessels facilitate the efficient movement of water from the roots to the shoots and leaves of a plant.
2. (in zoology). Any of various tubular structures through which substances are transported, especially a blood vessel or a lymphatic vessel.

Vessel Member. A vessel element, one of the dead cells which, joined end to end, form a vessel.

Vessel Element. A type of cell occurring within the xylem of flowering plants, many of which, end to end, form water-conducting vessels. Vessel elements are frequently very broad and have side walls thickened by deposits of lignin over most of the surface area. However the end walls are brokendown to provide connections with the cells both above and below them. Compare tracheid.

Vestibule

1. *anat.* A cavity or space which serves as an entryway or approach, as that of the mouth, nose, ear, or vagina.
2. *zool.* The cavity leading to the mouth or buccal cavity in various invertebrates.

Vestibulocochlear Nerve. The eighth cranial nerve (VIII), a sensory nerve from the internal ear composed of two branches, the cochlear and vestibular. Also called auditory, acoustic, or statoacoustic nerve.

Vestige

1. A small, imperfectly developed, or degenerate structure which represents an organ or structure which was fully developed and functional in an ancestor or in an earlier stage in development.
2. A rudimentary structure.

Vestigial Organ. Any part of an organism that has diminished in size during its evolution because the function it served decreased in importance or became totally unnecessary. Examples are the human appendix and the wings of the ostrich.

Vesture

1. Anything that covers or clothes; a covering.
2. *bot.* The hairy covering of a leaf or stem.

Vetch. A forage legume of the genus Victa or its beanlike seed.

Veterinary. A veterinarian or a veterinary surgeon.

Veterinary Medicine. The science and art of treating diseased and injured animals; the prevention and treatment of disease in animals, especially domestic animals.

Viable

1. Capable of growing and developing, said of seeds.
2. Capable of living, with reference to a fetus removed from the uterus or born prematurely.

Viatical. Growing along roadsides or pathways.

Vibraculum. A modified zooid of certain operculate ectoprocts which possesses a long bristle or seta which by sweeping movements removes debris from the surface of the colony.

Vibrio. Any comma-shaped bacterium. Generally, vibrios are Gram-negative (Gram's stain), motile, and aerobic. They are widely distributed in soil and water and while most feed on dead organic matter some are parasitic, *e.g.* Vibrio cholerae, the causal agent of cholera.

Vibrissa pl. **Vibrissae**

1. One of the long, stiff hairs present on the snout of various mammals, as the cat; a feeler or whisker.
2. One of a paia of stout bristles on each side of the face of a dipterous insect.

Vicariance. The splitting up of an original biota into several isolated biotas (vicariants) by past geological or climatic events. The vicariants then develop independently and different species evolve. The process is presented as an alternative to the traditional theories of speciation by dispersal that have previously been used to explain biogeographical pattern. The existence of areas that contain many species different from but related to species in another distant area is taken by many as evidence for vicariance. One major event that is postulated as a means by which vicariants could have arisen is the fragmentation of the ancient land masses into the present-day continents (continental drift). This could explain the disjunct distributions of many genera, *e.g.* Liriodendron (tulip trees) and southern beeches (Nothofagus).

Viceroy. A deep-orange colored butterfly (Basilarchia (Limenitis) archippus) which mimics the monarch butterfly.

Villiform

1. Having the shape and appearance of a villus.
2. Velvetlike in appearance.

Villous. Having a shaggy appearance due to a covering of long soft curly trichomes.

Villus. A microscopic outgrowth from the surface of some tissues and organs, which serves to increase the surface area of the organ. Numerous villi line the interior of the small intestine. Their shape may vary from finger-like (in the duodenum) to spadelike (in the ileum). Intestinal villi are specialized for the absorption of soluble food material : each contains blood vessels and a lymph vessel.

Villi also occur on the chorion of the mammalian placenta, where they increase the surface area for the exchange of materials between the fetal and maternal blood.

Vimen. A twig; a long, flexible branch or shoot.

Vine. A plant with a climbing or creeping stem; one whose stem rests upon or is attached to a supporting structure; a rambler or climber.

Vinegar. A liquid containing acetic acid, about 6%, resulting from the fermentation of alcoholic liquids, brought about by bacteria of the genus Acetobacter.

Vinegar Eel. The eelworm (Turbatrix (Anguillula) aceti), a nematode commonly found in old vinegar.

Vinegarroon. A whip scorpion (Mastigoproctus giganteus) of southwestern United States and Mexico.

Violaxanthin. A xanthophyll pigment that absorbs light in the blue region of the spectrum. Violaxanthin may in certain circumstances serve as a precursor of abscisic acid. It may also, with riboflavin, be involved in the photo-oxidation of endogenous auxins.

Violet. A common garden plant or flower of the genus Viola.

Viper

1. An Old World venomous snake of the family Viperidae, including the genera Vipera, Cerastes, Bitis, and Causus.
2. A venomous snake of the family Crotalidae.

Viral. Of, pertaining to, or caused by a virus.

Vireo. One of a number of small, insectivorous, passeriform birds of the genus Vireo, family Vireonidae.

Virescence *bot.* The state or condition of becoming green, as that resulting from the development of chloroplasts in uncolored structures.

Virgate

1. Wand-or rod-shaped; long, straight, and slender.
2. Bearing many twigs.

Virgin. *genetics.* A female which has not been mated to a male.

Virgin Birth. Parthenogenesis.

Virgin Soil. Soil which has never been cultivated.

Virgula. A transparent, fluid-filled gland which opens on the dorsal surface of the oral sucker in xiphidiocercariae.

Virilism. The development of male traits and characteristics in a female, as adrenal virilism resulting from over-production of androgens by the adrenal cortex.

Virility. The state or quality of being manly; having procreative power.

Virion. The inert extracellular phase of a virus, consisting of a strand of DNA or RNA surrounded by a protein coat.

Viroid An extremely small infections agent consisting solely of RNA with no enclosing coat or capsid. Viroids have been isolated from various plants in which they are able to replicate and cause characteristic disease symptoms. Examples are potato spindle tuber viroid, chrysanthemum chlorotic mottle viroid, hop stunt viroid, and avocado sunblotch viroid.

Virology. The scientific study of viruses.

Virulence. The disease-producing ability of a microorganism.

Virulent. Noxious, malignant, highly infectious.

Virus. A small infectious agent that is only able to replicate by modifying the genetic machinery of living host cells. Outside the host cell a virus consists of DNA or RNA surrounded by a protein shell (capsid) In this inert state a given virus has a characteristic size and shape (*e.g.* polyhedral, spherical, rodshaped, etc.). Some of the simpler viruses, *e.g.* tobacoo mosaic virus (TMV), can be crystallized.

Approximately 400 plant viruses are known, most of which are singlestranded RNA viruses. Some, *e.g.* TMV and cucumber mosaic virus, have a wide host range while others are limited to a few species. Viruses can produce a variety of symptoms, *e.g.* mosaics, leaf spots, and deformed growth of certain organs. The broken flower colours of certain ornamentals, *e.g.* Rembrandt tulips, are due to virus infection. Some viruses are symptomless though they may still markedly reduce yield. Viruses are transmitted by vectors and by infected seed and pollen. Control is by using virus-free seed or by breeding for hypersensitivity. Viruses are generally not found in meristematic shoot tips and virus-free stocks of certain species can be obtained by tissue culture of meristem explants. Cross protection is successful in some crops.

A virus that infects bacteria is termed a bacteriophage.

Viscera. Collectively, the internal organs of the body, especially those of the abdominal cavity.

Visceral

1. Of or pertaining to a viscus or viscera.
2. Of or pertaining to the branchial region of a vertebrate.

Visceral Arch. A branchial arch; a gill arch.

Visceral Cleft. A gill cleft or gill slit.

Visceral Functions. Those of an involuntary nature and under the control of the autonomic nervous system.

Visceral Furrow. A branchial groove.

Visceral Hump. The portion of the body of a gastroped which is contained within the colled portion of the shell.

Visceral Mass. The main portion of the body of a bivalve mollusk lying dorsal to the foot.

Visceral Musculature

1. The smooth muscles of hollow organs.
2. The musculature of the heart.
3. In aquatic vertebrates, the branchial muscles which move the gill arches and the jaws; in terrestrial bertebrates, the muscles derived from these.

Visceral Pouch. A pharyngeal pouch.

Visceral Skeleton. The branchial skeleton, comprising, in aquatic vertebrates, the gill arches, jaws, and cartilaginous structures supporting the gills; in terrestrial forms, the bones of the jaws, ear ossicles, hyoid bone, and cartilages of the larynx.

Viscid. Thick, sticky, adherent, adhesive, glutinous.

Viscus pl. Viscera. Any of the organs contained within one of the body cavities (cranium, thorax, abdomen, pelvis), especially one within the abdominal cavity.

Vision

1. The sense of sight; seeing.
2. The sense by which the color, shape, and form of an object can be perceived.
3. The sensation resulting from stimulation of a light receptor, as an eye.

Visual. Of or pertaining to the sense of vision.

Visual Acuity. Sharpness of vision; the ability to distinguish details of an object.

Visual Pigment. A pigment present in a photoreceptor organ which is essential for the perception of light.

Visual Purple. Rhacopsin.

Vital. Of, or pertaining to life; essential for life; related to life or living things.

Vital Capacity. The amount of air that can be expelled from the lungs by the most forceful expiratory effort following the deepest possible inspiration; average amount is about 4 liters.

Vitalism. The theory that activities of organisms are due to a vital principle or force and are not simply the result of chemical and physical processes. Compare mechanism.

Vital Stain. A stain used to dye living tissue without harming or killing the cells. Examples include trypan blue and vital red. Intravital staining involves the injection of a stain into an organism, some of the living cells taking up the dye. Supravital staining involves the removal of living tissue from a multicellular organism and its subsequent staining.

Vital Staining. A technique in which a harmless dye is used to stain living tissue for microscopical observation. The stain may be injected into a living animal and the stained tissue removed and examined (intravital staining) or the living tissue may be removed directly and subsequently stained (supravital staining). Microscopic organisms, such as Protozoa, may be completely immersed in the dye solution. Vital stains include trypan blue, vital red, and Janus green, the latter being especially suitable for observing mitochondria.

Vitamin. One of a number of organic compounds required by living organisms in relatively small amounts to maintain normal health. There are some 14 generally recognized major vitamins : the water-soluble vitamin B complex (containing 9) and vitamin C and the fat-soluble vitamin A, vitamin D, vitamin E, and vitamin K. Most B vitamins and vitamin C occur in plants, animals, and microorganisms; they function typically as coenzymes. Vitamins A, D, E, and K occur only in animals, especially vertebrates, and perform a variety of metabolic roles. Animals are unable to manufacture many vitamins themselves at must have adequate amounts in the diet. Foods may contain vitamin precursors (called pro-vitamins) that are chemically changed to the actual vitamin on entering the body. Many vitamins are destroyed by light and heat, *e.g.* during cooking.

Vitamin A. A fat-soluble vitamin necessary for the maintenance of mucous membranes and for the formation of rhodopsin, essential for vision in dim light.

Vitamin B Complex. A group of water-soluble vitamins that characteristically serve as components of coenzymes. Plants and many microorganisms can manufacture B vitamins but dietary sources are essential for most animals. Heat and light tend to destroy B vitamins.

Vitamin B_1 (thiamin(e)) is a precursor of the coenzme thiamine pyrophosphate, which functions in carbohydrate metabolism. Deficiency leads to beriberi in humans and to polyneuritis in birds. Good sources include brewer's yeast, wheatgerm, beans, peas, and green vegetables.

Vitamin B_2 (riboflavin) occors in green vegetables, yeast, liver, and milk. It is a constituent of the coenzymes

FAD and FMN, which have an important role in the metabolism of all major nutrients as well as in the oxidative phosphorylation reactions of the electron transport chain. Deficiency of B_2 causes inflammation of the tongue and lips and mouth sores.

Vitamin B_6 (pyridoxine) is yidely distributed in cereal grains, yeast, liver, milks, etc. It is a constituent of a coenzyme (pyridoxal phosphate) involved in amino acid metabolism. Deficiency causes retarded growth, dermatitis, convulsions, and other symptoms.

Vitamin B_{12} (cyanocobalamin) is manufactured only by microorganisms and natural sources are entirely of animal origin. Liver is especially rich in it. One form of B_{12} functions as a coenzyme in a number of reactions, including the oxidation of fatty acids and the synthesis of DNA. It also works in conjunction with folic acid (another B vitamin) in the synthesis of the amino acid methionine and it is required for normal production of red blood cells. Vitamin B_{12} can only be absorbed from the gut in the presence of a glycoprotein called intrinsic factor; lack of this factor or deficiency of B_{12} results in pernicious anaemia.

Other vitamins in the B complex include nicotinic acid, pantothenic acid, folic acid, biotin, and lipoic acid.

Vitamin C (ascorbic acid). A colourless crystalline water-soluble vitamin found especially in citrus fruits and green xegetables. Most organisms synthesize it from glucose but man and other primates and various other species must obtain it from their diet. It is required for the maintenance of healthy connective tissue; deficiency leads to scurvy. Vitamin C is readily destroyed by heat and light.

Vitamin D. A fat-soluble vitamin occurring in the form of two steroid derivatives : vitamin D_2 (ergocalciferol, or calciferol), found in yeast; and vitamin D_3 (cholecalciferol), which occurs in animals. Vitamin D_2 is formed from a steroid by the action of ultraviolet light and D_3 is produced by the action of sunlight on a cholesterol derivative in the skln. Fish-liver oils are the major dietary source. The active form of vitamin D is manufactured in response to the secretion of parathyroid hormone, which occurs when blood calcium levels are low. It causes increased uptake of calcium from the gut, which increases the supply of calcium for bone synthesis. Vitamin D deficiency causes rickets in growing animals and osteomalacia in mature animals. Both conditions are characterized by week deformed bones.

Vitamin E (tocopherol). A fat-soluble vitamin consisting of several closely related compounds, deficiency of which leads to a range of disorders in different species, including muscular dystrophy, liver demage. and infertility. Good sources are cereal grains and green vegetables. Vitamin E prevents the oxidation of unsaturated fatty acids in cell membranes, so maintaining their structure.

Vitamin K. A fat-soluble quinone found in most plants and many microorganisms. It is believed to play a part in the transfer of electrons from photosystem II to photosystem I in photosynthesis. In animals deficiency affects the normal blood-clotting mechanism.

Vitamin P-P. Niacin, the pellagra-preventative vitamin.

Vitellarium pl. **Vitellaria**

1. A yold gland, as those found in various invertebrates, as trematodes.
2. The portion of an insect ovariole which contains developing ova and mature nurse cells.

Vitellin. A phosphoprotein, the principal constituent of egg yolk.

Vitelline. Of, pertaining to, or producing yolk.

Vitelline Cells. Cells produced by the vitelline glands of trematodes which contain shell globules utilized in the formation of the eggshell.

Vitelline Membrane. The membrane surrounding the cytoplasm of an ovum; the cell membrane.

Vitellus. The yolk of an egg.

Vitrella. In an ommatidium, a group of two to five crystal cells grouped around a crystalline cone which they secrete.

Vitreous. Like glass : Hyaline.

Vitreous Body. The vitreous humor, a transparent, jellylike substance which fills the posterior cavity of the globe of the eye.

Vitreous Humour. The colourless jelly that fills the space between the lens and the retina of the vertebrate eye.

Vitrodentine. A hard, outer layer of mesodermal origin which covers the dentine of placoid scales and teeth of elasmobranchs.

Vitta. A resin canal or oil cavity. Vittae are often found in the fruits of plants in the Umbelliferae. The number and position (whether between or in the primary ridges of the fruit) are important diagnostic characters in the family.

Vivarium. A place for keeping and raising animals, especially terrestrial animals. Compare aquarium, terrarium.

Viviparity

1. (in zoology). A form of reproduction in animals in which the developing embryo obtains its nourishment directly from the mother via a placenta or by other means. Viviparty occurs in some insects and other arthropods, in certain fishes, amphibians, and

reptiles, and in the majority of mammals. Compare oviparity; ovoviviparity.

2. (in botany). *a.* A form of asexual reproduction in certain plants, such as the onion, in which the flower develops into a budlike structure that forms a new plant when detached from the parent. *b.* The development of young plants on the inflorescence of the parent plant, as seen in certain grasses and the spider plant.

Viviparous

1. *zool.* Giving birth to living young which develop within and are nourished through the uterus. Compare ovoviviparous, oviparous.

2. *bot.* Germination of a seed while still attached to the parent plant, as in the mangrove.

Vivipary

1. The differentiation of young plants or bulbils at the floral axils, instead of flowers. This is seen, for instance, in viviparous fescue (Festuca vivipara) and in the spider plant.

2. The premature germination of seeds or spores in situ on the maternal plant before they have been released. This occurs in the mangroves where seeds may develop into sizeable seedlings before they are shed from the parent tree.

Vivisection. Operating upon or cutting into a live animal, especially for investigational purposes and without the use of an anesthetic.

Vixen. A female fox.

Vocal. Of or pertaining to speech or voice.

Vocal Cords. A pair of elastic membranes that project into the larynx in air-breathing vertebrates. Vocal sounds are produced when expelled air passing through the larynx vibrates the cords. The pitch of the sound produced depends on the tension of the cords, which is controlled by muscles and cartilages in the larynx.

Vocal Folds. The true vocal cords, a pair of folds on the inner surface of the larynx extending from the thyroid cartilage posteriorly to the arytenoid cartilages, vibration of which results in production of sound.

Vocal Sac. One of a pair of sacs in the males of various amphibians located beneath the skin and opening into the mouth cavity.

Voice. Sounds, especially articulate sounds purposely produced, as in speech or song, resulting from the vibration of the vocal cords (folds). The quality of the sound is determined by resonating chambers (mouth pharynx nasal cavities) and articulators (lips, teeth, tongue, palate).

Void. To empty; to make empty or to evacuate.

[1]**Volant.** Flying; capable of moving through the air.

[2]**Volant.** A flying individual, as winged flies of the genus Lipotena, a parasite of deer.

Volar

1. Of or pertaining to the palm of the hand or the sole of the foot.
2. Pertaining to or utilized in flight.

Volatile. Readily vaporized or converted into a gas; evaporating readily at a low temperature.

Vole. One of a number of mouse-or ratlike rodents of the genera Microtus (meadow mouse, field mouse), Pitymys (pine vole), Arvicola (water vole), and Clethrionmys (bank vole).

Volitant

1. Volant.
2. Capable of moving rapidly.

Volition. Acting from choice or from the exercise of the will.

Voluble

1. Turning or rotating readily.
2. *bot*. Having the habit of twining.

Voluntary. Under the control of the will; acting from choice.

Voluntary Muscle (skeletal, striped, or striated muscle). Muscle that is under the control of the will and is generally attached to the skeleton. An individual muscle consists of bundles of long muscle fibres, each containing many nuclei, the whole muscle being covered with a strong connective tissue sheath (epimysium) and attached at each end to a bone by inextensible tendons. Each fibre contains smaller fibres (myofibrils) having alternate light and dark bands (sarcomeres), which are responsible for the muscle's contractile ability and its typical striped appearance under the microscope.

The end of the muscle that is attached to a nonmoving bone is called the origin of the muscle; the end attached to a moving bone is the insertion. As a muscle contracts it becomes shorter and fatter, moving one bone closer to the other. Since a muscle cannot expand, another muscle (the extensor, or antagonist) is required to move the bone in the opposite direction and stretch the first muscle (known as the flexor, or agonistic muscle).

Volunteer. A plant that has grown from self-sown seed. Volunteers may be important inoculum sources for some diseases.

[1]Volute

1. Spiral or scroll-shaped.
2. *bot*. Rolled up.

Volute

1. *zool.* A turn or whorl of a spiral shell.
2. A marine gastropod of the family Volutidae, especially one of the genus Voluta.

Volutin. Inclusion bodies of nucleic acid and related substances present in yeasts and certain bacetria.

Volva. The cuplike structure that encircles the base of the fruiting bodies of many basidiomycete fungi. It is part of the remnants of the universal veil.

Volvent. An unarmed type of nematocyst which wraps itself about and entangles prey.

Volvocales. An order of the Chlorophyceae containing motile unicellular (*e.g.* Chlamydomonas), colonial (*e.g.* Gonium), and coenobial (*e.g.* Volvox) algae. Members of the Volvocales have one chloroplast in each cell, often containing an eye spot. Usually asexual reproduction is by zoospores while sexual reproduction varies from isogamy to oogamy. In some classifications the unicellular forms are placed in a separate order, the Chlamydomonadales.

Vulva. The external opening of the vagina, comprising in women the female external genitalia—two pairs of fleshy folds of tissue (the labia).

Volvox. Any flagellate of the genus Volvox, a green, spherical, colonial form of the order Volvocales, usually regarded as a green alga; sometimes considered as a protozoan of the order Volvocida.

Vomer. A membrane bone of the nasal region, in mammals forming a part of the nasal septum.

Vomerine. Of, pertaining to, or borne on the vomer bone, as vomerine teeth in amphibians.

Vomeronasal Organ. Jacobson's organ, one of a pair of diverticula or grooves extending ventrally from the nasal cavity and opening into the mouth cavity in snakes and lizards; rudimentary in birds and mammals.

Vomit. To eject forcibly the contents of the stomach.

Voracious. Having an insatiable desire for food; ravenous.

Vortex pl. **Vortices**

1. A whorl.
2. A structure having the appearance of being produced by rapid rotation about an axis, as vortices pilorum (hair whorls).

Vorticella. A stalked, bell-shaped, ciliate protozoan of the genus Vorticella.

Vorticose. Whirling, having a whorled structure or appearance.

Vulpine. Of, pertaining to, or like a fox.

Vulture. One of a number of large, soaring, carrion-eating birds of the families Cathartidae (New World vultures) and Accipitridae (Old World vultures). To the former belong the turkey buzzard (Cathartes aura), the black buzzard, and the condor.

Vulva

1. The pudendum or external genitalia of a female.
2. The external genital opening in certain invertebrates, as Ascaris.

W

Wader. Any of a number of long-legged birds which frequent shallow waters in search of food, as cranes, herons, sandpipers.

Waggle Dance. A dance performed by returning worker bees which communicates to other bees information concerning direction and distance of food from the hive. Also called wagging dance.

Waist

1. The narrowest part of the body between thorax and hips.
2. A peduncle or petiole in insects or spiders.

Walking Fern. A fern (Camptosorus rhizophyllus) whose turned-down leaf tips, on contact with the substratum, give rise to new plants.

Walkingstick. A stick insect, a long, slender orthopteran insect of the family Phasmidae, with a wingless body resembling a stick.

Wall. The surface layer or layers of a cell, organ, or organism, especially when of a protective or supportive nature, as a cell wall, body wall.

Wallaby. A small kangaroo, a marsupial of the family Macropodidae, as Petrogale, the rock wallaby.

Wallace Effect. The idea, proposed by the naturalist A. R. Wallace, that reproductive barriers within a species may be developed and subsequently improved by selection. If there are a number of optimum phenotypes favoured by selection, intermediate organisms less fitted to the environment will be eliminated by natural selection. Thus hybrids between such phenotypes will be at a disadvantage and hybridization will be selected against.

Wallace's Line. An imaginary line that runs between the Indonesian islands of Bali and Lombok and represents the separation of the Australian and Oriental faunas. It was proposed by the naturalist A. R. Wallace (1823-1913) who had noted that the mammals in Southeast Asia are different from and more advanced than their Australian counterparts. He suggested this was because the Australian continent had split away from Asia before the better adapted placental mammals evolved in Asia. Hence the isolated Australian marsupials and monotremes were able to thrive while those in Asia were driven to extinction by competition from placental mammals.

Wallaroo. A kangaroo intermediate in size between a kangaroo and wallaby.

Wall Pressure. The force exerted upon cell contents by the cell wall. It is equal and opposite to the turgor pressure.

Walrus. A large, marine mammal of the genus Odobaenus characterized by a whiskered, blunt muzzle and elongated ivory tusks that lives in herds in polar waters.

Waltzer. One of a special strain of mice or rats which walks in a bizarre fashion due to an inherited defect in the inner ear.

Wamp. The American or common eider.

Wandering Cell. One not fixed; one that moves from place to place, as certain macrophages.

Warble

1. A swelling on the back of domestic animals (horses, cattle) which contains the larva of a warble fly.

2. The larva of the warble fly.

Warbe Fly. One of several flies of the family Oestridae whose larvae develop under the skin of various animals causing warbles. as Hypoderma bovis, the ox warble.

Warbler

1. A bird that warbles or sings in a trilling manner.
2. An Old World songbird of the family Sylviidae.
3. One of a number of small, brightly-colored, insectivorous birds of the family Parulidae.

Warburg Effect. The inhibition of carbon dioxide assimilation and photosynthesis by atmospheric oxygen, described by O. Warburg in 1920. This phenomenon was later discovered to be due to photorespiration.

Warfarin 3-(alpha-acetonylbenzyl)-4-hydroxycoumarin : a synthetic anticoagulant used both therapeutically in clinical medicine and, in lethal doses, as a rodenticide.

Warm-blooded. Having a relatively high and constant body temperature : Homoiothermous.

Warning Coloration (aposematic coloration). The conspicuous markings of an animal that make it easily recognizable and warm would-be predators that it is a poisonous, foul-tasting or dangerous species. For example, the yellow-and-black striped abdomen of the wasp warms of its sting.

Wart. *zool*

1. In mammals, a small circumscribed growth of the epidermis, usually of a hard, horny texture.
2. In holothurians, a modified tube foot.
3. In toads, a compact mass of poison glands.

Warthog. A large, grotesque, wild pig of Africa (Phachochoerus aethiopicus) with wartlike excrescences on the sides of its head; also called vlakvark.

Wasp. Any of a number of hymenopterous insects characterized by a slender body with abdomen attached by a slender stalk or peduncle. Females commonly possess a sting. Typical wasps and paper wasps (yellow jackets, hornets,) belong to the family Vespidae; solitary wasps to the Sphecidae. Some wasps are social, constructing nests and living in colonies.

Waste. Material eliminated from the body consisting of undigested food, unusable products of metabolism, glandular secretions, and excess substances not utilized by the body.

Water Bear. A tardigrade.

Water Beelte. Any of a number of beetles which frequent water or whose larvae live in water.

Water Buffalo. An often domesticated Indian buffalo (Bubalus bubalis) of Southeast Asia. Also called arna and carabao.

Waterbug. A croton bug or cockroach.

Water Bug. Any of a number of hemipterous insects which frequent ponds and streams, as the giant water bug (Bonacus grisseus).

Water Cells. Pouchlike diverticula of the stomach (rumen and reticulum) of camels.

Water Fern. An aquatic fern of the families Marsileaceae and Salviniaceae.

Water Flea. One of a number of small, aquatic crustaceans of the order Cladocera, as Daphnia, Alona, Leptodora.

Water Fowl

1. Any bird which frequents water, especially a swimming bird.
2. Swimming game birds (ducks and geese), as distinguished from shorebirds and upland game.

Water Hen. The Florida gallinule (Gallinula chloropus), the moorhen of Europe.

Water Hyacinth. An aquatic plant (Eichornia crassipes) often forming dense masses blocking waterways.

Water Lily. Any plant of the water lily family Nymphaeaceae, especially those of the genera Nuphar and Nymphaea.

Watermelon. A large, oval or spherical fruit of a vine (Citrullus vulgaris) or the plant which produces it.

Water Mold. An aquatic mold of the order Saprolegniales, as Saprolegnia, sometimes parasitic on fish or fish eggs.

Water Moulds. Saprolegniales.

Water Potential Symbol ψ. A measure of the energy available in an aqueous solution to cause the migration of water molecules across semipermeable membranes during osmosis. Values of water potential cannot be calculated absolutely but are highest in pure water, which for convenience is given the value zero, and fall with increasing solute concentration. Water always tends to move from areas of high (less negative) to areas of low (more negative) potential. This principle governs water conduction in plants. Water potential is the sum of osmotic potential, pressure potential, and matric potential. The term is replacing the concept of osmotic pressure and differs from osmotic pressure in taking capillary and imbibitional forces into account.

Water Ring. The circular or ring canal of a water-vascular system.

Water Snake. A harmless snake of the genus Natrix.

Water Strider. Any of several hemipterous insects of the families Gerridae and Veliidae, as those of the genera Gerris and Rhagovelia, with long, slender legs used in skating over the surface of the water.

Water Tube. One of the numerous tubes in the gill of a bivalve mollusk which open dorsally into the suprabranchial chamber.

Water-vascular System. In echinoderms, a system of fluid-filled canals and structures which function in locomotion and foodgetting. In a starfish, it comprises the madreporite, stone canal, ring canal (water ring), and radial canals with lateral canals connected to tube feet (podia) the inner ends of which bear ampullae.

Watson—Crick Model. The double-stranded twisted ladder-like molecular structure of DNA as determined by the US biochemist James Waston (1928) and the British biochemist Francis Crick (1916—) at Cambridge, England, in 1953. It is commonly known as the double helix.

Wattle

1. One of a pair of fleshy appendages which hang from the throat of various birds, especially domestic fowl and most galliform birds.
2. In reptiles, a median, ventral fold of skin hanging from the neck.

Wattlebird. A honey eater of New Zealand, the huia (Neomorpha acutirostris) with large orange and blue wattles.

Wax. Any of various solid or semisolid substances. There are two main types. Mineral waxes are mixtures of hydrocarbons with high molecular weights. Paraffin wax, obtained from petroleum, is an example. Waxes secreted by plants or animals are mainly esters of fatty acids and usually have a protective function. Examples are the beeswax forming part of a honeycomb and the wax coating on some leaves, fruits, and seed coats, which acts as a protective water-impermeable layer supplementing the functions of the cuticle. The seeds of a few plants contain wax as a food reserve.

Wax Gland. A gland that produces wax, as those of a honey-bee or wax insect.

Wax Insect. A homopterous insect which produces wax used commercially.

Wax Moth. A moth (Galleria mellonella) whose larvae (wax worms) live in the hives of bees feeding upon wax. Also called bee moth.

Wax Scale. One of several homopterous insects which produce wax used commercially, as the Chinese wax scale (Ericerus pe-la).

Wax Worm. The larva of the wax moth.

Wean. To deprive of mother's milk; to cause the young to cease to suckle or nurse at the breast.

Weasel A small, carnivorous, fur-bearing mammal of the genus Mustela.

Weaverbird. One of a number of finchlike birds of Asia and Africa of the family Ploceidae which construct elaborate nests by interlacing grass and other materials. Some are parasitic.

Weaver Finch One of a number of Old World passerine birds of the family Ploceidae which includes the English sparrow (Passer domesticus).

Web. A thin, membranelike structure, as *a.* that uniting the digits of various water animals; *b.* that formed of interlacing threads woven by spiders; *c.* that forming the nest or abode of various webworms; *d.* the vane of a feather.

Weberian Ossicles. A group of four small bones (scaphium, claustrum, intercalarium, tripus) which, in certain teleost fishes, lie between the swim bladder and perilymphatic space of the ear.

Web Spinner. An insect of the order Embioptera which constructs and lives in a silken gallery or tunnel, as Anisembia texana, of southern United States.

Webworm. One of a number of caterpillars, the larvae of moths of the family Arctiidae, which construct and live in large webs, as Hyphantria cunea, the fall webworm.

Weed. Any plant growing where it is not wanted. Many weeds are adapted to exploit disturbed areas of land and, unless measures are taken to prevent it, weeds are the first plants to establish themselves on cleared patches of ground. Many weeds are annual plants that produce large quantities of seed and often pass through several generations in a single year. An example of such a weed is shepherd's purse (Capsella bursa-pastoris). Weeds, especially those closely related to crop plants, may also harbour various peste and diseases. For example, the roots of the black nightshade (Solanum nigrum) are often infected by the potato cyst eelworm.

Weedkiller. Herbicide.

Weel. A structure consisting of hairlike processes arranged so as to prevent undesirable insect visitors from entering flowers.

Weep

1. *physiol.* To shed tears.
2. *bot.* To exude water; to bleed.

Weever. An edible marine fish of the genus Trachinus but bearing poisonous dorsal spines.

Weevil

1. Any of a number of snout beetles, as the cotton boll weevil.
2. One of a number of beetles whose larvae infest pods and seeds, as bean and pea weevils.

Weighting. In taxonomy, the assigning of greater or lesser importance to one character, as compared to another character, according to its known or assumed value. The initial choice of which characters to use in a classification is in itself a positive weighting process, termed selection weighting. Characters considered unreliable and consequently rejected, perhaps because they show too much enviranmental variation, are said to be given residual or rejection weighting. Once the characters have been selected some may be ascribed additional importance if, for example, they are known to be good diagnostically in other groups. When such weighting is applied before the classification is drawn up it is termed a priori weighting. An example would be the placing together of two taxa that share the one character chromosome number but differ in a number of other characters. Alternatively a classification may be constructed in which all the chosen characters are considered of equal importance; this is the normal procedure in numerical taxonomy. When the classification has been erected it will then be apparent which characters correlate well with other characters. Such characters are given a posteriori weighting. This second procedure provides a method for obtaining unbiased correlations of visible morphological characters with other characters, *e.g.* chemical, cytological, or genetic characters, that are not immediately apparent.

Weismannism. The theory of the continuity of the germ plasm published by August Weismann (1834-1914) in 1886. It proposes that the contents of the reproductive cells (sperms and ova) are passed on unchanged from one generation to the next, unaffected by any changes undergone by the rest of the body. It thus rules out any possibility of the inheritance of acquired characteristics, and has become fundamental to neo-Darwinian theory.

Wether. A castrated ram.

Wet Rot. A plant disease in which there is disintegration of tissues and release of cell fluids. Brown rot of stored fruits, such as plums and apples, is caused by fungi of the genus Sclerotinia. Wet rot of structural timber is caused by various fungi including Coniophora puteana and Poria vaillantii.

Wetting Agent. A chemical, such as detergent or soap, that lowers the surface tension of water. Wetting agents are added to fungicide, herbicide, and insecticide sprays to increase the area of the spray droplets in contact with the plant surface or insect body.

Whale. An air-breathing aquatic mammal of the order Cetacea, the largest of living mammals. They comprise two sub-orders, the Mysticeti or whalebone whales, and Odonto-ceti or toothed whales.

Whalebone (baleen). Transverse horny plates hanging down from the upper jaw on each side of the mouth of the toothless whales (Cetacea), forming a sieve. Water, containing plankton on which the whale feeds, enters the open mouth and is then expelled with the mouth slightly closed, so that food is retained on the baleen plates.

Whales. Cetacea.

Whale Shark. A large shark (Rhincodon typus) of tropical waters, sometimes reaching a length of 50 feet.

Wheat

1. One of a number of grasses of the genus Triticum, especially T. aestivum, cultivated wheat.
2. The cereal grain produced by these plants.

1. A basidiomycete (Puccinia graminis) whose life cycle includes stages on wheat and stages on the European or common barberry.
2. The disease caused by the wheat rust fungus.

Wheatworm. A nematode (Anguina tritici) which infests wheat.

Wheel Animacule. A rotifer.

Wheel Bug. An assassin bug (Arilus cristatus) with a pronotum bearing a wheellike crest. It sometimes inflicts vicious bites.

Whelk. A large, marine snail of the order Prosobranchiata, as the giant whelk (Busycon) and the edible whelk (Buccinum).

[1]**Whelp**. The young of a dog, wolf, or other carnivores.

[2]**Whelp**. To bring forth or give birth to young, applied especially to canine animals.

Whimbrel. The Hudsonian curlew (Numenius phaeopus).

Whiplash Flagellum (acronematic flagellum). A threadlike projection arising from motile algal and fungi cells that has a smooth surface. Internally the fibrillar structure is typical of the flagella and cilia of motile eukaryotic cells.

Whip Scorpion. An arachnid of the order Uropygi.

Whiptail. One of several lizards of the genus Cnemidophorus, with slender elongated tails.

Whipworm. A parasitic nematode (Trichuris trichiura) inhabiting the intestine of man or related species, common in the intestines of various mammals.

White Blood Cell. Leucocyte.

White Matter. Part of the tissue that makes up the central nervous system of vertebrates. It consists chiefly of nerve fibres enclosed in whitish myelin sheaths. Compare grey matter.

Whitewood. Basswood, a tree of the genus Tilia.

Wild Type. Describing the form of an allele possessed by most members of a population in their natural environment. Wild-type alleles are usually dominant.

Whorl

1. *bot*. A group of three of more structures, as leaves, arising at one point and arranged in the form of a circle; a verticil.

2. *anat.* *a.* A complete turn in the line of a finger print. *b.* A spiral arrangement of the hairs of the head; a vortex.
3. *zool.* A turn in the spire of a gastropod mollusk; a volution.

Whorled. Describing a form of leaf arrangement in which three or more leaves arise at each node, as in the bedstraws (family Rubiaceae).

Wild-type. The common form of a gene or organism in natural (wild) populations. Wild-type genes are typically dominant. They are usually designated '+'.

Wiggler. A wriggler; an animal that wiggles, as the larva or pupa of a mosquito or the nymph of a mayfly.

Wild. In a natural state; not domesticated; savage; uncivilized; not under the supervision or care of man.

Wildcat

1. The bobcat or bay lynx (Lynx rufus).
2. The European wildcat (Felis sylvestris).

Wildebeest. A gnu.

Wilt. A plant disease characterized by wilting Wilting often occurs in the advanced stages of root diseases when water uptake becomes inadequate. However the term is usually applied to diseases in which wilting occurrs in the absence of marked root damage. Such wilting may occur either because the vascular tissues are blocked or because water is being withdrawn by parasitic plants, such as witchweeds (Striga) and broomrapes (Orobranche). Blockage of vascular tissues is caused by various fungi and bacteria. It may be due either to the physical presence of vast numbers of microorganisms or to substances, such as gums and tyloses, that the host forms in response to invasion. Examples of wilt diseases are Dutch elm disease, caused by the fungus Ceratocystis ulmi, and wilts of potato, tobacco, and banana, caused by the bacterium Pseudomonas solanacearum.

Wilt Disease. Any of a number of diseases of plants characterized by wilting, as that caused by fungi of the genus Fusarium or by bacteria.

Wind Dispersal. The scattering or spreading of spores, pollen, seeds, or fruits by the agency of the wind.

Wind Pollination. Pollination by air-borne pollen.

Wind Timber. Trees deformed by the strong winds, as those seen on exposed slopes and mountain tops.

Wing

1. Either of the two narrow lateral petals of a 'pea' flower.
2. The membranous outgrowth of certain fruits, *e.g.* the samara.
3. A flange running down a stem or stalk as, for example, seen along the stems of the hairy vetchling (Lathyrus hirsutus).

Wing Cover. In an insect, an elytron.

Wing Covert. A tectrix.

Winged

1. Provided with wings or winglike structures.
2. Wounded or killed when in flight.

Wingless

1. Lacking wings or winglike processes.
2. Possessing only rudimentary wings.

Wing Pad. A compact, undeveloped wing of an insect nymph or pupa.

Wing Shell

1. A boring clam (Pholas campechiensis).

2. A bivalve of the genus Pteria.

Winkle

1. A periwinkle.
2. Any of a number of marine snails, especially those of the genus Busycon.

Winter Egg

1. A fertilized egg produced in late summer or fall by parthenogenetic organisms, as rotifers, aphids.
2. A thick-shelled egg with abundant yolk produced by certain flatworms.

Wintergreen. Checkerberry, a flavoring obtained from a low, creeping, evergreen plant (Gaultheria procumbens). Its leaves are the source of oil of wintergreen (methyl salicylate).

Winter Kill. The death of large numbers of organisms, as fishes, as occurs in shallow lakes and ponds containing much organic matter wheh ice covers the surface for prolonged periods.

Wireworm

1. The shiny, slender, hard-bodied larva of the click beetle which feeds on the roots of corn, wheat, cotton, and many other plants.
2. A slender-bodied millipede.

Wishbone. A furcula.

Witches'-broom. An abnormal, brushlike growth that in a symptom of a number of fungus or virus diseases in plants; also called hexenbesen.

Witches' Milk. Milk secreted by the mammary glands of a newborn infant.

Withers. The ridge between the scapulae or shoulder bones of a horse formed by spinous processes of the vertebrae.

Withy. A slender, flexible twig.

Womb. The uterus.

Wombat. A burrowing, badgerlike marsupial of Australia, as the common wombat (Vombatus hirsutus).

Wood. The hard structural and water-conducting tissue that is found in many perennial plants and forms the bulk of trees and shrubs. It is composed of secondary xylem and associated cells, such as fibres. The wood of angiosperms is termed hardwood, *e.g.* oak and mahogany, and that of gymnosperms softwood, *e.g.* pine and fir. New wood is added to the outside of the old wood each growing season by divisions of the vascular cambium (growth ring). Only the outermost new wood (sapwood) functions in water conduction; the inner wood (heartwood) provides only structural support.

Wood Alcohol. Methanol or methyl alcohol, CH_3OH, obtained by destructive distillation of wood. It is a violent poison.

Woodpecker. One of a large number of climbing birds of the family Picidae with a chisellike bill used for drilling into trees, as the redheaded woodpecker (Melanerpes erythrocephalus).

Wood Sugar. Xylose.

Woody. Of or pertaining to wood; composed of wood or woody fibers.

Woody Perennial. Perennial.

Wool

1. *zool. a.* The soft, curly, hairy covering of domesticated sheep and other animals. *b.* Short, crisp, curled hair. *c.* The thick, hairy covering of certain caterpillars.
2. *bot.* Long, soft, matted hairs, resembling animal wool.

Wool Fat. Lanolin, a fatlike wax which covers the fibers of sheep's wool.

Woolly

1. *zool.* Of, pertaining to, resembling, or consisting of wool.
2. *bot.* Lanate; bearing long, soft, and more or less matted hairs; tomentose.

Woolly Apple Aphid. A homopterous insect (Eriosoma lanigerum) which secretes white, waxen threads forming wool-like masses on twigs; a serious pest.

Woolly Bear. A woolly worm.

Woolly Worm

1. The woolly larva of several moths, especially tiger moths of the family Arctiidae.
2. A woolly bear or woolly bear caterpillar.

Worker. In social insects (ants, bees, wasps, termites), a member of a caste adapted for the performance of non-reproductive functions. They are imperfectly developed females.

Worm

1. Any small, elongated, creeping or crawling animal, especially those of the phyla Annelida, Platyhelminthes, Aschelminthes, and Acanthocephala; a helminth.
2. Any of a number of other phyla whose members are elongated, creeping animals, as a rhynchocoelan, sipunculid, echiurid, onycophoran, pentastomidan, or hemichordate.
3. The larva of various insects, especially caterpillars and grubs.

Worm Disease. In oysters, infestation by a polychaete worm (Polydora).

Worm Salamander. A salamander of the genus Batrachoseps, with a long, slender body and small limbs with a reduced number of digits.

Wormseed Oil. Oil of chenopodium.

Worm Shell. A gastropod mollusk with an elongated, coiled shell resembling a worm in appearance, as Vermicularia.

Wound Cork. A layer of phellem that forms over a damaged part of the plant. It prevents desiccation of the underlying tissues and the entry of pathogens.

Wound Hormone. Any substance produced by damaged cells that diffuses into nearby undamaged cells and there stimulates meristematic activity, resulting in the formation of a protective callus. Auxins, gibberellins, and certain products of wounding have been implicated in the wounding reaction.

Wound Wood. Callus.

Wracks. Fucales.

Wrasse. One of several brilliantly-colored food fishes of the family Labridae.

Wriggler. A wiggler.

Wrist. The region between the hand and the forearm; the carpus.

X

Xanthophyll. A member of a class of oxygen-containing carotenoid pigments, which provide the characteristic yellow and brown colours of autumn leaves.

X Chromosome. Sex Chromosome.

Xeromorphic. Describing the structural modifications of certain plants (xerophytes) the enable them to reduce water loss, particularly from their leaves and stems.

Xerophyte. A plant that is adapted to live in conditions in which there is either a scarcity of water in the soil, or the atmosphere is dry enough to provoke excessive transpiration, or both. Xerophytes have special structural (xeromorphic) and functional modifications, including swollen water-storing stems and specialized leaves that may be hairy, rolled, or reduced to spines or have a thick cuticle to lower the rate of transpiration. Examples of xerophytes are desert cacti and many species growing on sand dunes and exposed moorlands. Compare mesophyte; hydrophyte.

X-ray Crystallography. The use of X-ray diffraction to determine the structure of crystals or molecules, such as nucleic acids. The technique involves directing a beam of X-rays at a crystalline sample and recording the diffracted X-rays on a photographic plate. The diffraction pattern consists of a pattern of spots on the plate, and the crystal structure can be worked out from the positions and intensities of the diffraction spots. X-rays are diffracted by the electrons in the molecules and if molecules crystals of a compound are used, the electron density distribution in the molecule can be determined.

X-rays. Electromagnetic radiation of shorter wavelength than ultraviolet radiation and longer wavelength than gamma radiation. The range of wavelengths is 10^{-11} m to 10^{-9} m. X-rays can pass through many forms of matter and they are therefore used medically and industrially to examine internal structures. X-rays are produced for these purposes by an X-ray tube.

Xylem. A tissue that transports water and dissolved mineral nutrients in vascular plants. In flowering plants it consists of hollow vessels that are formed from cells (vessel elements) joined end to end. The end walls of the vessel elements are perforated to allow the passage of water. In less advanced vascular plants, such as conifers and ferns, the constituent cells of the xylem are called tracheids. In young plants and at the shoot and root tips of older plants the xylem is formed by the apical meristems. In plants showing secondary growth this xylem is replaced in most of the plant by secondary xylem, formed by the vascular cambium. The walls of the xylem cells are thickened with lignin, the extent of this thickening being greatest in secondary xylem. Xylem contributes greatly to the mechanical strength of the plant; wood is mostly made up of secondary xylem.

Xylenes. Dimethylbenzenes.

Y

Yak. A wild bovine (Poephagus grunniens) of the highlands of Tibet, hunted for its flesh and hair and sometimes domesticated.

Yam

1. A climbing vine (Dioscorea) or its root, widely used as a food in the tropics.
2. In the southern United States, the sweet potato.

Yard. A winter feeding area for deer.

Yaws. An infectious, nonvenereal disease of the tropics, caused by a spirochaete (Treponema pertenue); also called frambesia, pian.

Y Chromosome. A sex chromosome in the males of certain animals, as Drosophila.

Yeast

1. A semifluid substance consisting principally of unicellular fungi which forms on the surface or as a sediment in fermenting fruit juices, malt wort, and sugar-containing liquids and used to induce alcoholic fermentation, as a leavening agent in bread, in the manufacture of ethyl alcohol, and as a source of vitamins, especially those of the B-complex.
2. Any of a number of species of unicellular, ascomycete fungi, especially those of the genus Saccharomyces, which reproduce by budding, producing chains of cells but no true mycelium.

Yellows

1. A plant disease, caused by mineral deficiency or a virus or mycoplasma, in which there is yellowing of the foliage. Yellowing is a common symptom when there is a deficiency of elements important in chlorophyll production, namely, iron, magnesium, manganese, nitrogen, or sulphur. Barley yellow dwarf and beet yellows are caused by viruses and coconut lethal yellowing is caused by a mycoplasma.
2. A disease, of cabbage caused by Fusarium conglutinans.

Yellow Body. A corpus luteum.

Yellow Fever. A acute, infectious disease of tropical and subtropical regions caused by a virus transmitted by the bite of a female mosquito (Aedes aegypti).

Yellow Grub. The encysted metacercaria of a fluke (Clinostomum) found in the flesh of freshwater fishes, especially perch. The adult is a parasite of water birds. Also called black spot grub.

Yellow Jacket. A social wasp of the genus Vespula which usually constructs an underground nest of paper.

Yellowlegs. An American shorebird of the family Scolopacidae, as the greater yellowlegs (Totanus melanoleuca) and lesser yellowlegs (T. flavipes).

Yellow Spot. The macula lutea of the retina of the eye.

Yew. A coniferous tree or shrub of the yew family, Taxaceae, especially those of the genus Taxus, as T. canadensis, the American yew or ground hemlock.

Yield. Productivity; the rate at which a breeding stock produces an additional crop or additional stock.

Yogurt also **Yoghurt** or **Yoghourt**. A fermented milk of the consistency of custard made from concentrated milk and milk solids, fermentation being induced by addition of cultures of bacteria, usually Lactobacillus bulgaricus.

Yolk. The food stored in an egg for the use of the embryo. It can consist mainly of protein (protein yolk) or of phospholipids and fats (fatty yolk). The eggs of oviparous animals (*e.g.* birds) contain a relatively large yolk.

Yolk Plug. A mass of yolk-filled cells lying between the lips of the blastopore of a developing amphibian embryo.

Yolk Sac

1. A large, yolk-containing sac present in the embryos of fishes, birds, and reptiles formed by growth of the splanchnopleure downward over the massive yolk.
2. In placental mammals, a vestigial structure consisting of an endoderm-lined sac connected to the gut by a slender yolk stalk. It contains no yolk.

Yolk-sac Placenta. That present in egg-laying monotremes in which the yolk sac unites with the chorion to form a temporary placenta. Term sometimes applied to a comparable structure in elasmobranchs.

Yolk Stalk. The connection between the yolk sac and the gut.

Y-organ. An endocrine structure in crustaceans which produces a hormone essential for molting, located in the maxilla or base of the antenna.

Ypsiloid. The epipubic bone of a salamander.

Yucca. A xerophytic plant of the genus Yucca of the lily family, as Yucca brevifolia, the Joshua tree.

Yucca Moth. A moth of the genus Tegeticula, family Prodoxidae, essential for the pollination of yucca flowers.

[illegible]

[illegible]

[illegible]

[illegible]

[illegible] and the [illegible]

[illegible] in the manner of [illegible]

[illegible]

[illegible]

Z

Z-chromosome. One of the two sex chromosomes in the males of birds and some insects.

Zeatin (6-(4-hydroxy-3-methyl but-2-enyl) aminopurine). The first plant growth substance of the cytokinin types to be isolated from plant tissues. It was obtained from the kernels of sweet corn (Zea mays) hence its name. Subsequently other cytokinins similar in structure to zeatin (*i.e.* an adenine molecule substituted with an isoprenoid derivative) have been isolated. Some of these are found as minor bases in transfer RNA molecules (IPA).

Zeaxanthin. A xanthophyll present in the seeds or yellow corn; also present in various algae, bryophytes, and some vascular plants.

Zebra

1. A striped, African, horselike mammal of the family Equidae, as Equus burchelli, Burchell's zebra or bonteauagga.
2. A striped butterfly (Heliconius charitonius) of the family Nymphalidae.

Zebu. A domesticated, Asiatic bovine (Bos indicus) with a pronounced shoulder hump and a prominent dewlap.

Zein. A low-molecular-weight simple protein found as a major storage protein in maize grains.

Zinc Symbol : Zn. A metal element, atomic number 30, atomic weight 65.38, needed in trace amounts for successful plant growth. Zinc ions are required as cofactors by certain enzymes, *e.g*, carboxypeptidase, carbonic anhydrase, and alcohol dehydrogenase. It has been suggested that zinc may play a role in the mechanism of action of the growth substance ethylene. A common symptom of deficiency is leaf mottling.

Z-line. A thin, dark line or disc which bisects an I band (isotropic disc) in a striated muscle fiber.

Zeuglodont. An extinct, whalelike cetacean of the suborder Zeuglodontia with mammallike teeth.

Zinc. A mineral element, symbol Zn, at. no. 30, essential for plant growth. Zinc deficiency results in yellowing and malformation of leaves. In animals, it forms a part of certain enzyme systems and is present in crystallized insulin.

Zingiber. Ginger.

Zinnia. A widely grown ornamental flower of the genus Zinnia, a composite.

Zoantharian. Any coelenterate of the subclass Zoantharia, class Anthozoa, which includes the sea anemones and true corals.

Zoarium. A colony of colonial bryozoans.

Zoea Larva. A stage in the development of certain crustaceans between the protozoea and mysis stages characterized by a distinct cephalothorax, abdomen, and eight pairs of appendages, as in the shrimp.

Zona. An encircling belt, band, or girdle; a zone.

Zona Pellucida

1. A thin, transparent, noncellular layer surrounding a mammalian oocyte or ovum.
2. The zona radiata of certain vertebrate oocytes, as in reptiles.

Zona Radiata

1. The vitelltne membrane of certain vertebrate ova, as those of amphibians and birds.
2. A thin membrane with radial striations surrounding the oocyte of reptiles; also called zona pellucida.

Zonation. The location and distribution of organisms in definite zones.

Zone. A delimited area or region.

Zone Fossil. Index fossil.

Zonite. A body division or segment of a kinoryńch.

Zonula Cisiaris. The ciliary zonule (suspensory ligament) which attached the lens of the eye to the ciliary processes; the zonule of Zinn.

Zoo. A collection of animals, especially for exhibition purposes; a zoological garden.

Zoobenthos The animals in the bottom regions of a body of water.

Zoochlorella Unicellular green algae of the genus Chlorella which occur as symbionts in freshwater protozoans, the gastrodermis of Hydra, and in the amebocytes of sponges.

Zooecium. In an ectoproct, the body wall which encloses the soft parts (polypide).

Zooflagellate. An animallike flagellate of the class Zoomastigophorea; one lacking chlorophyll.

Zoogeography. The study of the geographical distributions of animals. The earth can be divided into several zoogeographical regions separated by natural barriers, such as oceans, desrets, and mountain ranges. The characteristics of the fauna of each region are believed to depend particularly on the process of continental drift and the stage of evolution reached when the various land masses became isolated. For example Australia, which has been isolated since Cretaceous times, has the most primitive native mammalian fauna, consisting solely of marsupials and monotremes.

Zooglea. A mass of bacteria embedded in a gelatinous matrix.

Zoogleal Film. A thin, gelatinous film containing bacteria, algae, fungi, and protozoans which coats the filtering medium in a sewage treatment plant.

Zooid. A member of a closely associated group of organisms, as *a*. individuals in a colony of protozoans, as Volvox; *b*. one of the individuals in a polymorphic hydroid colony; *c*. an individual of an ectoproct colony; *d*. one of a chain of individuals produced asexually, as in certain oligochaetes (Chaetogaster) or in turbellarians. (Stenostomum); *e*. a member of a tunicate colony.

Zoological

1. Of or pertaining to the science of zoology.
2. Of or pertaining to animals.

Zoology. The scientific study of animals, including their anatomy, physiology, biochemistry, genetics, ecology, evolution, and behaviour.

Zoonosis pl. **Zoonoses**. A disease of animals which is transmissible to man, as rabies.

Zooparasite. An animal parasite.

Zoophagous. Flesh-eating; feeding upon animals.

Zoophilous

1. Animal-loving, or having an affinity for animals.
2. Pollinated by animals other than insects, as bats, birds.

Zoophyte. An animal which has a plantlike form as a hydroid or bryozoan.

Zooplankton. The animal component of plankton. All major animal phyla are represented in zooplankton, as adults, larvae, or eggs : some are just visible to the naked eye but most cannot be seen without magnification. Near the surface of the sea there may be many thousands of such animals per cubic metre.

Zoosporangium. A sporangium that produces zoospores.

Zoospore. A motile usually naked spore with one or more flagella. It may be produced either by a zygote or a zoosporangium and is dependent on water for dispersal. In some species, *e.g.* the geen alga Ulothrix, two types of zoospore may be developed. In Ulothrix large macrozoospores with four flagella and small microzoospores with two flagella are seen. Zoospores may encyst under adverse conditions. Compare aplanospore.

Zootomy The anatomy of animals, especially those other than man; comparative anatomy.

Zooxanthellae. Dinoflagellate protozoans containing yellow chromatophores which live as symbionts in foraminiferans, radiolarians, and some metazoans. Compare zoochlorella.

Zorapteran. An insect of the order Zoraptera comprising the single genus Zoortypus, a colonial, termitelike insect of southern United States.

Zubr. European name for Indian humped cattle.

Zwitterion (ampholyte ion). An ion that has a positive and negative charge on the same group of atoms. Zwitterions can be formed from compounds that contain both acid groups and basic groups in their molecules. For example the amino acid glycine has the formula $H_2N.CH_2.COOH$. However, under neutral conditions, it exists in the different form of the zwitterion $H_3N.CH_2.COO^-$, which can be regarded as having been produced by an internal neutralization reaction (transfer of a proton from the corboxyl group to the amino group). Glycine therefore has some properties characteristic of ionic compounds, *e g*. a high melting point and solubility in water. In acid solutions, the positive ion $^{+}H_3NCH_2COOH$ is formed. In basic solutions, the negative ion H_3NCH_2 COO^{-} predominates. The name comes from the German zwed, two.

Zygantra. Posterior articular facets on the neural arches of certain reptiles. They articulate with zygosphenes.

Zygapophysis. One of two pairs of articular processes on the neutral arch of a vertebra.

Zygnemaphyceae (Conjugatophyceae). A class of the Chlorophyta whose members are distinguished by their distinctively symmetrical cells, anatomically complex plastids, and the lack of freeswimming forms. In addition they reproduce by conjugation. It contains freshwater filamentous forms (*e.g.* Spirogyra, Zygnema) and unicellular forms, the desmids. The desmids, are divided into the saccoderm desmids, commonly found in acidic pools and peat bogs, and the placoderm or true desmids, which are a major component of the phytoplankton. The cells of placoderm desmids are characteristically split into two virtually identical halves joined by a narrow bridge at the centre. The cell wall is highly ornamented and indented.

Zygodactyl Having two thoes in front and two behind, as in woodpeckers. Compare heterodactyl.

Zygoenesis. Reproduction in which male and female gametes fuse, forming a zygote.

Zygoid

1. Diploid.
2. Like a zygote, as in zygoid parthenogenesis.

Zy goma. The zygomatic arch.

Zygomatic Arch. An arch on the lateral surface of the skull formed by processes of the temporal and zygomatic bones.

Zygomatic Bone. The malar bone forming the prominence of the cheek.

Zygomorphic. Irregular; bilaterally symmetrical, with reference to flowers.

Zygomycetes. A class of the Zygomycotina containing both saprobic fungi and many that are parasitic, particularly on arthropods. It contains about 515 species in some 85 genera. There are two orders : the Mucorales; and the Entomophthorales, most of which are insect parasites.

Zygomycotina. A subdivision of the Eumycota containing fungi with a mycelial thallus, characteristically with aceptate hyphae. It contains about 620 species in some 115 genera. Its members do not produce motile cells an asexual reproduction is by nonmotile aplanospores. Sexual reproduction leads to the formation of a resting spore (zygospore). The Zygomycotina contains the two classes Zygomycetes and Trichomycetes.

Zygophore. A specialized hyphal branch in certain fungi, the tip which forms a gametangium which fuses with its mate to form a coenozygote, as in the Mucorales.

Zygopteran. A damselfly, an odonatan of the suborder Zygoptera.

Zygosphene. One of two articular processes on the neural arch of certain reptiles.

Zygospore. A zygote with a thick resistant wall, formed by some algae and fungi It results from the fusion of two gametes, neither of which is retained by the parent in any specialized sex organ (such as an oogonium) It enters a resting phase before germination. Compare oospore.

Zygote. A fertilized female gamete; the product of the fusion of the nucleus of the ovum or ovule with the nucleus of the sperm or pollen grain.

Zygotene. A stage in mitosis following the leptotene stage in which the pairing of chromosomes occurs. Also called synapsis or syndesis.

Zygotic. Of, pertaining to, or derived from a zygote.

Zymase. An enzyme complex present in plants, especially yeasts, which catalyzes the decomposition of sugars with resultant production of alcohol and carbon dioxide, as occurs in fermentation.

Zymase. The mixture of enzymes, isolated from yeasts, that brings about alcoholic fermentation. It includes pyruvate decarboxylase, which catalyses the formation of acetaldehyde from pyruvate, and alcohol dehydrogenase, which catalyses the reduction of acetaldehyde to ethanol. It also includes the enzymes of the glycolytic pathway.

Zymogen. Any inactive enzyme precursor that, following secretion, is chemically altered to the active form of the enzyme. For example, the protein-digesting enzyme trypsin is secreted by the pancreas as the zymogen trypsinogen. This is changed in the small intestine by the action of another enzyme, enterokinase, to the active form.

Zymogenic

1. Of, pertaining to, or causing fermentation.
2. Of or pertaining to a zymogen.

Zymology. The science dealing with fermentation; the study of enzymes and their actions; enzymology.